THE BUDDHIST DIRECTORY

THE DIRECTORY OF
ЭDHIST GROUPS AND CENTRES
⌐HER RELATED ORGANISATIONS
N THE UNITED KINGDOM
AND IRELAND

TENTH EDITION

© The Buddhist Society 2007

ISBN 978 0 901032 99 7

Published by:

The Buddhist Society
58 Eccleston Square
London SW1V 1PH

Tel: 020 7834 5858
Fax: 020 7976 5238
E-mail: info@thebuddhistsociety.org
Website: www.thebuddhistsociety.org

Edited by Stuart Corner & Louise Marchant

With special thanks to Dr R. B. Parsons for his work on previous editions
and Dario Alvarez for supporting contributions.

Front Cover: Photo of Tibetan Thangka by Mark Tilley

The Peaceful and Wrathful Deities
    Dharmakaya Samantabhadra (Skt.), Kuntuzangpo (Tib. *kun tu bzang po*) represents the quality
of the Clear Light Nature of the Omniscient Mind which is without beginning or end.
Samantabhadra in union with Samantabhadri, his consort, represents the union of wisdom and
compassion. Their naked bodies represent all transcendent qualities that are beyond descriptions
or any intellectual conception. Samantabhadra is the colour of the sky and represents the pure
nature of awareness.
    Samantabhadra, the primordial Buddha is pure omniscience, the essence of the enlightened
mind of all the Buddhas. Embracing Samantabhadri, the female primordial Buddha, their union
represents the fusion of wisdom and compassion, the ultimate indivisibility of samsara and nirvana
and the potential for Buddhahood inherent in all sentient beings.
    Samanta means, universally extending. Bhadra means great virtue. Samantabhadra means to
extend such great compassion that every sentient being is benefited and to practice so extensively
and profoundly that all virtue is perfected.

CONTENTS

Foreword...6

UK National Organisations 9

England..27

Wales..131

Scotland 139

Channel Islands 149

Ireland...151

Retreat Centres...159

Related Organisations 165

Resources: 181
Audio-Visual 181
Books by Post...184
Bookshops 186
Libraries 190
Other Buddhist Requisites...............................195
Publishers 200
Travel..204
Websites 204

Indexes:
Index of Towns and Districts...........................205
Index of Groups by Title 209
Index of Groups by Tradition 223

A brief summary of the Kalama Sutta
Also known as 'Advice to the Kalamas' or
'The Buddha's Charter of Free Enquiry':

Thus I have heard. Once the Buddha was wandering in the Kosalan country and came to a town of the Kalama people called Kesaputta.

After giving him praise as the Exalted One, a Fully Enlightened One, perfect in wisdom and practice, the people asked how they could separate true teachings from false teachings.

The Buddha replied: Do not accept things just because they are being repeated, or come from tradition, scriptures, rumour, guesswork, incorrect reasoning, a bias towards the subject, clever oration or mere respect for the teacher or speaker. When you know for yourself that something leads to harm and sorrow and is not welcomed by the wise, then abandoned it.

You can see that the presence of greed, hatred or ignorance leads to people taking life, stealing, committing adultery and telling lies, as well as encouraging others to do likewise. All these activities lead to harm and sorrow.

When freedom from greed, hatred and ignorance is achieved by the presence of love, compassion, joy and equanimity then people do not take life, steal, commit adultery and tell lies, as well as encouraging others to do likewise. The absence of all these blameful activities, you will observe, will lead to lasting benefit and happiness. Such behaviour is praised by the wise.

The people of Kesaputta rejoiced praised the Buddha for his teaching which uncovered what was concealed, pointed the way for those who are lost, carried a light into darkness. They then took refuge in the Triple Gem: the Blessed One, his Dharma teachings and the Community of Monastics, for the rest of their lives.

Anguttara Nikaya. See also Wheel Series publication, number 8.

The Four Reliance's taught by The Buddha (rton pa bzhi – Tibetan)
Rely on the truth the teacher teaches, not on his personality.
Rely on what he means, not on the words he speaks.
Rely on the real meaning, not on a partial provisional understanding.
Rely on your wisdom mind, not on judgemental intellect.

5

Foreword

This is the 10th edition of *The Buddhist Directory* to be published by The Buddhist Society. It seeks to provide a comprehensive guide to Buddhist centres and groups in the United Kingdom and the Republic of Ireland who wish to be included and contains 649 entries, not counting those in the *Related Organisations* and *Resources* sections, compared with 437 in the previous edition. Even so, as in previous editions, it has not been possible, for various reasons, to include *all* groups in the UK and some of the largest organisations are represented only by a single entry in the *UK National Organisations* section. This should be borne in mind particularly by anyone attempting to use the Directory for statistical purposes.

As explained in the previous edition, the Directory is now compiled from a computer database which is continually up-dated as new information becomes available. We therefore appeal to anyone who has information about new Buddhist groups or changes affecting existing groups, to send it to the Buddhist Society immediately and not wait until a new edition of the Directory is in preparation. If you do this, the task of preparing a new edition will be made easier and in the meantime the information will be available to inquirers, to The Buddhist Society.

IMPORTANT NOTICE

The fact that a teacher, group or centre is included in this Directory does not imply endorsement by the Buddhist Society. As a matter of policy, the Society does not offer opinions as to the authenticity, bona fides, reputability etc of any teacher, group or centre. This is in accordance with tradition, for Buddhism has never been a centralised religion with a governing body dispensing or withholding approval. It is up to each individual to test the ground for himself, guided by common sense and those indications that the Buddha himself gives in the Scriptures (e.g. in the Kalama Sutta – see opposite). *Caveat meditator!* Anyone seeking objective information about new religious groups may approach either of the following independent bodies, which have networks of contacts and wide experience of newer groups within the main world religions as well as of new religious movements:
INFORM, Houghton Street, London WC2A 2AE
(Telephone 020 7955 7654, Fax 020 7955 7679, E-mail inform@lse.ac.uk, Website www.inform.ac)

or THE CULT INFORMATION CENTRE, BCM Cults, London WC1N 3XX (Telephone 01689 833800 or 0870 7773800 Website www.cultinformation.org.uk)

Do not accept any of my words on faith,
Believing them just because I said them.
Be like an analyst buying gold, who cuts, burns,
And critically examines his product for authenticity.
Only accept what passes the test
By proving useful and beneficial in your life.
The Buddha

How to use this Directory.

1.   If you are interested in a specific organisation of which you know the name, there is an *Index of Groups by Title* at the back of the book. This index covers all the entries except those in the *Resources* section. Entries for organisations having a national role, and especially for those having branches or associated groups in various parts of the country, will be found in the *UK National Organisations* section. Please note that some major organisations are represented *only* by an entry in this section, so that in these cases it will be necessary to consult the national contact to find your nearest group.

2.   If you are interested in groups belonging to a particular Buddhist tradition, consult the *Index of Groups by Tradition.*

3.   If you want to find Buddhist groups in a particular area, you should consult the main body of the Directory where the entries are arranged by counties in alphabetical order.

The situation regarding local government boundaries seems to have largely stabilised after the widespread changes of the 1990's so it seems desirable to adopt an arrangement reflecting the divisions currently in use, as given in the *Municipal year book and public services directory.* As far as Scotland and Wales are concerned, this means following the boundaries of the unitary authorities established in 1996. For England, however, also following the *Municipal year book,* the entries have been arranged according to the counties established in 1974, since even where these have

7

been abolished as administrative units, the successor authorities are arranged within the same boundaries. For Northern Ireland, however, the pre-1996 counties have been retained, since these appear to be generally accepted.

University Buddhist Societies

These, like university societies in general, tend to manifest impermanence to a marked degree. For this reason, no special effort has been made to track them down and only those have been listed where we can be reasonably certain that the contact details will remain valid for the lifetime of the Directory. However, other university Buddhist societies certainly exist and can usually be contacted through the Students Union.

Funerals, Weddings, Namings.

In the first instance, helpful advice may be obtained regarding Buddhist funeral services, weddings, memorial services, and the naming of children by contacting the main centres.

The Internet

This is coming increasingly to dominate the dissemination of information about Buddhism and Buddhist activities, as in almost all aspects of our national life and it would not have been possible to compile the present edition of this Directory without making constant use of it. The e-mail addresses and website URL's of Buddhist groups and centres are given wherever possible. However, it should be borne in mind that everything connected with the Internet is liable to change without notice. If the URL listed fails to yield a result, the group should be looked for using Internet search engines (as many as possible). It is also worth trying these even if no website is listed, as new websites are constantly being set up and these frequently provide more information than can be given here. They should also provide more up-to-date contact information.

UK NATIONAL ORGANISATIONS

AGON SHU UK
Tradition: Agon Shu
Meetings: 3 Queen Square, London, WC1N 3AU
Charity No.: 1050059
Postal Address: Agon Shu UK, 3 Queen Square, London, WC1N 3AU
Telephone Contact: 020 7278 1988
Fax: 020 7837 1958
Email: londoncentre@agon.org.uk
Website(s): www.agon.org/us/

Agon Shu is based on the original teachings of the Buddha. Established in Japan in 1978 by Kiriyama Kancho, Agon Shu is founded on the wisdom of the Agama Sutras originally taught by the Buddha over 2,500 years ago. At the same time, Agon Shu is thoroughly contemporary, democratically making higher wisdom available to anyone. Agon Shu is also involved in social and educational activities throughout the world including funding of hospitals, elder care, AIDS hospices, environmental development, disaster relief, and educational assistance.

AMARAVATI BUDDHIST MONASTERY
Tradition: Theravada
Meetings: Great Gaddesden, Hemel Hempstead, Hertfordshire HP1 3BZ
Postal Address: Amaravati Buddhist Monastery, Great Gaddesden, Hemel Hempstead, Hertfordshire HP1 3BZ
Telephone Contact: 01442 842455 (2.30 - 4.30pm)
Fax: 01442 843721
Website(s): www.amaravati.org or www.forestsangha.org

Amaravati is a monastery based on the study and practice of Theravada Buddhism. There is a resident community of monks, nuns and postulants under the direction of the Venerable Ajahn Sumedho, a disciple of Ajahn Chah. Facilities include a Temple (meditation hall); simple accommodation for visitors; a library; a children's room and grounds which are spacious enough for large gatherings on Buddhist festival days. Members of the community sometimes visit affiliated groups, schools, etc. on invitation. The community produces a number of publications. The monastery steward, the English Sangha Trust (see Related Organisations) manages donations in support of the Monastery and resident community. For general information about the monastery, write to the Secretary including a SAE.

The typical daily routine includes morning puja at 5.00am, the meal offering at 11am and evening puja at 7.30pm but the schedule can vary during the year. There is a meditation workshop on Saturday afternoons from 1.30pm-3.30pm.

Visitors are welcome. However, overnight accommodation must be arranged in advance - write to the Guest Monk/Nun for details. Guests join in the life of the community, following the daily routines, including pujas and work periods and keeping the Eight Precepts. There is no charge. Public activities and overnight accomodation are suspended during January, February and March when the community is in silent retreat.

See separate entry for information about the Amaravati Retreat Centre.

The Forest Sangha Newsletter and a number of publications in English and Thai are available; please send a SAE for a current list. There is no charge, but publications can only be sent if the cost of postage is covered.

The monastery is in the lineage of the Thai teacher Venerable Ajahn Chah of Wat Pah Pong, and is related to Wat Pah Nanachat (International Forest Monastery) in Thailand.

AMIDA TRUST
Tradition: Pure Land
School: Amida-Shu
Meetings: The Buddhist House, 12 Coventry

Entry continued on the following page.

9

Road, Narborough, Leicester LE19 2GB
Charity No.: 1060589
Postal Address: The Buddhist House, 12
Coventry Road, Narborough, Leicester LE19 2GB
Telephone Contact: 0116 286 7476
Email: amida@amidatrust.com
Website(s): www.amidatrust.com

Amida Trust, a registered charity, is the sponsoring body of Amida-shu, a Buddhist denomination of the Pureland School under the guidance of Rev. Dr. Dharmavidya, affiliated to the European Buddhist Union, the World Buddhist University, the Network of Engaged Buddhists and the Buddhist Peace Fellowship. Amida-shu follows the Japanese tradition of Pureland Buddhism, but is organisationally an independent foundation. Amida-shu includes the religious society called the Amida Order with both ordained and lay members engaged in Buddhist ministry, education, pastoral care, chaplaincy, community work, Sangha building, interfaith activity, Dharma propagation and campaigns on ethical issues. Membership of Amida Trust is open to any person sympathetic to the Trust's work whereas entry to Amida-shu is conditional upon a faith commitment to the Amidist approach to Buddhadharma. Among its many activities the Trust sponsors a full professional training in psychotherapy from a Buddhist psychology perspective and training programmes in ministry and chaplaincy with practical and theoretical components. The trust also sponsors overseas projects with a centre in Delhi offering Dharma teaching and literacy education and an affiliated project in Zambia offering primary health care and education. There are affiliated Amida-shu groups in several countries.

BODHICHARYA UK
Tradition: Tibetan
Meetings: Contact for details
Postal Address: Bodhicharya UK. UK Office and Rigul Co-ordination, Margaret Ford, 28 Carrick Drive, Coatbridge, Lanarkshire, Scotland ML5 1JZ

Email: co-ordination-uk@bodhicharya.org
Website(s): www.bodhicharya.org

The group was founded in May 1998. It is part of an international network under the direction of Ringu Tulku Rinpoche.

BUDDHIST SOCIETY
Tradition: All
Meetings: 58 Eccleston Square,
London SW1V 1PH
Charity No.: 1113705
Postal Address: The Registrar, The Buddhist Society, 58 Eccleston Square, London SW1V 1PH
Telephone Contact: 020 7834 5858
Fax: 020 7976 5238
Email: info@thebuddhistsociety.org
Website(s): www.thebuddhistsociety.org

Founded in 1924 by Christmas Humphreys Q.C., The Buddhist Society was one of the original centres for Buddhist teaching and practice in the West. Since then it has consistently provided a programme of talks, practice, meditation and study classes under the guidance of teachers trained in the traditions of Buddhism.

The Society's Objects are To publish and make known the principles of Buddhism and to encourage the study and practice of those principles. The Society adheres to no one school of Buddhism and in its structured programme of classes gives the newcomer an impartial introduction to the fundamental tenets common to all of the Schools of Buddhism and, later on, an introduction to some of the main Buddhist training traditions.

Information about the Society's Public Lectures, its Introducing Buddhism Course and the various practice, study and meditation classes can be obtained from the Society's website or by writing, calling or telephoning.

The Society provides an annual Summer School in

Entry continued over the following page.

The Buddhist Society,

58, Eccleston Square, London SW1V 1PH
phone: 020 7834 5858
email: info@thebuddhistsociety.org **website**: www.thebuddhistsociety.org
Registered Charity No: 1113705

The Buddhist Society presents the major Buddhist schools and traditions, and in its extensive library there are books on all Buddhist subjects.

The Society holds lectures, classes and activities in the teachings of the Theravada, Mahayana, Zen, Pure Land and Tibetan Schools. Some are open to the public, including the 'Introducing Buddhism' class, which offers the newcomer an introduction to the whole field of Buddhism. There are also classes and lectures for members only; these include 'The Fundamentals of Buddhism' which is an Intermediate course and 'Themes of the Great Way', a course on Indian Mahayana. The Correspondence Course is suitable for people living outside London and unable to attend regular classes at the Society. The annual one-week residential Summer School is available to members and non-members.

The Buddhist Society is open from 2pm to 6pm Monday to Friday with classes in the evening and from 2pm to 5pm on Saturdays.

THE MIDDLE WAY

The Middle Way, the Buddhist Society's quarterly journal, features articles by noted Buddhist teachers, scholars and practicing Buddhists on various aspects of the Buddha's teaching. There are articles on theory and practice as well as some on the history of the Buddhist religious traditions. Each issue includes book reviews, the Society's programme of classes, courses, public talks and activities.

The Middle Way is **published in May, August, November & February**. All paid-up Members of the Society automatically receive *The Middle Way* free of charge. The Middle Way is also available to non-members on subscription. Renewal reminders are sent out both to Members and Subscribers quarterly.

August/September and a Correspondence Course.

The Society's Journal The Middle Way is published quarterly and is free to members or available on subscription. Lists of the Society's publications and recordings are available on request.

The Society's Library aims to include all the books essential for the study of the Buddhadharma and in addition there is a bookstall with a representative selection of Buddhist books for sale.

For a membership application forms or details of how to subscribe separately to The Middle Way, please see the Society's website, write, call or telephone.

The Society is open for enquiries 2pm - 6pm Monday to Friday. 2pm - 5.00pm Sat.

COMMUNITY OF INTERBEING, U.K.
Tradition: Vietnamese
School: Thich Nhat Hanh
Charity No.: 105871
Postal Address: Matthew Melliar-Smith, 5 Walshams, Stockland, Devon EX14 9DT
Telephone Contact: 0870 041 1242
Website(s): www.interbeing.org.uk & www.plumvillage.com

The Community of Interbeing is the name that has been chosen for the network of people who practice Mindfulness according to the Zen Buddhist teachings of Thich Nhat Hanh. It is part of the wider international community who follow the practice and teachings of Thich Nhat Hanh worldwide.

Zen Master Thich Nhat Hanh was born in Vietnam in 1926 and ordained as a Buddhist monk at the age of 16. He has worked tirelessly for peace throughout the Vietnam war and ever since. Martin Luther King nominated him for the Nobel Peace Prize in 1967. He has lived in exile in France

for many years, establishing Plum Village, a rural retreat centre, in 1982.

Thich Nhat Hanh's teaching is based on conscious breathing and being fully aware of the present moment. Through the practice of meditation in everyday life and by showing compassion to all living beings, peace becomes possible within ourselves and extends to everyone we touch.

Anyone who is interested can join in the activities of the Community. Information about current events and regional contacts can be obtained from the address below. Selected regional contacts are also listed in the geographical sections of this Directory.

If you would like a copy of the journal Here and Now contact Ann Irving, The Old Stables, 44 Main Street, Sudborough, Northants. NN14 3BX Telephone 01832 731557.

Membership Secretary: Sandra Kirk, 17 Southfields, Glastonbury, Somerset BA6 8DW. Tel: 01458 833325

DECHEN COMMUNITY
Tradition: Tibetan
School: Kagyu-Sakya
Meetings: Various
Postal Address: Dechen Community Sakya Centre, 121 Sommerville Road, St.Andrews, Bristol, BS6 5BX
Telephone Contact: 0117 924 4424
Email: info@dechen.org
Website(s): www.dechen.org

The Dechen Community is an association of Buddhist centres and groups belonging to the Sakya and Karma-Kagyu schools of Tibetan Buddhism under the direction of Karma Thinley Rinpoche and Lama Jampa Thaye.

Karma Thinley Rinpoche, meditation master and scholar of the Sakya and Karma-Kagyu traditions

UK National Organisations

of Tibetan Buddhism, was born in Eastern Tibet in 1931. He was recognised as the incarnation of the Sakya Lama Beru Kunrik, and later recognised as the fourth incarnation in the line of the famous Karma Thinleypas.

During his childhood and youth Rinpoche received a vast array of teachings of the Sakya, Kagyu and Nyingma traditions. After leaving Tibet for India in 1959, Rinpoche spent a few years acting as abbot of a Karma Kagyu nunnery. In 1971 Rinpoche settled in Canada since which time he has established numerous centres in Canada, and the UK, as well as his monastic seat, Tegchen Legshey Ling in Kathmandu.

Lama Jampa Thaye, born in England in 1952, met Karma Thinley Rinpoche in 1973. Over the past three decades he has inherited a great range of teachings of the Sakya, Kagyu and Nyingma traditions. As a result of his studies and practice, he was appointed Rinpoche's dharma-regent and subsequently given the authority to bestow Vajrayana initiations.

He is the author of a number of guides to Buddhist practice, including Diamond Sky (1989), Garland of Gold (1990), Way of Tibetan Buddhism (Thorson's, 2001) and Rain of Clarity (2006).

There are Dechen Buddhist centres in Bristol, Manchester, London and Harrogate and groups in Bath, Birmingham, Cheshire, Colne, Exeter, Liverpool, Pembrokeshire, Southport, Truro and Wirral. Internationally there are also Dechen groups in Bulgaria, France, Germany, Mexico and Poland.

DIAMOND WAY BUDDHISM UK
Tradition: Tibetan
School: Karma-Kagyu
Charity No.: 1093406
Postal Address: Diamond Way Buddhism UK c/o London Diamond Way Buddhist Centre, 27 Johns Mews, London, WC1N 2NS

Telephone Contact: 020 7916 2282
Email: info@dwbuk.org
Website(s): www.diamondway-buddhism.co.uk

The Diamond Way opens the most skilful methods of the Buddha to the modern world. It helps us discover and develop our inner richness for the benefit of all beings. The teachings which have come through the great meditation masters of Tibet have developed an accessible and modern style. While many schools of Buddhism in the West today are still very cultural and focus mainly on calming the mind, the Diamond Way works with people's confidence and desire, using every situation in life to develop fearlessness and joy.

Diamond Way Buddhism UK is part of an international network of over 400 lay Buddhist centres of the Karma Kagyu Lineage, under the spiritual guidance of the 17th Karmapa, Thaye Dorje and directed by Lama Ole Nydahl. There are currently 9 groups in the UK, which have a democratic structure and function through unpaid, voluntary work on the basis of idealism and friendship.

DZOGCHEN COMMUNITY UK
Tradition: Tibetan
School: Dzogchen
Meetings: (Various)
Charity No.: 1019101
Postal Address: The Secretary, Dzogchen Community UK, 152 Sturton Street, Cambridge, CB1 2QF
Email: amely@blueyonder.co.uk
Website(s): www.dzogchencommunity.org

Follows the teachings of Chogyal Namkhai Norbu Rinpoche, author of the following books: 'The Crystal and the Way of Light' and 'Dzogchen the Self Perfected State' (Snow Lion).

The main European centre of this community is Merigar, Arcidosso 58031 (GR), Italy. There are other main 'Gars' in Argentina, Australia, USA and

Entry continued on the following page.

Venezuela. The UK Community has a retreat centre 'Kunsel-Ling' in the mountains of mid Wales.

Up to date weekly information about practices in the London area as well as other events can be found on 020 7912 1190

All enquiries about membership should be addressed to Ruth Sparks: flamingo54@tiscali.co.uk

Regional Contacts:

Bristol: Catriona Mundle catrionamundle@blueyonder.co.uk

Cambridge: Peter White peter@cambridgeacupuncture.net

Cardiff: Len Sinclair lgsinc123@hotmail.com

Cumbria: Lindsay Young Tel: 015 2426 2381/077 6030 1266

Devon: Lol Kane lolkane@onetel.com

London / SE: Judy Allan juditta@macunlimited.net

Manchester: Marc Franks marcfranks@btinternet.com

Midlands: Barry Patterson barry@redsandstonehill.net

FEDERATION OF AMBEDKARITE BUDDHIST ORGANISATIONS UK
Tradition: Theravada
School: Ambedkarite
Postal Address: C Gautam, Vice President, Federation of Ambedkarite Buddhist Organisations, Milan House, 8 Kingsland Road, London E2 8DA
12 Featherstone Road, Southall, Middlesex, 4B2 5AA
Telephone Contact: 0208 571 5131 or 07956 918053 or 01745 582703 or 0871 433 1032

Email: cgautam@ambedkar.org.uk

The Federation has been set up to propagate Ambedkar's thought and Buddhist ideas throughout the world. The Federation in fact represents the amalgamation of the many Ambedkarite Buddhist groups which have come into being in various towns and cities in the UK. It thus forms a unified front for our activities and concerns at a national level. Ours is a movement following Dr Babasaheb Ambedkar's revival of Buddhism in modern India for the underprivileged sectors of society. We celebrate Ambedkar's Birthday and Vesak Day (offering Dana to monks and nuns) annually. A Journal New Era appears every year at Dr Ambedkar's birthday celebration.

FOUNDATION FOR THE PRESERVATION OF THE MAHAYANA TRADITION
Telephone Contact: 020 7820 8787
Fax: 020 7820 8605
Email: admin@jamyang.co.uk
Website(s): www.fpmt.org or www.jamyang.co.uk

Lama Thubten Yeshe (1935 -1984) and Lama Zopa Rinpoche, together as teacher and disciple since their exile in India, met their first Western Student in 1965 and by 1971 had settled at Kopan, near Kathmandu in Nepal. Due to demand, they began teaching Buddhist philosophy and meditation to increasing numbers of travellers, which in turn started groups and centres in their own countries.

In 1975 Lama Yeshe named the fledgling network the Foundation for the Preservation of the Mahayana Tradition. The FPMT now runs more than 132 centres in 31 countries and other activities and projects, including the building of a 500ft statue of the Buddha Maitreya in India (see www.maitreyaproject.org).

The Foundation's International Office publishes the Mandala Journal, supplemented by newsletters. It provides a forum for the exchange

UK National Organisations

of information and ideas among students of the FPMT, encouraging a feeling of international community. To receive Mandala, or to find out more about the organisation, please visit www.fpmt.org or write to International Offices at 1632 SE 11th Avenue, Portland, OR 97212-4702 USA Telephone: (1) (503) 808-1588 Fax: (1) (503) 808-1589.

FPMT centres in the UK are Jamyang Buddhist Centre London, Jamyang Leeds, Jamyang Brighton, Jamyang Colchester, Jamyang Coventry, Jamyang Salisbury, Shen Phen Thubten Choeling and the Yeshe Study Group.

FRIENDS OF THE WESTERN BUDDHIST ORDER
Tradition: FWBO
Charity No.: 1017329
Postal Address: FWBO Communications Office, 59 Roman Road, Bethnal Green, London, E2 0QN
Or
The London Buddhist Centre, 51 Roman Road, Bethnal Green, London, E2 0QN
Telephone Contact: 020 8981 0091 (Director Communications)
Or 0845 458 4716
Fax: 020 8981 0091 (Communications Office)
Email: communications@fwbo.org or info@lbc.org.uk
Website(s): www.fwbo.org

The FWBO was founded in 1967 by Sangharakshita, an Englishman who spent 20 years in the east, 16 of them as a Buddhist monk. Having returned to Britain in the mid-1960s he saw the need for a new Buddhist movement. His vision was to create something faithful to traditional Buddhist values while being relevant to the modern world. The FWBO is an ecumenical movement, aligned to no one traditional school, but drawing on the whole stream of Buddhist inspiration.

The FWBO has many public centres where meditation is taught, and promotes 'Right Livelihood' projects in which Buddhists can work together and turn their work into a spiritual practice.

GOLDEN BUDDHA CENTRE
Charity No.: 1072818
Postal Address: Golden Buddha Centre, Zeal Cottage, South Brent, Devon, TQ10 9ED
Telephone Contact: 01364 73711
Or 01803 732082
Email: gb@goldenbuddha.org
Website(s): www.goldenbuddha.org

The Golden Buddha project began in 1998 with the aim of providing a focus for the growing number of people wishing to live a Buddhist way of life in retirement.

Zeal Cottage is the first step in the Golden Buddha project. It provides opportunities for personal and group retreats together with a regular meditation programme and library facilities. The cottage adjoins Dartmoor National Park, and is edged by a flowing stream. This is a beautiful location two miles from the town of South Brent. The Centre is not affiliated to any single teacher or tradition and will host a variety of retreats and other Buddhist activities. The Golden Buddha Patrons include senior monks from the three main traditions of Buddhism.

Buddhists can apply to use the facilities for retreats or study purposes either individually or on a group basis. They are also welcome to take part in work retreat programmes and support the project in practical ways. Future plans include the acquisition of properties nearby for longer term accommodation for older Buddhists, together with advice and support for those wishing to rent or purchase property in the vicinity.

For further details send a SAE.

UK National Organisations

INTERNATIONAL ZEN ASSOCIATION UK
Tradition: Zen
School: Soto
Charity No.: 1069941
Postal Address: International Zen Association UK, c/o Bristol Soto Zen Dojo, Gloucester Road, Bishopston, Bristol BS7 8AT
Telephone Contact: 0117 942 4347
Email: enquiries@izauk.co.uk
Website(s): www.izauk.co.uk

Follows the Soto Zen tradition. Dojos and groups in: Bournemouth, Bristol, Leeds, London (North, South and West), Manchester, Norfolk and Oxford.

KAGYU SAMYE LING MONASTERY AND TIBETAN CENTRE - ROKPA TRUST
Tradition: Tibetan
School: Karma-Kagyu
Meetings: Eskdalemuir, Langholm, Dumfriesshire, DG13 0QL, Scotland
Charity No.: 1059293
Postal Address: The Booking Office, Samye Ling Monastery and Tibetan Centre, Eskdalemuir, Langholm, Dumfriesshire DG13 0QL
Telephone Contact: 013873 73232 Ext 22
Fax: 013873 73223
Email: scotland@samyeling.org
Website(s): www.samyeling.org

Founded in 1967. It was the very first Tibetan Centre in the West, taking its name from Samye (the inconceivable place) the very first Buddhist centre in Tibet, established in the 8th century. During the past 30 years, Samye Ling has developed into a key focus for a number of important activities. Its natural growth has taken place under the guidance of Dr Akong Tulku Rinpoche, assisted in recent years by Abbot and Retreat Master Lama Yeshe Losal. Functioning under the auspices of the Rokpa Trust (See Related Organisations) Samye Ling today exists as:

A centre for the preservation of Tibetan religion, culture, medicine, art, architecture and handicrafts.

An international centre of Buddhist training with regular courses in Buddhist philosophy and meditation.

The mother centre for its branch centres in Europe and Africa (see the geographical sections of this Directory for centres in the UK).

The hub of a international network of humanitarian activities (see Rokpa Trust - Related Organisations).

The driving force behind the Holy Island project (see Scotland, North Lanarkshire).

A place of therapy - where a cross-cultural enrichment of therapeutic skills takes place through courses and weekend workshops.

A voice in interfaith understanding.

A community of some 70 people, both monastic and lay volunteers, who maintain the Centre's activities.

Please see website for details of the programme.

LONGCHEN FOUNDATION
Tradition: Tibetan
School: Kagyu-Nyingma
Meetings: Oxford, London, Bristol, Kent, and North Wales. In Germany: Cologne, Berlin, Heidelberg, Stuttgart,
Charity No.: 802247
Postal Address: Longchen Programmes, Gelli Faia, Porthmadog, North Wales LL49 9UW
Tim Malnick, 27 Maple Road, Bristol BS7 8RD
Telephone Contact: 01766 513131
Email: longchenlHE@bigfoot.com
Website(s): www.longchenfoundation.com

The Longchen Foundation was established by Chigyam Trungpa Rinpoche and Dilgo Khyentse Rinpoche, two of the great Tibetan teachers of the 20th century, to pass on the authentic Mahayana

Entry continued over the following page.

16

The Longchen Foundation

The Longchen Foundation is an authentic lineage in the Nyingma tradition of Tibetan Buddhism, established by Chögyam Trungpa Rinpoche and Dilgo Khyentse Rinpoche, under the direction of Rigdzin Shikpo.

We offer talks, retreats and training focusing on the union of Mahayana and Dzogchen. Our courses are suitable for anyone interested in meditation, from complete beginners to those who wish to deepen their experience.

The Lion's Roar is a course of weekend teachings over three years, introducing the view and practice of Dzogchen.

The Path of Freedom consists of weekly evening meetings in local groups around the country, covering core Buddhist teachings from the Longchen perspective.

To find out more please visit:

www.longchenfoundation.com

or email:

admin@longchenfoundation.com

Registered Charity No. 802247

17

UK National Organisations

MahaAti (Dzogchen) teachings of the Nyingma lineage to the west. The spiritual director and principal teacher, Rigdzin Shikpo, one of Trungpa Rinpoche's earliest western students and a qualified lama of the Nyingma tradition, was entrusted by them to teach in direct response to the needs of westerners and is among the most experienced and inspiring Buddhist teachers in Britain.

The Foundation is a community of Buddhist teachers, meditation instructors and students practising these teachings with the vision of liberating the hearts of beings. For details of weekend courses, retreats, publications, newsletters, please visit our website.

The Lions Roar is a course that introduces the view and innermost teachings of the Longchen tradition and offers a deep and authentic grounding in the practice of meditation. It is suitable for total beginners and experienced meditators. The course is available in Britain and in Germany.

Local groups led by senior students are in Bristol, Oxford, North London, South-east London, Maidstone, North Wales and Birmingham.

LUMBINI NEPALESE BUDDHA DHARMA SOCIETY UK
Tradition: Nepalese
Charity No.: 1116370
Postal Address: The Lumbini Nepalese Buddha Dharma Society UK, 11 Mulberry Drive, Slough, Berkshire SL3 7JU
Or 16 Wyatt Close, Hayes, Middlesex UB4 0BT
Telephone Contact: 01753 549370 (Dr Dharma Bhakta Shakya, Secretary)
Or 020 8573 3534 (Mr Amrit Ratna Sthapit, President)
Or 07899 900460 (Mr Amrit Ratna Sthapit, President)
Email: lumbini1997@hotmail.com
Website(s): www.lumbini.org.uk

Established in 1997 to serve the needs of the expatriate Nepali community in the UK but open to everyone regardless of nationality or background on a strictly non-political, non-racial, voluntary basis.

The aims and objectives of the Society are: to make the Buddha's teachings known to a wider public; to build a forum for positive discussion, exchange of ideas and constructive dialogue; to establish links with similar organisations in Nepal, the United Kingdom and other countries; to organise voluntary work to help suffering humanity in Nepal and other countries and to promote awareness of and to publish information about the religions and cultural heritage of Nepal.

Publication: Lumbini (Annual).

NETWORK OF ENGAGED BUDDHISTS (UK)
Tradition: All
Postal Address: Network of Engaged Buddhists (UK), Maitrisara, 18 Bhandariclose, Oxford, OX4 3DT
Telephone Contact: 01865 777297
Email: secretary@engagedbuddhist.org.uk
Website(s): www.engagedbuddhists.org.uk

This is a network of people trying to combine inner peace seeking and outward social concern in a mutually supportive and enriching way. It provides opportunities for sharing problems, feelings and experience in this great lifelong undertaking, embracing the concerns of ecological well-being, world peace and social justice. In trying to understand the problems of personal and social violence it is both affinity group and pressure group, attempting both personal and social transformation.

The Fellowship has a broad, non-sectarian interfaith character and a wide range of members interests is reflected in its lively newsletter, Indra's Net and an eforum NebSangha which is accessible from the website.

NEW KADAMPA TRADITION
Tradition: Tibetan
School: New Kadampa Tradition
Charity No.: 1015054
Postal Address: The Secretary, New Kadampa Tradition Office, Conishead Priory, Ulverston, Cumbria LA12 9QQ
Telephone Contact: 01229 588533 Or 01229 584029
Fax: 01229 580080/588533
Email: info@kadampa.org
Website(s): www.kadampa.org

An association of independent Mahayana Buddhist centres following the Kadampa Tradition passed down from Buddha Shakyamuni, principally through the Indian Buddhist Master Atisha and the Tibetan Buddhist Master Je Tsongkapa.

The Spiritual Director is Venerable Geshe Kelsang Gyatso Rinpoche, a highly accomplished Meditator and Teacher. Born in Tibet and resident in the UK since 1977, he is the author of 20 books to date on all aspects of Buddhist Sutra and Tantra.

Currently (December 2006) there are over 300 centres and groups associated with the New Kadampa Tradition throughout the United Kingdom and Eire. These range from 40 residential Centres following a full programme of daily study and meditation classes to branch groups meeting weekly.

All Centres follow one or more of three study programmes:

The General Programme provides a basic introduction to Buddhist view, meditation and action that is suitable for beginners.

The Foundation Programme provides an opportunity for deeper understanding and experience of Buddhism through systematic study of five of Geshe Kelsang's books.

The Teacher Training Programme is designed for people who wish to train as authentic Buddhist Teachers.

Residential Centres also host a number of day, weekend and week-long courses ranging from introductions to Buddhism to more advanced studies of Mahayana Buddhism, as well as an annual retreat in January and a number of week-long retreats throughout the year. Correspondence courses are available.

All Centres of the New Kadampa Tradition collectively host an annual three day Spring Festival in May and a two week Summer Festival in August both festivals being held in Cumbria.

For more details on all Centres of the New Kadampa Tradition and their activities contact the Secretary.

OGYAN CHOKHOR LING
Tradition: Tibetan
School: Nyingma
Meetings: Canterbury & London N12
Telephone Contact: 01227 728379
Email: gawang@nyingma.com
Website(s): www.nyingma.com/ogyan-cho-khor-ling

Ogyan Chokhor Ling is the European Sangha of Ven. Lopon P Ogyan Tanzin Rinpoche. We are Vajrayana Buddhist practitioners within the Dudjom Lineage of the Nyingma school of Tibetan Buddhism.

When Ven. Lopon P Ogyan Tanzin Rinpoche first came to Britain in 2004 he was able to build on foundations already laid for the Dudjom tradition in the UK. HH. Dudjom Rinpoche himself had visited London in the 1970s, and the wonderful teachings he gave at that time planted the best of seeds for the development of practice in the Dudjom tradition here. Then in the 1980s, Ven. Lama Yeshe Dorje Rinpoche, a heart student of H.H. Dudjom Rinpoche and Dharma brother of Lama Tanzin

Entry continued on the following page.

Rinpoche, made two visits to Kent, and gave further teachings.

In the 1990s Ven. Lama Tharchin Rinpoche of Vajrayana Foundation (http://www.vajrayana.org) another heart student of H.H. Dudjom Rinpoche and Dharma brother of Lama Tanzin Rinpoche, made two extended teaching visits to the UK.

Lama Tanzin Rinpoche continues the work begun by these other renowned lamas of the tradition. He spends around 3 months a year teaching and leading retreats in the UK.

We welcome experienced practitioners to our practice groups and events at various locations in the UK whether inspired by the Dudjom practices, or wishing to discover more about them. We also have programmes to support those setting out for the first time on the Buddhist path.

For information please contact Ngakpa Ga'wang

ORDER OF BUDDHISTS CONTEMPLATIVES
Tradition: Zen
School: Soto
Postal Address: Throssel Hole Buddhist Abbey, Carrshields, Hexham, Northumberland NE47 8AL
Telephone Contact: 01952 615574 (OBC European Advisor)
Or 01434 345204 (Throssel Hole Buddhist Abbey)
Website(s): www.obcon.org

The Order of Buddhist Contemplatives is dedicated to the practice of the Serene Reflection Meditation tradition, known as Ts'ao-Tung Ch'an in China and Soto Zen in Japan. The Order was incorporated in 1983 by Rev. Master Jiyu-Kennett to serve as the international umbrella organization for the monasteries, priories (local temples), and meditation groups led by priests of our lineage in Britain, Canada, Germany, the Netherlands, and the United States.
A British-born Buddhist master trained in

Malaysia and Japan, Rev. Master Kennett came to the United States in 1969. A year later, Shasta Abbey, a Buddhist seminary and training monastery, was founded in northern California. In 1972 she founded Throssel Hole Priory, now Throssel Hole Buddhist Abbey, in the north of England. The practice of the Order emphasizes serene reflection meditation, mindfulness in daily life, and adherence to the Buddhist Precepts.

Included within it are a number of Temples, Priories and affiliated meditation groups in Britain (see geographical section of the guide for details) as well as the largest monastery of the Order in Europe, Throssel Hole Buddhist Abbey in Northumberland. It also publishes a quarterly journal.

PADMA LING UK
Tradition: Tibetan
School: Nyingma
Postal Address: Padma Ling, 2 Church Court, Church Road, Lyminge, Kent, CT18 8FB
Telephone Contact: 01303 86 28 77 (Chantal)
Or 07969 40 89 60
Email: info@padmaling.org.uk
Website(s): www.padmaling.org.uk

We are the UK branch of several Padma Ling centres in Europe, founded under the auspicious spiritual guidance of Tulku Jigme Norbu La, also known as the Venerable Jigme Gyetrul Rinpoche.

We receive teachings during regular visits from Rinpoche; and in the future also wish to be able to invite Rinpoche's father to teach in the UK, His Eminence the Terton Namkha Drimed Rabjam Rinpoche and other Lamas from the Ripa Lineage. We meet in group to practice Shinay Meditation, Sangye Menla, The Heart Essence of Padmasambhava, Yeshe Tsogyal and Gesar of Ling Sadhanas.

We will be registered as a UK Charity within the coming year.

Kent, Lyminge/Folkestone:

Shinay Meditation:Every Monday 7.30-9pm

Padmasambhava + Tsok/Yeshe Tsogyal + Tsok/Sangye Menla/ Gesar of Ling: Monthly depending on lunar calendar, please check the website for details www.padmaling.org.uk

London, varied venues: please contact Chantal

Shinay Meditation: Monthly, as part of the Sangye Menla practice.

Padmasambhava/Yeshe Tsogyal/Sangye Menla/Gesar of Ling: Monthly depending on lunar calendar, check the website for details.

PALYUL CENTRE UK
Tradition: Tibetan
School: Nyingma
Meetings: 3 Rotherfield Street, Islington, London N1 3EE
Charity No.: 109465
Postal Address: Palyul Centre UK, 3 Rotherfield Street, Islington, London N1 3EE
Telephone Contact: 020 7359 5964 (Centre)
Or 07933 941550
Or 07841 286362
Fax: 020 7359 5964
Email: office@palyul.org.uk
Website(s): www.palyul.org.uk

Palyul Centre UK was established by Khenpo Pema Choephel Rinpoche under the guidance of His Holiness Penor Rinpoche to provide a better understanding of Tibetan Buddhism, especially of the Palyul Tradition, and make Buddhist teachings available and accessible to the growing number of students and practitioners in the west. Its principal purpose is to provide a place for contemplation, study, and meditation and through this to help with the most important task of preserving and spreading the teachings of Lord Buddha in this

rapidly changing world to the benefit of all sentient beings.

Palyul Centre UK opened its permanent premises on July 7th 2003. Please contact for details of future activities.

The Palyul Tradition:

The first throne holder of the Palyul lineage was the Vidyadhara (Knowledge holder) Kunzang Sherab who assumed the spiritual leadership of the newly-built Palyul monastery in 1665. Within the Nyingma School, the Palyul tradition traces its lineage back through the great treasure revealer, Migyur Dorje to the Dakini, Yeshe Tsogyal, her guru, Padmasambhava, to the first human teacher, Garap Dorje who received transmission from Avalokiteshvara and so on, originating in the Dharmakaya sphere of Samantabhadra.

The highly disciplined monks of the Palyul lineage have perpetuated a tradition that has come to be known as the tradition of accomplishment. This series of practices and retreats commence with the 30 day foundation practice retreat, followed by the 44 day tummo tsa-lung practice; the 400,000 repetitions of the foundation practices; the 40 day tigal transmission; the 40 day inner clear light tigal practice; the 30 day darkness practice; the training in sound; the dream state; and the pure realms. Finally, during the three year retreat, the recitations of the three roots and the practice of trekchî are accomplished.

PURE LAND BUDDHIST FELLOWSHIP
Tradition: Pure Land
Meetings: By arrangement
Postal Address: Pure Land Buddhist Fellowship, c/o Jim Pym, Flat 1F2, 208 Morningside Road, Edinburgh, EH10 4QQ.
Telephone Contact: 0131 446 3473 (Jim Pym
Email: Jimpym@aol.com

Entry continued on the following page.

UK National Organisations

The Pure Land Buddhist Fellowship (PLBF) is an informal national network linking together Buddhists whose belief and practice is that of the Pure Land or Other Power tradition of Mahayana Buddhism. Although many of our members are associated with the Japanese Jodoshinshu (Shin) school, there are many other traditions which advocate reliance on the power of Buddhas or Bodhisattvas rather than on our own efforts. Thus the PLBF is non-sectarian.

We publish our own quarterly journal, Pure Land Notes, which carries articles, letters, poems and reviews. Details can be obtained by writing to the editor. We also try to answer queries and provide information on the beliefs and practises of Pure Land Buddhism. We also have occasional meetings and details appear in the journal. We do not have a centre and the addresses given are for contact purposes only.

RIGPA FELLOWSHIP
Tradition: Tibetan
School: Nyingma
Meetings: 330 Caledonian Road, London N1 1BB
Charity No.: 279315
Postal Address: Rigpa Fellowship, 330 Caledonian Road, London N1 1BB
Telephone Contact: 020 7700 0185
Email: enquiries@rigpauk.org.uk
Website(s):www.rigpa.org.uk

Rigpa Fellowship is an international Buddhist organisation with centres and groups in eleven countries around the world under the spiritual direction of Sogyal Rinpoche, author of the highly acclaimed spiritual classic The Tibetan Book of Living and Dying

Rigpa seeks to make the teachings of Buddha available to benefit as many people as possible and to offer those following the Buddhist teachings a complete path of study, practice and retreats led by Sogyal Rinpoche, on topics such as

meditation, compassion, healing and spiritual care for the dying. Please contact the office for a programme of events.

Rigpa has branches in Birmingham, Edinburgh, Lewes and Norwich, please see the entries under those cities in the appropriate sections of the Directory. There are also Study and Practice Groups which meet in various parts of the country, please contact Sally Williams for details.

For information about Zam Trading, Rigpa's trading arm, please see the entry in the Resources section.

RISSHO KOSEI-KAI OF THE UK
Charity No.: 1072329
Postal Address: John Gisbey, 32 Acton Road, Whitstable, Kent CT5 1JJ
Telephone Contact: 07979 713229
Email: rkkgisubi@googlemail.com
Website(s): www.kosei-kai.or.jp

A lay Buddhist organisation, founded in Japan in 1938 by Rev. Nikkyo Niwano, to further the bodhisattva ideal and contribute to world peace by daily practice of the Lotus Sutra teachings. The Sutra of the Lotus Flower of the Wonderful Law (The Lotus Sutra) is a holy scripture of the Mahayana tradition.

SAMATHA TRUST
Tradition: Theravada
Meetings: The Samatha Centre, Greenstreete, Llangunllo, Knighton Wales
Charity No.: 266367
Postal Address: Hon Secretary, The Samatha Trust, The Samatha Centre, Greenstreete, Llangunllo, Knighton, Powys,
Telephone Contact: 01223 740407 (Rachael Hall, beginners courses)
Email: info@samatha.org
Website(s): www.samatha.org

The Trust's purpose is to foster the development of

Entry continued over the following page.

Buddhist Meditation Practice
www.samatha.org

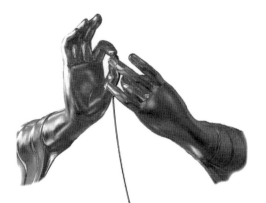

The meditation technique taught is based on mindfulness of breathing; beginning with samatha to develop calm and inner strength, leading on to clarity and understanding. It is particularly suitable for those looking for a way to develop meditation practice and the benefits it can bring, whilst continuing with the challenges of everyday life. This path, unifying calm and insight was followed by the Buddha himself and sits at the heart of the Theravadin tradition.

email: info@samatha.org
Or write to:
The Secretary
The Samatha Centre,
Greenstreete,
Llangunllo, Powys
LD7 1SP
The Samatha Trust
is a Registered Charity

As well as practising meditation local groups engage in dahmma discussion, chanting using traditional pali texts and practical work to establish dhamma within. Increased peace and awareness bring an ability to make the most of oneself in daily life.

Classes and groups meet regularly across the UK - see the specific entries in the directory. There are also weekend courses for beginners and longer courses for experienced meditators at the Centre in Wales.

Samatha meditation, a traditional technique of self-cultivation leading to inner strength, tranquillity and knowledge. The meditation method has its origins in ancient India, but developed over recent centuries in Thailand and was brought to Britain in 1963.

The Trust has a national Centre in Wales, a converted farmhouse with individual accommodation, forest meditation-huts and a purpose-built shrine hall, where regular courses for beginners and experienced meditators are held in a rural setting. The grounds consist of more than eighty acres of hill country, including rivers, footpaths and substantial areas of woodland. Pictures and further information will be found on the Trust's pages on the World Wide Web (see below).

Local classes offering instruction in meditation are held in many parts of Britain. Other activities from time to time include groups for experienced meditators; study-groups working on aspects of Southern Buddhist (Theravada) theory, practice and texts; chanting; celebration of pujas; and occasional work relating to Mahayana and other traditions.

SANG-NGAK-CHO-DZONG
Tradition: Tibetan
School: Nyingma
Meetings: Various
Charity No.: 1019886
Postal Address: Administrative Secretary, Sang-ngak-cho-dzong, PO Box 65, Penarth, Vale of Glamorgan, CF64 1HH (For enquiries about Sang-ngak-cho-dzong and the apprenticeship programme.)
Email: queries@arobuddhism.org
Website(s): www.arobuddhism.org

Sang-ngak-cho-dzong is dedicated to the establishment of the ngakphang sangha in the West. It was founded in 1977 by Ngak'chang Rinpoche under the patronage and encouragement

of HH Dudjom Rinpoche. It is affiliated to the 'Confederate Sanghas of Aro' an international association of charitable organisations dedicated to the preservation of the lineage of Khyungchen Aro Lingma (1886 - 1923) with branches in Austria, Finland, Germany, Holland, Malta, Norway, Sweden, Switzerland, and the USA.

Sang-ngak-cho-dzong follows the Tibetan Nyingma Ngak'phang tradition, according to the Aro gTer lineage. The Aro gTer is a non-monastic non-liturgical tradition of Vajrayana. It emphasises the importance of everyday life as practice.

Local Groups meet regularly for practice and the meetings include periods of silent sitting meditation and yogic song from the Aro gTer. Some also include an informal talk or introductory teachings by ordained Buddhist practitioners.

Open Teaching Retreats are held on three weekends each year. These provide an accessible introduction to the theory and practice of Nyingma Vajrayana but are suitable for both beginners and experienced practitioners. They are designed for those who wish to explore the possibility of 'apprenticeship' but students with commitments to other teachers are warmly welcomed. Retreats include empowerments; direct guidance in practice; in-depth discussion and personal interviews with the Lamas. Details of the retreats, open teaching days and other events can be found in the free quarterly newsletter, available from the Administrative Secretary.

Membership of Friends of Sang-ngak-cho-dzong costs £20 a year. Friends support the work of the charity in making the ngak'phang tradition better known in the West. Friends also receive free access to the on-line magazine Vision which contains articles, poems, photographs and interviews. Sang-ngak-cho-dzong also produces booklets, tapes, cards and transcripts of teachings.

SGI-UK
Tradition: Nichiren
Charity No.: 1104491
Postal Address: The Secretary, SGI-UK, Taplow Court, Taplow, Nr MAIDENHEAD Berkshire SL6 OER
Telephone Contact: 01628 773163
Fax: 01628 773055
Email: mike.yeadon@sgi-uk.org
Website(s): www.sgi-uk.org

Soka Gakkai International - (Buddhist Society for the Creation of Value) is a world-wide lay society founded upon the Buddhist teachings of Nichiren (1222 - 1282). SGI provides support for people in their practice of Buddhism and their study of Nichiren's writings, which stress the importance of the Lotus Sutra. SGI-UK has about three hundred local groups throughout the UK. These groups hold monthly discussion meetings, where people exchange experience of, and insights from, their practice of Buddhism. Guests are warmly welcomed. The address of your local group can be obtained from the contact below.

SGI-UK is also a movement for peace, education and culture, based on the philosophy and ideals of Nichiren Buddhism, engaging in a wide range of local and national activities to this end. Some recent examples of these have been: Conflict and Peace Forums dealing with conflict resolution and peace journalism, academic conferences and lectures on Buddhism and Asian philosophies, cultural activities and arts festivals.

VIPASSANA FELLOWSHIP
Tradition: Theravada
School: Vipassana
Postal Address: Vipassana Fellowship, 33 Fir Street, Southport, PR8 6HD
Telephone Contact: 08704 325 325
Email: fellowship@vipassana.com
Website(s): www.vipassana.com

The Vipassana Fellowship exists to promote the practice of Samatha and Vipassana meditation in a Buddhist context. Its teachings are based on the Pali Canon and the early commentaries. It was founded in 1997 by Andrew Quernmore.

In recent years retreats have been offered in England, Finland and Sri Lanka. Days of meditation are organised in Northwest England and occasionally in London and elsewhere. There is also a well-established 90-day online meditation course that takes place several times each year suitable for beginners and experienced meditators.

The Buddhist Homelands scheme promotes the practice of Buddhist meditation in the countries of early Buddhism.

WESTERN CH'AN FELLOWSHIP
Tradition: Chinese
School: Ch'an
Meetings: Mid Wales.
Charity No.: 1068637
Postal Address: Simon Child, 24 Woodgate Avenue, Bury, Lancashire BL9 7RU
Telephone Contact: 0161 761 1945 (Simon Child)
Or 01934 842231 (Dr John Crook)
Fax: 0161 763 3221 (Simon Child)
Email: secretary@westernchanfellowship.org
Website(s): www.westernchanfellowship.org

The Western Ch'an Fellowship offers intensive retreats in orthodox Ch'an (Chinese Zen) following introductory Western Zen Retreats. It also offers retreats introducing Mahamudra and basic Tantra. Other activities include walks in wilderness areas, pilgrimages to Buddhist lands, a Dharma study group and support for affiliated and associated groups in various part of the UK (for details see the geographical sections of the Directory. Affiliated groups are those whose activities closely follow the Objects of the WCF constitution, whereas Associated Groups are more eclectic but include WCF Fellows or other WCF supporters and participants.

Entry continued on the following page.

25

Retreats are also held in Warsaw and Oslo. The periodical New Ch'an Forum provides articles on Zen, lay practice, retreats and an ongoing constructive critique of Buddhism in the West.

Teachings are based on the Lin-chi and Caodong traditions of China as taught in this century by Master Hsu-Yun and the contemporary Master Sheng Yen of the Institutes of Chung-Hwa Buddhist Culture in Taiwan and New York (Ch'an Meditation Center, 90-56 Corona Avenue, Elmhurst NY 11373)

Teacher: John Crook PhD DSc (Lin-chi and Caodong lineage holder Chuan-deng Jing Di).

Dharma advisor: Master Sheng Yen.

For information about groups listed above, see the relevant geographical sections of the Directory. For information about other groups, please contact the Fellowship.

ZEN PRACTICE CENTRE TRUST (Affiliated to the Kanzeon Sangha)
Tradition: Zen
School: Soto/Rinzai
Meetings: Various
Charity No.: 289863
Postal Address: David Scott, c/o Everyman Bistro, 9 Hope St., Liverpool L1 9BH
Telephone Contact: 0151 709 0813 (David Scott)
Or 0151 706 0125 (David Scott)
Email: dl.scott@virgin.net
Website(s): www.zenbuddhism.co.uk or www.liverpool-zen.org.uk

The Zen Practice Centre Trust operates under the auspices of the abbot of Kanzeon Sangha, Genpo Merzel Roshi, who is also the spiritual leader of the White Plum Sangha (the umbrella organisation for teachers given transmission by Taizan Maezumi Roshi, the founder of Los Angeles Zen Center). For details of all White Plum retreats, sessins, Big

Mind workshops and local sitting groups in the U.K please contact those listed below or see the two websites.

ENGLAND

AVON

BATH

BATH DIAMOND WAY BUDDHIST CENTRE
Tradition: Tibetan
School: Karma-Kagyu
Meetings: 4 Stuart Place, Bath, BA2 3RQ
Affiliated to: Diamond Way Buddhism UK, UK
National Organisations
Charity No.: 1093406
Postal Address: Bath Diamond Way
Buddhist Centre, 4 Stuart Place, Bath, BA2 3RQ
Telephone Contact: 01225 400923
Or 07866 203318
Email: bath@dwbuk.org
Website(s): www.diamondway-
buddhism.co.uk

The Bath group is located in a quiet area about 2
miles from the city centre. We have a small library
with Buddhist books and magazines, lecture tapes
and a selection of meditation booklets.

Regular Meditation Times:

Wednesday 7:00pm: Introductory talk and guided
16th Karmapa meditation, for people who are new
to Buddhism and those who have been practising
for many years. There is plenty of time to answer
any questions you may have.

Sunday 7:00pm: Guided 16th Karmapa meditation.

THERAVADA GROUP
Tradition: Theravada
Meetings: Hartridge Buddhist Monastery,
England, Devon, Honiton
Postal Address: Carol and Bill Huxley,
Lavender House, 17 Bloomfield Park, Bath BA2
2BY
Telephone Contact: 01225 314500 (Carol
& Bill Huxley)
Email: lavenderhouse@bt.internet.com

THERAVADA MEDITATION CLASS
Tradition: Theravada
Meetings: In the centre of Bath at the Central
United Reform Church.
Affiliated to: London Buddhist Vihara,
England, London, W 4
Telephone Contact: 01225 448988
(Sumana)
Email: deborah.smith@psychologist.ms
Website(s): www.psychologist.ms

Theravada Meditation Class taught by Sumana,
Deborah Smith, an experienced Theravada
Buddhist who is closely connected with the
London Buddhist Vihara. The Classes are every
Monday at 7.30 - 9.30pm involving meditation,
instruction, a Buddhist talk and discussion.
Beginners and advanced meditators are very
welcome.

DECHEN IN BATH
Tradition: Tibetan
School: Kagyu-Sakya
Meetings: Stillpoint, Broad Street Place, Bath
BA1 5LH
Affiliated to: Dechen Community, UK National
Organisations
Charity No.: 282717
Telephone Contact: 0117 924 4424
Email: bristol@dechen.org
Website(s): www.dechen.org

Introductory Classes are held Tuesdays at 8 p.m.
These evenings comprise a meditation followed by
a short talk on an aspect of the foundations of
Buddhism, and will end with a cup of tea and time
to ask questions. All are welcome.

BATH/BRISTOL

BATH/BRISTOL SAMATHA GROUP
Tradition: Theravada
Affiliated to: Samatha Trust, UK National
Organisations

Entry continued on the following page.

Telephone Contact: 0117 925 5183 (Chris Gilchrist)
Or 0117 941 1902 (Rupert Gethin)
Email: info@samatha.org
Website(s): www.samatha.org

BRISTOL

BRISTOL BUDDHIST CENTRE (FWBO)
Tradition: FWBO
Meetings: 162 Gloucester Road, Bishopston, Bristol BS7 8NT
Affiliated to: Friends Of The Western Buddhist Order, UK National Organisations
Charity No.: 900165
Postal Address: Bristol Buddhist Centre, 162 Gloucester Road, Bishopston, Bristol BS7 8NT
Telephone Contact: 0117 924 9991
Or 0117 953 1106
Fax: 0117 924 9991
Email: office@bristol-buddhist-centre.fsnet.co.uk
Website(s): www.bristol-buddhist-centre.fsnet.co.uk

Weekly drop-in introductory meditation and Dharma classes are held at the Centre on Tuesday evenings at 7.30pm and Wednesdays at 1.00pm. We also run other introductory and more in-depth classes and courses, as well as day and weekend events on meditation, Dharma study, yoga, art, communication, healing, etc. Weekend retreats in the country take place every month. The Centre shop sells books, tapes, cards, posters, meditation stools and cushions, and so on.

BRISTOL CH'AN GROUP
Tradition: Chinese
School: Ch'an
Meetings: The Coach House, 40A Eastfield, Westbury-on-Trym, Bristol BS9 4BE
Affiliated to: Western Ch'an Fellowship, UK National Organisations
Postal Address: Bristol Ch'an Group, 6 Tyne Road, Bristol, BS7 8EE
Telephone Contact: 0117 924 8819 (Sally

and Mike Masheder)
Or 0117 907 0462 (Bruce McLaughlin)
Email: bristol@westernchanfellowship.org
Website(s):
www.westernchanfellowship.org/bristol

See details under Western Ch'an Fellowship (UK National Organisations).

Meetings on Wednesday evenings at 7:30 for meditation and an informal discussion. Organises programme of short weekend retreats.

Meditation Instructor: Dr John Crook.

BRISTOL DIAMOND WAY BUDDHIST CENTRE
Tradition: Tibetan
School: Karma-Kagyu
Meetings: 6c Robertson Drive, St. Annes, Bristol BS4 4JB
Affiliated to: Diamond Way Buddhism UK, UK National Organisations
Charity No.: 1093406
Postal Address: Bristol Diamond Way Buddhist Centre 6c Robertson Drive, St. Annes, Bristol BS4 4JB
Telephone Contact: 07929313315 (Bartek or Iwona)
Email: bristol@dwbuk.org
Website(s): www.diamondway-buddhism.co.uk

The Bristol group is located in St Annes.

Regular Meditation Times

Tuesday 7:00pm: Introductory talk and guided 16th Karmapa meditation, for people who are new to Buddhism and those who have been practising for many years. There is plenty of time to answer any questions you may have.

BRISTOL SHAMBHALA MEDITATION GROUP
Tradition: Tibetan

England

School: Kagyu-Nyingma
Meetings: 13 Clifton Vale, Clifton, Bristol
Affiliated to: London Shambhala Meditation
Centre, England, London, SW 4
Charity No.: 1073977
Telephone Contact: 0117 970 6586
Or 01275 843581
Email: bristol@shambhala.org.uk
Website(s): www.bristol.shambhala-
europe.org

See London Shambhala Centre, London SW4 for
further details.

BRISTOL SOTO ZEN DOJO
Tradition: Zen
School: Soto
Meetings: 91-93 Gloucester Road, Bishopston,
Bristol BS7 8AT
Affiliated to: International Zen Association
UK, UK National Organisations
Charity No.: 1069941
Postal Address: Bristol Zen Dojo, 91-93
Gloucester Road, Bishopston, Bristol BS7 8AT
Telephone Contact: 0117 942 4347
(answerphone)
Email: greatlengths@connectfree.co.uk
Website(s): www.izauk.org

Zazen: Tuedays: 7.00am; Wednesdays: 6.30pm;
Thursdays: 7.00am; Fridays: 6.00pm; Sundays:
8.30am.

Introduction: Wednesday 6pm

Half-Day: 1st Sunday of each month at 8.30am

DOGEN SANGHA BUDDHIST GROUP
Tradition: Zen
School: Soto
Meetings: 21 Melbourne Road, Bishopstown,
Bristol, BS7 8LA
Postal Address: Dogen Sangha Buddhist
Group, 21 Melbourne Road, Bishopstown, Bristol,

BS7 8LA
Telephone Contact: 0117 924 3828 (Mike
Luetchford)
Fax: 0117 924 3828
Email: info@dogensangha.org.uk
Website(s): www.dogensangha.org.uk

Contact Michael Eido Luetchford for full details of
the programmes.

Located in the ancient port city of Bristol in the
South West of England, Dogen Sangha Buddhist
Group holds weekly Zazen practice and talks on
Buddhism based on the teachings of Zen Master
Dogen, the 13th century monk and philosopher
who established the practice of Zazen in Japan.

DZOGCHEN BRISTOL
Tradition: Tibetan
School: Dzogchen
Affiliated to: Dzogchen Community UK, UK
National Organisations
Email: catrionamundle@blueyonder.co.uk
Website(s): www.dzogchencommunity.org

See UK NATIONAL ORGANISATIONS

LAM RIM BRISTOL BUDDHIST CENTRE
Tradition: Tibetan
School: Gelugpa
Meetings: Lam Rim Bristol, 12 Victoria Place,
Bedminster, Bristol, BS3 3BP
Affiliated to: Lam Rim Buddhist Centre,
Wales, Monmouthshire, Penrhos
Charity No.: 294470
Postal Address: Lam Rim Bristol Buddhist
Centre, 12 Victoria Place, Bedminster, Bristol, BS3
3BP
Telephone Contact: 0117 963 9089
Or 0117 923 1138
Or 0117 968 4784
Email: mike@lamrim.org.uk
Website(s): www.lamrim.org.uk

The Centre follows the Tibetan Gelugpa Tradition

Entry continued on the following page.

29

under the guidance of Ven. Geshe Damchö Yonten. Geshe Lobsang Thinley (the resident monk) teaches every Tuesday.

Meetings are on Monday evening (7.30, basic meditation), Tuesday evening (7.00, Tara Puja plus teachings), Thursday evening (7.30, introductory talks and discussion) and some weekends.

Within the Lam Rim Centre is the Centre for Whole Health where complementary medicine is practised and a large hall where courses in Tai Chi, Yoga, Shiatsu, massage etc are offered.

LONGCHEN FOUNDATION
Tradition: Tibetan
School: Kagyu-Nyingma
Meetings: Bristol
Affiliated to: Longchen Foundation, UK National Organisations
Charity No.: 802247
Telephone Contact: 01179 441030 (Stephen Hinde)
Email: longchenIHE@bigfoot.com
Website(s): www.longchenfoundation.com

The Longchen Foundation was established by Chögyam Trungpa Rinpoche and Dilgo Khyentse Rinpoche, two of the great Tibetan teachers of the 20th century, to pass on the authentic Mahayana MahaAti (Dzogchen) teachings of the Nyingma lineage to the west. The spiritual director and principal teacher, Rigdzin Shikpo, one of Trungpa Rinpoche's earliest western students and a qualified lama of the Nyingma tradition, was entrusted by them to teach in direct response to the needs of westerners and is among the most experienced and inspiring Buddhist teachers in Britain.

The Foundation is a community of Buddhist teachers, meditation instructors and students practising these teachings with the vision of liberating the hearts of beings. For details of weekend courses, retreats, publications,

newsletters, please visit our website.

The Lions Roar is a course that introduces the view and innermost teachings of the Longchen tradition and offers a deep and authentic grounding in the practice of meditation. It is suitable for total beginners and experienced meditators. The course is available in Britain and in Germany.

SAKYA THINLEY RINCHEN LING
Tradition: Tibetan
School: Kagyu-Sakya
Meetings: 121 Sommerville Road, St Andrews, Bristol
Affiliated to: Dechen Community, UK National Organisations
Charity No.: 282717
Postal Address: Sakya Thinley Rinchen Ling, 121 Sommerville Road, St Andrews, BRISTOL BS6 5BX
Telephone Contact: 0117 924 4424
Fax: 0117 924 4424
Email: bristol@dechen.org
Website(s): www.dechen.org

Sakya Thinley Rinchen Ling is the principal Sakya centre of the Dechen Community. It was founded in Bristol in 1977 by Karma Thinley Rinpoche and Lama Jampa Thaye. Its purpose is to transmit the contemplative and philosophical teachings of the Sakya tradition which is currently led by H.H. the 41st Sakya Trizin. Over the last three decades Sakya Thinley Rinchen Ling has grown into one of the leading centres of Tibetan Buddhism in the United Kingdom.

SANG-NGAK-CHO-DZONG
Tradition: Tibetan
School: Nyingma
Meetings: Please contact Ngakma Metsal for details.
Affiliated to: Sang-Ngak-Cho-Dzong, UK National Organisations
Charity No.: 1019886

Postal Address: 01453 546030
Email: metsal@ukonline.co.uk
Website(s): www.aroter.org

See UK National Organisations.

THERAVADA BUDDHIST CENTRE
Tradition: Theravada
Meetings: Bristol Theravada Buddhist Centre, 11 Fernbank Road, Redland, Bristol, BS6 6QA.
Affiliated to: Buddhavihara Temple, England, West Midlands, Birmingham
Charity No.: 1082096
Postal Address: Bristol Theravada Buddhist Centre, 11 Fernbank Road, Redland, Bristol, BS6 6QA.
Telephone Contact: 07783 204820
Email: info@theravadabuddhisminbristol.org
Website(s): www.theravadabuddhisminbristol.org

The Theravada Buddhist Centre is a newly established centre (October 2006) in Bristol open to anyone wanting to practise Vipassana meditation and learn about Theravada Buddhism, the oldest surviving school of Buddhism. The centre is run by Phramaha Bhatsakorn Piyobhaso, a resident Thai monk based in Bristol.

Talks take place every Wednesday evening from 7pm to 9pm and are open to everyone. They are suitable both for those who are interested in learning how to meditate and to understand the the role of meditation in daily life as well as those who want to find out more about classical Buddhism. The talks include regular discussions on the cornerstones of Theravada Buddhism, namely, the Triple Gem, the Four Noble Truths and the Middle Way.

UNIVERSITY OF BRISTOL SAMATHA GROUP
Tradition: Theravada
Meetings: University of Bristol Ecumenical Chaplaincy.

Affiliated to: Samatha Trust, UK National Organisations
Postal Address: Rupert Gethin, University of Bristol, Department of Theology and Religious Studies, 3 Woodland Road, Bristol BS8 1TB
Email: Rupert.Gethin@bristol.ac.uk
Website(s): www.samatha.org

Beginners' class in mindfulness of breathing in the tradition of the Samatha Association.

Please contact Rupert Gethin for further detail.

WESTBURY-ON-TRYM

WESTBURY ON TRYM MEDITATION GROUP
Postal Address: Hebe Welbourn, Westbury Meditation Group, Elsie Briggs House, 39 Church Road, Westbury on Trym Bristol BS9 3EQ
Telephone Contact: 0117 950 6451

Meets on Wednesdays at 7.30pm. Christian setting, Zen practice, drawing on locally available teaching.

BEDFORDSHIRE

BEDFORD

BEDFORD AREA BUDDHIST INFORMATION
Affiliated to: Amaravati Buddhist Monastery, UK National Organisations
Postal Address: David Stubbs, 1 Peaches Close, Harrold, Bedfordshire MK 43 7DX
Telephone Contact: 01234 720892 (David Stubbs - evenings only).
Fax: 01234 721600
Email: Buddhism@image-maker.demon.co.uk

Since the Bedfordshire Buddhist Society has now disbanded, Mr Stubbs acts as a contact for Buddhists in the area, especially for lay supporters of Amaravati Buddhist Monastery.

LEIGHTON BUZZARD

LEIGHTON BUZZARD MEDITATION GROUP
Tradition: All
Telephone Contact: 07876 441599
Email: anne.solomon@ntlworld.com

An informal group of Buddhists of various traditions which meets on the 2nd Tuesday and 4th Wednesday of the month for meditation, informal discussion and to keep in touch. Telephone for details of meeting place.

BERKSHIRE

NEWBURY

NEWBURY CH'AN GROUP
Tradition: Chinese
School: Ch'an
Affiliated to: Western Ch'an Fellowship, UK National Organisations
Telephone Contact: 01635 46139
Email: newbury@westernchanfellowship.org
Website(s):
www.westernchanfellowship.org/newbury

A meditation group meeting weekly in the Ch'an (Chinese Zen) tradition.

Meetings are on Tuesdays at 7:30pm.

For further details contact: Dave and Aurie McKay

READING

BERKSHIRE THERAVADAN GROUP
Tradition: Theravada
Meetings: 58 Norries Avenue, Wokingham, RG40 1UG
Affiliated to: Cittaviveka, Chithurst Buddhist Monastery, England, West Sussex, Chithurst
Postal Address: c/o Anthea West, 58 Norries Avenue, Wokingham, RG40 1UG

Telephone Contact: 0118 979 8101
Email: anthea@west8068.freeserve.co.uk

The group meets on 2nd and 4th wednesdays at 8pm for short evening puja, meditation and discussion on aspects of the teachings.

READING BUDDHIST PRIORY
Tradition: Zen
School: Soto
Meetings: Reading Buddhist Priory, 176 Cressingham Road, Reading RG2 7LW
Affiliated to: The Order Of Buddhists Contemplatives, UK National Organisations
Charity No.: 1092463
Postal Address: Reading Buddhist Priory, 176 Cressingham Road, Reading RG2 7LW
Telephone Contact: 0118 986 0750
(Please telephone between 9.30am and 12.30 or between 2.30 and 5.30 Tues - Sat)
Email: info@readingbuddhistpriory.org.uk
Website(s):www.readingbuddhistpriory.org.uk

The Reading Priory was opened in January 1990 as an extension of Throssel Hole Buddhist Abbey, Hexham, Northumberland (See UK National Organisations).

Both Throssel Hole Buddhist Abbey and Reading Buddhist Priory are part of the Order of Buddhist Contemplatives, the international umbrella organisation. A senior monk is based at the Priory where there is a regular schedule of Meditation, services and day retreats. Meditation instruction is available and people new to the practice are very welcome to visit. The Prior also visits local southern groups as well as giving public talks and leading weekend retreats.

READING DIAMOND WAY BUDDHIST CENTRE
Tradition: Tibetan
School: Karma-Kagyu
Meetings: Life Story, 17 Eldon Square, Reading, RG1 4DP

England

Affiliated to: Diamond Way Buddhism UK, UK National Organisations
Charity No.: 1093406
Postal Address: Reading Diamond Way Buddhist Centre, Life Story, 17 Eldon Square, Reading, RG1 4DP
Telephone Contact: 07952 722249 (Joel)
Email: reading@dwbuk.org
Website(s): www.diamondway-buddhism.co.uk

The Reading group is located in the heart of the town, in a lovely Georgian House within easy walking distance of the rail station. Everyone is welcome to join us for a cup of tea, talk and meditation on Monday nights. On the first Monday of every month we have an introduction to Diamond Way buddhism for beginners and for more advanced practices we meet on Sunday mornings. We have a small library with Buddhist books and magazines, lecture tapes and a selection of meditation booklets.

Regular Meditation Times:

Sunday 10:00am: Foundational Practices (Tib. Ngondro). Call to confirm.

Monday 7:30pm: A brief talk on a Buddhist topic followed by 16th Karmapa guided meditation.

Wednesday 7:30pm: A brief talk on a Buddhist topic followed by 16th Karmapa guided meditation.

First Monday of every Month: Introduction and 16th Karmapa guided meditation: for people who are new to Buddhism and those who have been practicing for many years. There is plenty of time to answer any questions you may have.

SLOUGH

LUMBINI NEPALESE BUDDHA DHARMA SOCIETY UK
See UK NATIONAL ORGANISATIONS

TAPLOW

SGI-UK
See UK National Organisations.

BUCKINGHAMSHIRE

MILTON KEYNES

MILTON KEYNES FWBO
Tradition: FWBO
Affiliated to: Friends Of The Western Buddhist Order, UK National Organisations
Postal Address: Milton Keynes FWBO, c/o Cambridge Buddhist Centre, 36-38 Newmarket Road, Cambridge, CB5 8DT
Telephone Contact: 01223 577553
Email: info@cambridgebuddhistcentre.com
Website(s): www.cambridgebuddhistcentre.com

Regular meetings for meditation, study and puja as well as activities for newcomers.

MILTON KEYNES SERENE REFLECTION MEDITATION GROUP
Tradition: Zen
School: Soto
Affiliated to: The Order Of Buddhists Contemplatives, UK National Organisations
Telephone Contact: 01908 560620 (Keith Ayling)
Or 07814 522800 (Keith Ayling)
Or 01280 813962 (Hilaire MacCarthy)

The group meets on the first Monday evening of the month at 7.30pm. Meditation instruction is available and newcomers are welcome. The group receives regular visits from monks of the Order of Buddhist Contemplatives. Please phone for details.

NIPPONZAN MYOHOJI PEACE PAGODA
Tradition: Nichiren shu
Meetings: Willen, Milton Keynes
Affiliated to: Nipponzan Myohoji Monastery,
Willen, Milton Keynes MK15 0BA
Telephone Contact: 01908 663652
Fax: 01908 663652
Website(s): mkbuddhism.tripod.com

Nipponzan Myohoji is a monastic order, Japanese
in origin, coming out of the Nichiren school (no
connection with Nichiren Shoshu or Soka Gakkai).
The Teacher and founder is the Most Venerable
Nichidatsu Fuji who passed away in 1985.

Four resident monks/nuns form the basis of the
temple. Our 'Sangha' has a medium base of
frequent visitors; very many friends and helpers
when projects are involved. This is due to the very
outgoing nature of the temple.

Our basic practice is the chanting of the mantra
Namu myoho-renge-kyo to the accompaniment of
a prayer drum. This prayer is the essence of the
Lotus Sutra and works as a medicine to heal
people and society. There is daily chanting in the
temple (in traditional Japanese style including a
Zen garden - plenty of space for visitors).

The Order organises frequent walks in troubled
areas, sometimes fasts and has a strong interest in
the inter-faith movement as well as in the anti-
nuclear movement and in non-violence. It also
seeks to build more peace pagodas (stupas
dedicated to world peace); the current temple is
still under construction, although it is in use.

CAMBRIDGESHIRE

CAMBRIDGE

CAMBRIDGE AMARAVATI GROUP
Tradition: Theravada
In members homes

Amaravati Buddhist Monastery, UK National
Organisations
01223 246 257 (Dan Jones)
danjones@supanet.com

This group grew from a few local Buddhists, who
were interested in the teachings from Amaravati
Buddhist monastery near Hemel Hempstead. They
meet fortnightly on Sunday evenings in each
others' houses to meditate together, with a brief
Buddhist ceremony beforehand, and a cup of tea
and chat afterwards. Amaravati monastery is in
the Theravadin tradition of Buddhism, generally
found in countries such as Thailand, Sri Lanka and
Burma, although most of the monks and nuns at
Amaravati are Westerners.

The type of meditation taught there is usually
Vipassana or Insight Meditation. The group
functions as a way for meditators to come
together, rather than as a taught class, and is open
and sociable. Over the years people have joined
who are interested in different forms of Vipassana
meditation, or in different Buddhist traditions
altogether. The group also acts as a contact point
for people interested in visiting Amaravati, to find
out more directly about this sort of meditation and
Buddhist way of life.

CAMBRIDGE BUDDHIST CENTRE
Tradition: FWBO
Meetings: 38 Newmarket Road, Cambridge
CB5 8DT
Affiliated to: Friends Of The Western
Buddhist Order, UK National Organisations
Charity No.: 297894
Postal Address: Cambridge Buddhist Centre,
38 Newmarket Road, Cambridge CB5 8DT
Telephone Contact: 01223 577553
Email: info@cambridgebuddhistcentre.com
Website(s):
www.cambridgebuddhistcentre.com

As well as courses in meditation and Buddhism,
the Centre holds regular drop-in classes for

newcomers and experienced meditators, and a full programme of yoga classes and courses. Around the Centre is a thriving mandala of other activities, including residential communities and Windhorse Trading, a large team-based right livelihood business.

CAMBRIDGE BUDDHIST SOCIETY
Meetings: Friends Meeting House, Jesus Lane, Cambridge
Telephone Contact: 01223 249732
Email: info@cambridgebuddhistsociety.org.uk
Website(s):
www.cambridgebuddhistsociety.org.uk

The Cambridge Buddhist Society organises monthly talks covering all aspects of Buddhism, with speakers from all the Buddhist traditions and schools.

The talks usually take place on the last Friday of each month at the Friends Meeting House on Jesus Lane, at 7:30 pm.The society has an e-mailing list. Everyone is welcome to the talks which are free; after the talks there is usually tea and the opportunity to speak to the teachers or have a chat with some other local Buddhists.

CAMBRIDGE CH'AN GROUP
Tradition: Chinese
School: Ch'an
Meetings: Friends Meeting House, 91-93 Hartington Grove, Cambridge
Affiliated to: Western Ch'an Fellowship, UK National Organisations
Telephone Contact: 07766 686345 (David Brown)
Or 01954 267410 (Ann Brown)
Email: cambridge@westernchanfellowship.org
Website(s):
www.westernchanfellowship.org/cambridge

Refer to entry for Western Chan Fellowship under UK National Organisations for a full description of

Ch'an Meditation and of the UK National Organisation.

The Cambridge Ch'an Group meets on the 1st and 3rd Wednesday of each month, at 7.30pm at The Friends Meeting House, 91-93 Hartington Grove, Cambridge)off Hills Road). Meditation instruction is available from an authorised instructor.

If you are interested in the opportunity to learn and practice a very effective method of meditation, whether you are a beginner or a more experienced meditator, you are welcome to attend. Please note that this is predominantly a practice session, the focus is on developing and sustaining an effective meditation practice. However there is opportunity for Q&A and most weeks we hold a discussion of a Buddhist text that illuminates effective meditation practice.

It would be appreciated if newcomers would contact David Brown on 07766 686345 a day or two in advance before attending. In particular, if you do require initial instruction, we ask that you notify the instructor in advance then arrive by 7.20pm.

CAMBRIDGE SAMATHA MEDITATION GROUP
Tradition: Theravada
Meetings: Friends Meeting House, Jesus Lane, and, during University term time, in Pembroke College.
Affiliated to: Samatha Trust, UK National Organisations
Charity No.: 266367
Postal Address: David & Rachael Hall, 47 Cavendish Avenue, Cambridge CB1 7UR
Telephone Contact: 01223 249732
Email: rmh1001@cam.ac.uk
Website(s): www.samatha.org

A Thai breathing mindfulness samatha-vipassana (calm and insight) technique is the central practice. The group runs introductory courses and groups for more experienced meditators.

Entry continued on the following page.

CAMBRIDGE SERENE REFLECTION MEDITATION GROUP

Tradition: Zen
School: Soto
Affiliated to: The Order Of Buddhists Contemplatives, UK National Organisations
Telephone Contact: 01223 411018
Email: richard.potter@potterhorgan.clara.co.uk

The group meets twice a month on Tuesdays at 7.30pm. Please contact for details.

COMMUNITY OF INTERBEING - CAMBRIDGE SANGHA

Tradition: Vietnamese
School: Thich Nhat Hanh
Affiliated to: The Community Of Interbeing, UK, UK National Organisations
Telephone Contact: 01223 842941 (Jane)
Website(s): www.interbeing.org.uk

Contact for information about local and regional activities for meditation and Days of Mindfulness. See UK National Orgaisations for details of The Community of Interbeing.

DZOGCHEN CAMBRIDGE

Tradition: Tibetan
School: Dzogchen
Affiliated to: Dzogchen Community UK, UK National Organisations
Email: peter@cambridgeacupuncture.net
Website(s): www.dzogchencommunity.org

See UK NATIONAL ORGANISATIONS

NEZANG BUDDHIST MEDITATION GROUP

Tradition: Tibetan
School: Karma-Kagyu
Meetings: Morley Memorial Primary School, Blinco Grove (off Hills Road), Cambridge
Telephone Contact: 01223 366 079 (Mary Rose Baugh)

Or 01277 222 941 (Jane Sandemann)

The Tibetan Karma Kagyu tradition is followed under the direction of Ato Rinpoche. Open meetings are held monthly except in August and December at 2.00pm on a Saturday. Meetings start with a talk by Lama Ato Rinpoche and are followed by prayer chanting and a short period of silent meditation. Teachings and meditation instructions are given. Please do not disturb others by arriving late.

There is no charge, but donations are welcome to cover costs.

PADMA LING

See UK NATIONAL ORGANISATIONS

PETERBOROUGH

PETERBOROUGH BUDDHIST GROUP (FWBO)

Tradition: FWBO
Affiliated to: Friends Of The Western Buddhist Order, UK National Organisations
Postal Address: Peterborough Buddhist Group. 36-38 Newmarket Road, Cambridge, CB5 8EG
Telephone Contact: 01223 577 553
Website(s): www.fwbo.org

CHESHIRE

CHESTER

CHESTER SAMATHA MEDITATION GROUP

Tradition: Theravada
Meetings: Bishop Lloyd's Palace, Watergate Street, Chester
Affiliated to: Samatha Trust, UK National Organisations
Postal Address: Chester Samatha Group, c/o

England

Manchester Centre for Buddhist Meditation, 19-21 High Lane, Chorlton, Manchester M21 1DJ
Telephone Contact: 01244 336283
Email: mountway@aol.com
Website(s): www.samatha.org

A small group offering practical instruction in samatha (mindfulness of breathing) meditation.

Meetings: Tuesdays at 7pm.

CHESTER ZEN GROUP
Tradition: Zen
School: Soto
Telephone Contact: 01978 759447
Fax: 01244 313685
Email: pardos@globalnet.co.uk

Lineage: Tangen Harada

Teacher: Hogen Daido Yamahata

MACCLESFIELD

KHANDRO LING
Tradition: Tibetan
School: Nyingma / Rime
Meetings: 17-27 Pierce Street, Macclesfield SK11 6ER
Charity No.: 1101397
Telephone Contact: 01625 434831
Email: gordonellis@talktalk.net
Website(s):
www.diamondheartfoundation.org.uk

Established under the inspiration of H.H. Khordong Terchen Tulku, Chhimed Rigdzin Rinpoche, and guided in consultation with James Low, his most senior student, we offer a full range pf practice and study with a programme of weekly and weekend courses. In our developing courses we shall begin offering a three year training programme in Kum Nye under the guidance of John Peacock, as well as a one day meditation retreat programme the first Saturday of the month.

NORTHWICH

COMMUNITY OF INTERBEING - NORTHWICH SANGHA
Tradition: Zen
School: Thich Nhat Hanh
Affiliated to: The Community Of Interbeing, UK, UK National Organisations
Telephone Contact: 0160 675916 (Joyce)
Email: joyce@jaisbote.f9.co.uk
Website(s): www.interbeing.org.uk

Contact for information about local and regional activities for meditation and Days of Mindfulness. See UK National Orgaisations for details of The Community of Interbeing.

WARRINGTON

WARRINGTON SAMATHA GROUP
Tradition: Theravada
Affiliated to: Samatha Trust, UK National Organisations
Telephone Contact: 01928 734996
Email: amteccorrosion@onetel.net.uk
Website(s): www.samatha.org

WILMSLOW

WILMSLOW (SAMATHA) BUDDHIST MEDITATION GROUP
Tradition: Theravada
Meetings: Wilmslow URC Church Hall
Contact rob.adkins@mac.com for current meeting place.
Affiliated to: Samatha Trust, UK National Organisations
Postal Address: Vicky Stringer, 14 Churwell Ave, Heaton Mersey, Stockport, SK4 3QE
Telephone Contact: 0161 442 7079
Email: vicki@vickistringer.freeserve.co.uk
Website(s): www.samatha.org

Entry continued on the following page.

The meditation class for beginners meets at 8:00pm on Thursday evenings. All are welcome. Please contact us to confirm time and venue.

CLEVELAND

MIDDLESBOROUGH

TEESIDE SERENE REFLECTION MEDITATION GROUP
Tradition: Zen
School: Soto
Affiliated to: The Order Of Buddhists Contemplatives, UK National Organisations
Telephone Contact: 01642 319864 (John Adams)
Or 01429 231937 (Billy Barnett)
Website(s):
www.northeastserenereflection.org.uk

The group meets on Wednesdays at 7.45pm. Meditation instruction is available and newcomers are welcome. The group receives regular visits from a senior monk from Throssel Hole Buddhist Abbey.

TEESSIDE THERAVADIN BUDDHIST GROUP
Tradition: Theravada
Meetings: Friends Meeting House, 131 Cambridge Road, Middlesborough
Affiliated to: Aruna Ratanagiri, England, Northumberland, Belsay
Postal Address: Teesside Theravadin Buddhist Group, 26 Osbourne Road, Oxbridge, Stockton on Tees, TS18 4DJ
Telephone Contact: 07786 032732
Or 01642 643071(Colin Walker)
Email:
teessidetheravadinbuddhistgroup@ne.communigate.co.uk
Website(s):
www.communigate.co.uk/ne/teessidetheravadinb uddhistgroup/contact.phtml

This is the first and only Theravadin Buddhist Group (so far!) to be set up in Teesside. The aim of the group is to provide a friendly source of advice, instruction and support for all those interested in practising or learning more about Buddhism.

The group is affiliated to and supported by Harnham Buddhist Monastery in Northumberland and at the first meeting of the group, on 29 November 2000, Ven. Punnyo and Ven. Revato from Harnham came along to lend their support and to deliver a dhamma talk.

The group meets once a fortnight on a Thursday evening at 7.30pm. Please contact us for more information.

CO DURHAM

DURHAM

DURHAM SAMATHA MEDITATION GROUP
Tradition: Theravada
Meetings: Room 2, Alington House, 4 North Bailey (nr. Cathedral), Durham City, DH1 4NE
Affiliated to: Samatha Trust, UK National Organisations
Postal Address: Peter Harvey, 10 Cedar Drive, Farewell Hall, Durham City, DH1 3TF
Telephone Contact: 0191 384 3913
Email: peter.harvey@sunderland.ac.uk
Website(s): www.samatha.org

Classes in Theravada Samatha meditation, based on mindfulness of breathing, are given by a member of the Samatha Trust. The classes begin in early October, but people are welcome to join at any time. The group meets on Mondays at 7.30pm. A practice-oriented talk is followed by a guided meditation and then an opportunity for one-to-one discussion of people's practice. Information is provided on retreats at the Samatha Trust's centre in Powys, Wales. The meditation teacher is author of several books on Buddhism.

CORNWALL

CORNWALL SERENE REFLECTION MEDITATION GROUP
Tradition: Zen
School: Soto
Meetings: The Newquay Centre, St Michaels Road, Newquay.
Affiliated to: The Order Of Buddhists Contemplatives, UK National Organisations Lotus Gate, The Avenue, Truro TR1 1HR
Telephone Contact: 01872 273887 (Pollie Harington)

The group has weekly meetings. They take place on the first Sunday of the month followed by three Wednesday evening meetings. Please phone for details before attending. Sunday meeting 10-12, Wednesday evening meetings 7.30 - 9.30. There are also regular day retreats led by Rev Master Myfanwy McCorry of Dragon Bell Temple Exeter.

SANG-NGAK-CHO-DZONG
Tradition: Tibetan
School: Nyingma
Affiliated to: Sang-Ngak-Cho-Dzong, UK National Organisations
Charity No.: 1019886
Telephone Contact: 01736 351501 (Naljorma A'dzin)
Or 01736 850373 (James Kilty)
Email: adzin_yeshe@yahoo.co.uk or
Or james@kilty.demon.co.uk
Website(s): www.aroter.org
See UK National Organisations.

HELSTON

LIZARD CH'AN GROUP
Tradition: Chinese
School: Ch'an
Meetings: Gear Hill, Mawgan, Nr Helston, Cornwall TR12 6AE

Affiliated to: Western Ch'an Fellowship, UK National Organisations
Postal Address: Gear Hill, Mawgan, Nr Helston, Cornwall TR12 6AE
Telephone Contact: 01326 221651 (Sophie Muir)
Email: lizard@westernchanfellowship.org
Website(s): www.westernchanfellowship.org/lizard

Refer to entry under Western Ch'an Fellowship under UK National Organisations. Meeting currently monthly, each 3rd Tuesday evening, 5.30 - 7.30pm; to resume fortnightly, 1st & 3rd Tuesday, Spring 2007. Practice opens with a short refuge & liturgy and continues with two half hour periods of sitting meditation with walking meditation in between. Some readings may be shared, usually with a period of silence and dedication to close.

Half and full day weekends retreats are offered, led by invited teachers.

Retreat cabin in wooded, creek side setting available for periods of short retreat, 3 days - 1 week. Enquires as above.

WEST CORNWALL ZEN CENTRE
Tradition: Zen / Ch'an
Meetings: West Cornwall Zen Centre, Tavern Coth Cottage, Churchtown, Mullion, Helston, TR12 7HN
Telephone Contact: 01326 241758 (Richard Rowlett)
Please telephone for full details, and leave a message. Buddhist Chaplaincy contact for hospitals and hospices in cornwall. Member of College of Health Care Chaplains and Association of Hospice & Palliative Care Chaplains.

ILLOGAN

ILLOGAN BUDDHIST GROUP (FWBO)
Tradition: FWBO

Entry continued on the following page.

England

Affiliated to: Friends Of The Western Buddhist Order, UK National Organisations
Telephone Contact: 01209 890 997 (Dharmacharini Sampada)

LOSTWITHIEL

KAGYU SAMYE DZONG CORNWALL
Tradition: Tibetan
School: Karma-Kagyu
Meetings: Hedra, Genville Road, Lostwithiel, Cornwall, PL22 0EP and Rock Cottage
Affiliated to: Kagyu Samye Ling Monastery And Tibetan Centre, UK National Organisations
Postal Address: Kagyu Samye Dzong, Hedra, Genville Road, Lostwithiel, Cornwall, PL22 0EP
Telephone Contact: 01208 873785
Fax: 01208 873785
Email: garuda@talk21.com
Website(s): www.cornwallbuddhism.com

Providing a space for practitioners to come together, enjoying the support of sangha and group practice.

PENZANCE

PENZANCE MEDITATION GROUP
Tradition: Theravada
Affiliated to: Hartridge Buddhist Monastery, England, Devon, Honiton
Telephone Contact: 01736 762135 (Lee)

REDRUTH

BUDDHIST MEDITATION GROUP
Tradition: Theravada
Meetings: Members Homes
Affiliated to: Hartridge Buddhist Monastery, England, Devon, Honiton
Telephone Contact: 01209 214031 (Vanessa)
Or 01209 842305 (Rose)

Meetings are held every Wednesday evening and 7.00pm to 10.00pm. There is a period of meditation, followed by study from books, tapes or talks, plus frequent visits by Monks or Nuns. Cost is met by donations (Suggested £2). Phone first to find location of meeting.

TRURO

DECHEN IN CORNWALL
Tradition: Tibetan
School: Kagyu-Sakya
Meetings: Friends' Meeting House, Paul's Terrace, Truro TR1 1HD
Affiliated to: Dechen Community, UK National Organisations
Charity No.: 282717
Telephone Contact: 07790 134180
Email: cornwall@dechen.org
Website(s): www.dechen.org

Introductory Classes: The Path of the Buddha are held every other Tuesday consisting both of a short talk on different aspects of Buddhism and an introduction to Buddhist meditation, followed by an opportunity for questions and answers and refreshments. The classes are designed for those who are new to Buddhism and the Sakya tradition.

WHITECROSS

WHITECROSS BUDDHIST MEDITATION CENTRE
Tradition: All
Meetings: The Buddhist Meditation Centre, Gilly Lane, Whitecross, Penzance
Affiliated to: Hartridge Buddhist Monastery, England, Devon, Honiton
Postal Address: The Trustee, Gilly Lane, Whitecross, Penzance, Cornwall TR20 8BZ
Telephone Contact: 01736 762135 (Lee Stevenson)
Or 01736 710284 (Carole Blackwell)
Or 01736 799170 (Molly Venning)
Email: lee.stev@tiscali.co.uk

We welcome people of all denominations. There is no resident teacher, but at the meetings every Monday at 7.00pm we have chanting, meditation, reading, questions and answers. All welcome.

CUMBRIA

DZOGCHEN CUMBRIA
Tradition: Tibetan
School: Dzogchen
Affiliated to: Dzogchen Community UK, UK National Organisations
Telephone Contact: 015 2426 2381
Or 077 6030 1266
Website(s): www.dzogchencommunity.org
See UK NATIONAL ORGANISATIONS

CARLISLE

SANG-NGAK-CHO-DZONG
Tradition: Tibetan
School: Nyingma
Meetings: Please contact Yvette Haines for details
Affiliated to: Sang-Ngak-Cho-Dzong, UK National Organisations
Charity No.: 1019886
Telephone Contact: 01228 545565
Email: yvette-haines@btinternet.com
Website(s): www.aroter.org

See UK National Organisations.

THERAVADA BUDDHIST GROUP
Tradition: Theravada
School: Starlight Healing Centre 01228 599799
Affiliated to: Aruna Ratanagiri, England, Northumberland, Belsay
Postal Address: Jean Nelson, Theravada Buddhist Group, 23 Longdyke Drive, Carlisle, Cumbria CA1 3HJ
Telephone Contact: 01228 543491

KENDAL

BUDDHIST GROUP OF KENDAL (THERAVADA)
Tradition: Theravada
Meetings: Fellside Centre, Low Fellside, Kendal, Cumbria LA9 4NH (The main entrance to the Fellside Centre is in Sepulchre Lane.)
Postal Address: The Secretary, Buddhist Group of Kendal (Theravada), Fellside Centre, Low Fellside, Kendal, Cumbria LA9 4NH
Telephone Contact: 01539 729793

Monthly open meetings are held on Sundays from 2.00pm - 4.30pm. Instruction is given in the teachings of Theravada Buddhism and meditation. All teachers have been authorised to teach Buddhism by the Theravada Sangha (community of Buddhist monks). Newcomers are welcome.

President: H J Russel-Williams. Teaching Supervision: T Gomes. Treasurer: J Gerrard (Upasaka Sumedha)

Meetings Co-ordinator: J Griffiths (Upasaka Mahinda). Secretary: J Gomes (Upasika Jayasili)

Spiritual Advisers: Venerable Balangoda Ananda Maitreya Mahanayaka Thera Abhidhaja Maharatthaguru Agga Maha Pandita DLitt DLitt (1896-1998) and Venerable Henepola Gunaratana Maha Thera MA PhD.

KESWICK

KESWICK SERENE RELECTION MEDITATION GROUP
Tradition: Zen
School: Soto
Affiliated to: The Order Of Buddhists Contemplatives, UK National Organisations
Telephone Contact: 01900 85036 (Gill James)
Email: gilljames@brackenthwaite.freeserve.co.uk

The group meets weekly on Thursdays at 7.30pm. Phone for details.

DERBYSHIRE

BAKEWELL

BAKEWELL SAMATHA GROUP
Tradition: Theravada
School: Samatha Trust, UK National Organisations
Telephone Contact: 01629 814617 (Rosemary Rose)
Email: rosemarose@google.com
Website(s): www.samatha.org

Weekly meditation and discussion classes on Thursdays 8pm during term-time.

The group meets just south of Matlock in the Scarthin Bookshop, The Promenade, Scarthin, Cromford, Derbyshire.

Directions: Heading towards Derby on the A6 turn right at the Cromford traffic lights just after Masson Mill (the Sir Richard Arkwright Mill). Heading towards Buxton on the A6, it is clearly signposted when you arrive at Cromford. Turn left at the lights. Go just a few yards and turn right up a small lane - you will see an advert for the shop. The Bookshop overlooks the Millpond behind the Greyhound Inn. Go 50 yards up Scarthin from the Market Place. Please come to the side door.

DERBY

COMMUNITY OF INTERBEING - MINDFULNESS SANGHA
Tradition: Zen
School: Thich Nhat Hanh
Affiliated to: The Community Of Interbeing, UK, UK National Organisations
Telephone Contact: 01332 732171 (Chris)
Email: chris.goacher@ntlworld.com
Website(s): www.interbeing.org.uk
Contact for information about local and regional activities for meditation and Days of Mindfulness.

See UK National Orgaisations for details of The Community of Interbeing.

GLOSSOP

HIGH PEAK THERAVADA BUDDHIST GROUP
Tradition: Theravada
Meetings: Bradbury House, Market Street, Glossop.
Affiliated to: Aruna Ratanagiri, England, Northumberland, Belsay
Postal Address: Carmel Brown, 11 Jubilee Close, Haslingden, Lancs., BB4 4RN
Telephone Contact: 01706 219747 (Carmel Brown)
Or 01457 765845 (Mai Watson)

We meet on the first Friday of each month. We usually take the five Refuges and Precepts, sit in silence together and then hold an informal discussion on a particular aspect of Buddhist Practice.

Beginners and non-Buddhists are very welcome and guidance in meditation techniques will be offered.

MATLOCK

MATLOCK SERENE REFLECTION MEDITATION GROUP
Tradition: Zen
School: Soto
Meetings: The Order Of Buddhists Contemplatives, UK National Organisations
Telephone Contact: 01629 581335 (Julie Dumelow)
Or 07759 091424 (Don Astley)

The group meets every Tuesday evening at 7.30 - 9.30. There are regular visits from a monk from Throssel Hole Buddhist Abbey. Please phone for details.

DEVON

ASHPRINGTON

SHARPHAM CENTRE FOR CONTEMPORARY BUDDHIST ENQUIRY
Meetings: Sharpham House, Ashprington, Totnes, Devon
Charity No.: 285767
Postal Address: The Secretary, Sharpham Centre, Sharpham House, Ashprington, TOTNES, Devon TQ9 7UT
Telephone Contact: 01803 732542
Fax: 01803 732037
Email: centre@sharpham-trust.org
Website(s): www.sharpham-trust.org

Although inspired and informed by Buddhist teachings, the centre does not adhere to any particular school.

The public programme offers Tuesday evening meditations and talks as well as regular meditation days and workshops on Buddhist themes and related topics. Guest speakers and workshop leaders come from various Buddhist schools or from other traditions and perspectives. There are also introductory evening classes on Buddhism and on how Buddhism interfaces with contemporary culture and issues. Beginning meditation instruction and support is available on request.

Please contact the secretary at Sharpham Centre for further details.

DARTMOOR

SOUTH DEVON CH'AN GROUP
Tradition: Chinese
School: Ch'an
Meetings: Leusdon Memorial Hall near Poundsgate in Dartmoor
Affiliated to: Western Ch'an Fellowship, UK

National Organisations
Postal Address: Wren Cottage, Silver Street, Buckfastleigh TQ11 0BQ
Telephone Contact: 01364 643560 (Pete Lowry)
Or 07737 526048
Email: southdevon@westernchanfellowship.org
Website(s): www.westernchanfellowship.org/southdevon

Refer to entry under Western Ch'an Fellowship under UK National Organisations.

Monthly half-day retreats held in a stunning, remote location. A rare chance to experience the intensive format of a Chan retreat for an afternoon. Usually every 2nd Sunday in the month. Sessions are free, donations are invited for the hall hire. Please contact the group leader Pete Lowry before coming for the first time.

EXETER

COMMUNITY OF INTERBEING - WEST COUNTRY SANGHA
Tradition: Vietnamese
School: Thich Nhat Hanh
Affiliated to: The Community Of Interbeing, UK, UK National Organisations
Telephone Contact: 01392 676402 (Jude)
Website(s): www.interbeing.org.uk

Contact for information about local and regional activities for meditation and Days of Mindfulness. See UK National Orgaisations for details of The Community of Interbeing.

DRAGON BELL TEMPLE
Tradition: Zen
School: Soto
Meetings: 14 Albion Place, Exeter EX4 6LH
Affiliated to: The Order Of Buddhists Contemplatives, UK National Organisations
Charity No.: 506094

Entry continued on the following page.

England

Postal Address: Dragon Bell Temple, 14 Albion Place, Exeter EX4 6LH
Telephone Contact: 01392 479648
Email: hmyfanwy@onetel.com
Website(s): www.dragonbelltemple.org.uk

Dragon Bell Temple is a Buddhist Temple in the Soto Zen tradition and a temple of the Order of Buddhist Contemplatives. Located in central Exeter, it is run as a neighbourhood temple, offering a place of quiet and focus in the city, solely dedicated to meditation and the practice of Buddhism.

There is a regular programme of Introductory Evenings, Services, Festivals, Dharma Talks, Meditation and Day Retreats. Overnight accommodation may be available by prior arrangement for guests who have a long distance to travel. Please contact for details of the current programme.

EXETER DIAMOND WAY BUDDHIST CENTRE
Tradition: Tibetan
School: Karma-Kagyu
Meetings: 13 Toronto Road, Exeter, EX4 6LE
Affiliated to: Diamond Way Buddhism UK, UK National Organisations
Charity No.: 1093406
Postal Address: Buddhist Centre Exeter, 13 Toronto Road, Exeter, EX4 6LE
Telephone Contact: 01392 427601
Email: exeter@dwbuk.org
Website(s): www.diamondway-buddhism.co.uk

The Exeter centre is just 10 mins walk from the city centre.

The house was bought in March 2004 and is a traditional English terrace built in the 1880s. It has been modernised whilst keeping many of it's original features - with the addition of a landscaped garden! The ground floor has a very relaxed living space where the focus is usually the open kitchen and garden, or the open fire in the lounge. There are two big rooms for people to live in.

The meditation room is in the top of the house and is now being prepared. Although using traditional Buddhist art, it is being designed to have a very contemporary feel.

The centre will become a place for a relaxed and dynamic community for those interested in meditation practise, learning about the nature of mind, and combining these with modern active lives.
Regular Meditation Times

Thursday 7:30pm: Introduction and 16th Karmapa guided meditation: for people who are new to Buddhism and those who have been practicing for many years. There is is an introductory talk before the meditation and plenty of time to answer any questions you may have.

SAKYA THINLEY NAMGYAL LING
Tradition: Tibetan
School: Kagyu-Sakya
Meetings: Exeter University School of Education Campus, Heavitree Road, Exeter EX1 2LU (500 yards from bus station)
Affiliated to: Dechen Community, UK National Organisations
Charity No.: 282717
Postal Address: Dr. Paul Rogers, 2 Dewdneys Court, Upton Pyne, Exeter EX5 5EQ
Telephone Contact: 01392 253040 (Paul Rogers)
Email: exeter@dechen.org
Website(s): www.dechen.org

Sakya Thinley Namgyal Ling was established in 1983. Lama Jampa Thaye visits periodically to bestow initiations and textual teachings from the Sakya tradition. In addition, the centre has hosted visits from H.H. Sakya Trizin and H.E. Ngor Phende Rinpoche. A continuing programme of meditation classes is offered to the public.

Introductory Classes, Every Tuesday, 7.30-9.00pm consist of a short talk on different aspects of

England

Buddhism and an introduction to Buddhist meditation, and are designed for those who are new to Buddhism and the Sakya tradition.

HONITON

HARTRIDGE BUDDHIST MONASTERY (The Devon Vihara)
Tradition: Theravada
Meetings: Odle Cottage, Upottery, Nr. Honiton, Devon EX14 9QE
Affiliated to: Amaravati Buddhist Monastery, UK National Organisations
Charity No.: 289636
Postal Address: Hartridge Buddhist Monastery, Odle Cottage, Upottery, Nr Honiton, Devon EX14 9QE
Telephone Contact: 01404 891251
Fax: 01404 890023
Email: hartridge@onetel.com

Hartridge Monastery follows the forest tradition of Theravada Buddhism, a simple and contemplative way of life that was lived and encouraged by the Buddha. It is associated with three other Monasteries in the UK: Amaravati, Cittaviveka and Aruna Ratanagiri.

Please contact the monastery for details of current activities. To receive a copy of the current newletter by email, please contact nick.ray@blueyonder.co.uk.

NEWTON ABBOT

GAIA HOUSE
Tradition: Theravada
School: Vipassana
Meetings: Gaia House, West Ogwell, Newton Abbot, Devon TQ12 6EN
Charity No.: 900339
Postal Address: The Managers, Gaia House, West Ogwell, Newton Abbot, Devon TQ12 6EN
Telephone Contact: 01626 333613

Fax: 01626 352650
Email: generalenquiries@gaiahouse.co.uk
Website(s): www.gaiahouse.co.uk

Set in a former convent among the gentle hills and woodlands of South Devon, Gaia House offers a sanctuary of contemplative calm open to all. Founded in 1984, Gaia House is the only non-affiliated retreat centre in Britain which offers guidance in different meditative disciplines from the Buddhist traditions. Our retreats are designed for both experienced meditators and beginners, of any faith or none, who seek to cultivate a path of wisdom and compassion. All retreats (with the exception of the Family and Friends retreat) are held in silence and explore the essential themes of calm attentiveness, equanimity, insight, peace and freedom.

Gaia House offers Insight Meditation (known as Vipassana in the Buddhist tradition) and Zen Retreats throughout the year.

The Centre provides comprehensive Dharma teachings and spiritual practices to realise wisdom and compassion in daily life.

HOLE FARM GROUP
Tradition: Theravada
Meetings: Hole Farm, Bickington, Newton Abbot, TQ12 6PE
Postal Address: Hole Farm, Bickington, Newton Abbot, TQ12 6PE
Telephone Contact: 01626 821508 (Sumitta)

A small group that meets on Tuesdays at 7.30pm for meditation and Dhamma discussion. Phone to ask directions.

SOUTH BRENT

GOLDEN BUDDHA CENTRE

See UK NATIONAL ORGANISATIONS

45

England

TOTNES

BARN RURAL RETREAT CENTRE
Tradition: All
Meetings: Lower Sharpham Barton, Ashprington, Totnes, Devon TQ9 7DX
Affiliated to: Sharpham Centre For Contemporary Buddhist Enquiry, Ashprington, Devon, England
Charity No.: 285767
Postal Address: The Managers, The Barn, Lower Sharpham Barton, Ashprington, Totnes, Devon TQ9 7DX
Telephone Contact: 01803 732661
Fax: 01803 732718
Email: barn@sharphamcolleg.org
Website(s): www.sharpham-trust.org/barn.htm

Situated on a stunning hillside location overlooking the River Dart, the Barn offers a year-round retreat facility. For periods ranging from one week to six months visitors practise integrating meditation, work in the woodlands and organic vegetable garden, and community life. Three forty minute sittings are held daily.

Although based on Buddhist teachings, The Barn is non-denominational and welcomes people from other backgrounds. There are twice weekly sessions with visiting meditation teachers, as well as regular opportunities to attend lectures and meditation at near-by Sharpham College.

Two residential managers and up to seven retreatants are accommodated in single rooms. The Barn is part of the Sharpham Trust, Charity No. 285767

DORSET

BOURNEMOUTH

BOURNEMOUTH ZEN DOJO
Tradition: Zen
School: Soto
Affiliated to: International Zen Association UK, UK National Organisations
Charity No.: 1069941
Telephone Contact: 07837 303972 (Jason Miller)
Website(s): www.izauk.org

Zazen Timetable

Friday 19.00 - 20.30

Introduction Friday 18.30

Please phone Jason for details of the location where we sit.

COMMUNITY OF INTERBEING - BOURNEMOUTH SANGHA
Tradition: Vietnamese
School: Thich Nhat Hanh
Affiliated to: The Community Of Interbeing, UK, UK National Organisations
Telephone Contact: 01202 434121 (Allegra)
Website(s): www.interbeing.org.uk

Contact for information about local and regional activities for meditation and Days of Mindfulness. See UK National Orgaisations for details of The Community of Interbeing.

EAST DORSET BUDDHIST GROUP
Tradition: All
Meetings: St. Michaels Church Centre, Colehill Lane, Colehill, Wimborne, Dorset BH21 7AB.
Postal Address: Philip Crook, September Cottage, Lower Row, Holt, Wimbourne, Dorset BH21 7DZ.
Or Steve Wilkens, Green Glade, 13 Kyrchil Lane, Colehill, Wimborne, Dorset BH21 2RT.
Telephone Contact: 01202 884977 (Philip Crook)
Or 01202 880661 (Steve Wilkens)

The group aims to provide a starting point for those new to Buddhism, to provide information on the availability of further training and to provide a regular contact for practicing Buddhists. Meetings usually consist of a short period of sitting practice followed by a talk and discussion on an aspect of Buddhist teaching. New members and visitors are welcome. The group meets at 10:30am on the second and fourth Thursdays of the month except for the proximity of public holidays.

LYME BAY

COMMUNITY OF INTERBEING - LYME BAY SANGHA, DORSET
Tradition: Zen
School: Thich Nhat Hanh
Affiliated to: The Community Of Interbeing, UK, UK National Organisations
Telephone Contact: 01308 897265 (Anita)
Website(s): www.interbeing.org.uk

Contact for information about local and regional activities for meditation and Days of Mindfulness. See UK National Orgaisations for details of The Community of Interbeing.

MARTINSTOWN

COMMUNITY OF INTERBEING - MARTINSTOWN SANGHA, DORSET
Tradition: Zen
School: Thich Nhat Hanh
Affiliated to: The Community Of Interbeing, UK, UK National Organisations
Telephone Contact: 01305 889387 (Lesley & Russel)
Website(s): www.interbeing.org.uk

Contact for information about local and regional activities for meditation and Days of Mindfulness. See UK National Orgaisations for details of The Community of Interbeing.

WEYMOUTH

SOUTH DORSET BUDDHIST GROUP
Tradition: Theravada
Meetings: 3 New Close Gardens, Rodwell, Weymouth, Dorset DT4 8RG
Affiliated to: Hartridge Buddhist Monastery, England, Devon, Honiton
Postal Address: Barbara Cohen Walters (Sati Sati), 3 New Close Gardens, Rodwell, Weymouth, Dorset DT4 8RG
Telephone Contact: 01305 786821

We are a group that meets every Thursday at 7.45pm. to chant and meditate together and to study the Buddhist teachings. We offer each other support in the practice of Buddhism and in trying to live in a way that is kind, compassionate and aware.

We are under the guidance of Ajahn Sumedho and the monks and nuns of the Theravada tradition.

EAST RIDING OF YORKSHIRE

WITHERNSEA

A SHARED OFFERING
Tradition: All
Meetings: Meditation space to the rear of 11 Chellsway, Carrs Meadow, Withernsea HU19 2EN
Telephone Contact: 01964 612374
Email: ann_surgey@hotmail.com

On the 4th Sunday of each month a meditation/contemplation space is made available to the rear of 11 Chellsway, Withernsea from 10 - 4pm. Individuals may meditate, read, listen to recorded talks, sit under a tree in the garden, or have a 'base' from which to reach the countryside, beach or cemetery. There is no obligation to stay

Entry continued on the following page.

47

for the whole day. Speaking is kept to a minimum, so it is best to ring previously to discuss individual needs. Refreshments are available. No charge is made. Please bring a packed lunch to share; alternatively there plenty of shops and cafes locally if you prefer. Some basic meditation equipment is available but you are welcome to bring your own. All denominations welcome.

EAST SUSSEX

BRIGHTON

BODHI GARDEN DHARMA CENTRE
Tradition: All
Meetings: 7A Ship Street Garden, (Lane between Ship Street and Middle Street), Brighton
Affiliated to: English Buddhist Monastery Trust, Related Organisations
Charity No.: 1088804
Postal Address:
Bodhi Garden Dharma Centre,
c/o 7 Hanover Crescent, Brighton BN2 9SB
Telephone Contact: 07796 331167
(Richard Gilpin)
Email: info@bodhigarden.org
Website(s): www.bodhigarden.org

A non-sectarian Dharma centre run by the English Buddhist Monastery Trust (see Related Organisations).

This charity operates as an umbrella space for several local Buddhist groups, including those from the Theravadan, Tibetan and Zen traditions. The centre also offers day retreats and weekend workshops led by invited teachers from across the traditions. The centre operates on the principle of 'dana' ('generosity', 'support').

Please contact for details of current programme.

BRIGHTON BUDDHIST CENTRE (FWBO)
Tradition: FWBO
Meetings: 17 Tichborne Street, Brighton, East Sussex BN1 1UR
Affiliated to: Friends Of The Western Buddhist Order, UK National Organisations
Charity No.: 273682
Postal Address: Brighton Buddhist Centre, 17 Tichborne Street, Brighton, East Sussex BN1 1UR
Telephone Contact: 01273 772090
Email: info@brightonbuddhistcentre.co.uk
Website(s):
www.brightonbuddhistcentre.co.uk

The Centre holds regular drop-in meditation classes as well as courses in meditation and Buddhism for newcomers. Around the Centre is a thriving mandala of other activities including residential communities, Right Livelihood businesses and the Evolution Arts and Natural Health Centre.

BRIGHTON CH'AN GROUP
Tradition: Chinese
School: Ch'an
Telephone Contact: 01275 846261 (John Mitchell)
Email: john@ditchling8ut.freeserve.co.uk

BRIGHTON DIAMOND WAY BUDDHIST CENTRE
Tradition: Tibetan
School: Karma-Kagyu
Meetings: 13 Montpelier Apartments, Montpelier Road, Brighton BN1 2LY
Affiliated to: Diamond Way Buddhism UK, UK National Organisations
Charity No.: 1093406
Postal Address: Brighton Diamond Way Buddhist Centre, 13 Montpelier Apartments, Montpelier Road, Brighton BN1 2LY
Telephone Contact: 01273 202871
Or 07736 061108
Email: brighton@dwbuk.org
Website(s): www.diamondway-buddhism.co.uk

The Brighton Group was founded three years ago and is located very centrally - on top of 'Taj Supermarket', opposite Waitrose on Western Road. On Thursdays, there is a short talk on a Buddhist topic, followed by a guided meditation. Newcomers are always welcome, also for a chat and a cup of tea after the meditation. We have a small library of Buddhist books and a selection of Diamond Way Buddhist magazines and meditation booklets.

If you are already practicing Diamond Way Buddhism, you are also welcome to join us on Sundays at 6.00pm where we do a longer meditation session together and on Tuesdays at 7:30pm where we practice Diamond Mind Meditation.

Regular Meditation Times

Thursday 7:30pm: 16th Karmapa guided meditation.

Tuesday 7.30pm: Diamond Mind meditation. For those that have already started the ngondro.

BRIGHTON SERENE REFLECTION MEDITATION GROUP
Tradition: Zen
School: Soto
Affiliated to: The Order Of Buddhists Contemplatives, UK National Organisations
Telephone Contact: 01273 552747 (Duncan & Diane Sellers)

Please contact for details of regular weekly meetings.

BRIGHTON SHAMBHALA STUDY GROUP
Tradition: Tibetan
School: Kagyu-Nyingma
Meetings: Yoga Haven, Kendal House, Donkey Mews, Brunswick St, East Hove. BN3 1AW.
Affiliated to: London Shambhala Meditation

Centre, England, London, SW 4
Charity No.: 1073977
Postal Address: Brighton Shambhala Study Group, Yoga Haven, Kendal House, Donkey Mews, Brunswick St, East Hove. BN3 1AW.
Telephone Contact: 01273 557610
Email: brighton@shambhala-europe.org
Website(s): www.brighton.shambhala-europe.org

BRIGHTON THERAVADAN GROUP
Tradition: Theravada
Meetings: The Bodhi Garden, Ship Street, Brighton.
Affiliated to: Cittaviveka, Chithurst Buddhist Monastery, England, West Sussex, Chithurst
Telephone Contact: 07888 821524 (Sam)

The Brighton Theravada Group meet on Monday evenings at The Bodhi Garden, Ship Street, doors open 7:15 and the group meeting usually lasts until about 9:30. The group organises visits to Forest Sangha monaseries and other events. We are sometime blessed with visiting teachers.

BRIGHTON ZEN DOJO
Tradition: Zen
School: Soto
Meetings: Bodhi Garden Dharma Centre, 7a Ship Street Gardens, Between Ship Street and Middle Street, Brighton BN1 1AJ
Affiliated to: International Zen Association UK, UK National Organisations
Charity No.: 1069941
Telephone Contact: 01273 682974 (Jay or Heather)
Email: zen@zenbrighton.co.uk
Website(s): www.izauk.org

Zazen: Fridays 8.00 pm & Wednesdays 7.30 - 8.30 am

Introductions: Fridays 7.30pm

England

JAMYANG BRIGHTON

Tradition: Tibetan
School: Gelugpa
Meetings: The Bodhigarden, 7a Ship Street Gardens, Brighton, BN1 1AJ
Affiliated to: Foundation For The Preservation Of The Mahayana Tradition, UK National Organisations
Telephone Contact: 01273 778835 Or 07758 150722.
Email: meditate@brightonjamyang.org.uk
Website(s): www.brightonjamyang.org.uk

As of March 2007 we meet in the Bodhi Garden every Thursday at 7.30pm - 9.00pm to study Tibetan Buddhist philosophy. Each study session consists of a guided meditation, a reading from a text and some discussion.

Brighton Jamyang is a satellite group of Jamyang Tibetan Buddhist Centre in London (www.jamyang.co.uk), which supports the work of His Holiness the Dalai Lama and is affiliated to the Foundation of the Preservation of the Mahayana Tradition (www.fpmt.org), an organisation devoted to the transmission of the Mahayana Buddhist tradition and values, based on the teachings of Lama Tsongkhapa.

MAITRIKARA

Tradition: Tibetan
School: Nyingma
Charity No.: 1086822
Postal Address: L Gethin, 24 Freshfield Street, Brighton BN2 2ZG
Telephone Contact: 01273 675803 (Larrie Gethin)
Fax: 01273 675803
Email: info@maitrikara.org.uk
Website(s): www.maitrikara.org.uk

Affiliated to Centre d'Etudes de Chanteloube in the Dordogne, France, it follows the Nyingma school of Tibetan Buddhism, under the guidance of Jigme Khyentse Rinpoche, who visits Maitrikara once or twice per year. There are two groups which meet weekly, offering opportunities for pujas, meditation, discussion and study, as well as seminars and retreats.

Please contact for further details.

CROWBOROUGH

CROWBOROUGH DIAMOND WAY BUDDHIST CENTRE

Tradition: Tibetan
School: Karma-Kagyu
Meetings: The Noyle, Blackness Road, Crowborough, East Sussex TN6 2LP
Affiliated to: Diamond Way Buddhism UK, UK National Organisations
Charity No.: 1093406
Postal Address: Crowborough Diamond Way Buddhist Centre, The Noyle, Blackness Road, Crowborough, East Sussex TN6 2LP
Telephone Contact: 01892 665677
Email: crowborough@dwbuk.org
Website(s): www.diamondway-buddhism.co.uk

Welcome to the Crowborough meditation group. We offer regular guided meditation evenings that include a short introduction to Buddhism for newcomers. All are welcome and there is no charge for coming along.

As well as holding regular meditation evenings we shall be organising frequent lectures and meditation courses in the future.

If you are new to Buddhism and would like to find out more, please feel free to come along, give us a call or send us an email. We look forward to seeing you there.

Regular Meditation Times
Tuesday 7:30pm: Introduction and 16th Karmapa guided meditation: for people who are new to Buddhism and those who have been practicing for many years. There is plenty of time to answer any questions you may have.

England

HASTINGS

HASTINGS AND ROTHER BUDDHIST MEDITATION GROUP
Tradition: Zen
School: Soto
Meetings: 4 St Mary's Terrace, Hastings, East Sussex TN34 3LS
Telephone Contact: 01424 460707
Email: petereaster@macunlimited.net

Meditation every Thursday at 7.30pm followed by a Dharma discussion facilitated by an ordained member of the International Association of Zen UK.

HASTINGS BUDDHIST MEDITATION AND STUDY GROUP
Meetings: Cincla Cottage, Pett Level, Hastings TN35 4EE
Postal Address: Alan Dipper, Cincla Cottage, Pett Level, Hastings TN35 4EE
Telephone Contact: 01424 813176

A small meditation and study group. Meets on Fridays 6.30pm. Following the example of Mr. Christmas Humphreys and the Venerable Myoko-ni.

HIGH HURSTWOOD

RIVENDELL RETREAT CENTRE
Tradition: FWBO
Tradition: Rivendell Retreat Centre, Chillies Lane, High Hurstwood, East Sussex TN22 4AB
Affiliated to: Friends Of The Western Buddhist Order, UK National Organisations
Charity No.: 270460
Postal Address: Croydon Buddhist Centre, 96-98 High Street, Croydon CRO 1ND
Telephone Contact: 020 8688 8624
Email: info@rivendellretreatcentre.com
Website(s): www.rivendellretreatcentre.com

A former vicarage set in its own grounds amid beautiful Sussex countryside. Rivendell regularly holds introductory weekend retreats as well as longer retreats for people at all levels of experience.
To book please contact: Croydon Buddhist Centre Mon - Fri, usually 11.30 am - 2.30pm, and Sat 10am - 1.00pm

HOVE

COMMUNITY OF INTERBEING - BRIGHTON SANGHA
Tradition: Vietnamese
School: Thich Nhat Hanh
Affiliated to: The Community Of Interbeing, UK, UK National Organisations
Telephone Contact: 0870 777 3348 (Barry & Vivien)
Email: barry@eliades.org
Website(s): www.sussexinterbeing.org.uk

Contact for information about local and regional activities for meditation and Days of Mindfulness. See UK National Orgaisations for details of The Community of Interbeing.

Regular meetings on Saturdays. 10.00- 12.00am.

LEWES

COMMUNITY OF INTERBEING - LEWES SANGHA
Tradition: Vietnamese
School: Thich Nhat Hanh
Affiliated to: The Community Of Interbeing, UK, UK National Organisations
Postal Address: 01273 475260 (Judy Lewis)
Website(s): www.interbeing.org.uk

Contact for information about local and regional activities for meditation and Days of Mindfulness. See UK National Orgaisations for details of The Community of Interbeing.

England

RIGPA SOUTH DOWNS
Tradition: Tibetan
School: Nyingma
Affiliated to: Rigpa Fellowship, UK National Organisations
Telephone Contact: 01273 476596
Email: cheryl@cherylwebb.wanadoo.co.uk
Website(s): www.rigpa.org.uk

See UK National Organisations.

ESSEX

ASHDON

MARPA HOUSE - Chos Khor Ling
Tradition: Tibetan
School: Karma-Kagyu
Meetings: Marpa House, Rectory Lane, Ashdon, Saffron Walden, Essex CB10 2HN
Charity No.: 271104
Postal Address: The Secretary, Marpa House, Rectory Lane, Ashdon, Saffron Walden, Essex CB10 2HN
Telephone Contact:01799 584415 (The Secretary)
Email: mail@marpahouse.org.uk
Website(s): www.marpahouse.org.uk

The aim of the centre is to encourage a deeper understanding of the nature of mind, developing unshakable confidence through the study and practice of the Mahamudra and Dzogchen traditions of Tibet.

The Centre is residential and also offers retreat facilities. Guest or day visitors are always welcome. Bookings should be made in writing or by telephone. There are morning and evening pujas plus two silent meditations each day. Weekend retreats and occasional courses and open days are also organised. A regular Newsletter is published.

We have a non-residential London centre, (see Amrita Dzong, London, E2).

COLCHESTER

COLCHESTER BUDDHIST CENTRE (FWBO)
Tradition: FWBO
Meetings: 11 Manor Road, Colchester, Essex CO3 3LX
Affiliated to: Friends Of The Western Buddhist Order, UK National Organisations
Charity No.: 1046724
Postal Address: Colchester Buddhist Centre, 11 Manor Road, Colchester, Essex CO3 3LX
Telephone Contact: 01206 576330
Email: colchester.buddhist@tiscali.co.uk
Website(s): www.colchesterbuddhistcentre.com

Meets regularly for meditation, study, Puja and retreats. Activities for newcomers. Outreach to schools and other organisations by appointment.

JAMYANG COLCHESTER
Tradition: Tibetan
School: Gelugpa
Meetings: The Trinity Centre, 21 Trinity St, Colchester, CO1 1JN
Affiliated to: Foundation For The Preservation Of The Mahayana Tradition, UK National Organisations
Postal Address: The Trinity Centre, 21 Trinity St, Colchester, CO1 1JN
Telephone Contact: 07909 680497
Email: jamyangcolchester@googlemail.com
Website(s): www.jamyang.co.uk/colchester

Jamyang Colchester is a satellite study group of Jamyang Buddhist Centre in London. Meeting regularly to listen to and discuss Dharma teachings and to meditate.

HARLOW

HARLOW BUDDHIST SOCIETY
Tradition: Theravada
Meetings: Dana House, 385 Longbanks,

England

Harlow, Essex CM18 7PG
Affiliated to: Amaravati Buddhist Monastery, UK National Organisations
Charity No.: 275471
Postal Address: Sanghapalo, Harlow Buddhist Society, Dana House, 385 Longbanks, Harlow, Essex CM18 7PG
Telephone Contact: 01279 303287 (Sanghapalo)
Or 01279 862947 (Paul Marshall)
Or 01279 724330 (Pamutto)
Email: spalo@ntlworld.com
Website(s): www.danahouse.co.uk

Formed 1968. The Society meets on Monday evenings and broadly follows the Theravada tradition. There is regular contact with the Amaravati and Chithurst monasteries. The Society organises its own retreats and other activities, including a Beginner's Meditation class and a Self-Help Therapy Group.

HARLOW DIAMOND WAY BUDDHIST CENTRE
Tradition: Tibetan
School: Karma-Kagyu
Meetings: 1 Church Leys, Harlow, Essex CM18 6BX
Affiliated to: Diamond Way Buddhism UK, UK National Organisations
Charity No.: 1093406
Postal Address: Harlow Diamond Way Buddhist Centre, 1 Church Leys, Harlow, Essex CM18 6BX
Telephone Contact: 01279 425141
Email: harlow@dwbuk.org
Website(s): www.diamondway-buddhism.co.uk

The Harlow centre was formed on 14 September 2000 and is ideal for residents of Harlow and residents of North London who are close to the M11, with the Friends Meeting House only 1 mile from the M11 Harlow exit. There is a small library available with books and tapes.

Regular Meditation Times

Monday 8:00pm: Introduction and 16th Karmapa guided meditation: for people who are new to Buddhism and those who have been practicing for many years. There is plenty of time to answer any questions you may have.

LEIGH ON SEA

LEIGH BUDDHIST GROUP
Tradition: Theravada
Affiliated to: Amaravati Buddhist Monastery, UK National Organisations
Postal Address: Rob Howell, 61 Thames Drive, Leigh-on-Sea, Essex
Telephone Contact: 01702 482134 (Rob Howell)

Meets every Wednesday at 8pm for discussions and meditation. Occasional weekend visits by monks and nuns from Amaravati Buddhist Monastery. Buddhists of all traditions are welcome to the meetings. Class leader Rob Howell.

LONGCHEN FOUNDATION
Tradition: Tibetan
School: Kagyu-Nyingma
Meetings: Leigh on Sea
Affiliated to: Longchen Foundation, UK National Organisations
Telephone Contact: 01702 710410
Email: moira@london.com
Website(s): www.longchenfoundation.com

The Longchen Foundation was established by Chögyam Trungpa Rinpoche and Dilgo Khyentse Rinpoche, two of the great Tibetan teachers of the 20th century, to pass on the authentic Mahayana MahaAti (Dzogchen) teachings of the Nyingma lineage to the west. The spiritual director and principal teacher, Rigdzin Shikpo, one of Trungpa Rinpoche's earliest western students and a qualified lama of the Nyingma tradition, was entrusted by them to teach in direct response to

Entry continued on the following page.

the needs of westerners and is among the most experienced and inspiring Buddhist teachers in Britain.
The Foundation is a community of Buddhist teachers, meditation instructors and students practising these teachings with the vision of liberating the hearts of beings. For details of weekend courses, retreats, publications, newsletters, please visit our website.

The Lions Roar is a course that introduces the view and innermost teachings of the Longchen tradition and offers a deep and authentic grounding in the practice of meditation. It is suitable for total beginners and experienced meditators. The course is available in Britain and in Germany.

Local groups led by senior students are in Bristol, Oxford, North London, South-east London, Maidstone, North Wales and Birmingham.

GLOUCESTERSHIRE

CIRENCESTER

CIRENCESTER SERENE REFLECTION MEDITATION GROUP
Tradition: Zen
School: Soto
Affiliated to: The Order Of Buddhists Contemplatives, UK National Organisations
Telephone Contact: 01451 861146 (Allie McLeod)

The group meets fortnightly on a Thursday at 7.30pm - 9.30pm. There are regular vidits from the Prior of Reading Buddhist Priory. Please phone for details.

CIRENCESTER ZEN GROUP
Tradition: Zen
Meetings: Cirencester Zen Group, 1 Queen

Street, Cirencester, Glos GL7 1HD
Please write for details.

NEWENT

NEWENT THERAVADA GROUP
Tradition: Theravada
Affiliated to: Amaravati Buddhist Monastery, UK National Organisations
Telephone Contact: 01531 821902 (John Teire)
Email: john.teire@virgin.net

STROUD

CHALFORD HILL SHAMBHALA STUDY GROUP
Tibetan
Kagyu-Nyingma
London Shambhala Meditation Centre, England, London, SW 4
1073977
John & Sophie Seex, 3 Roseberry Terrace, Chalford Hill, Gloucestershire, GL6 8EE
01453 889609
johnseex@f2s.com
www.shambhala.org.uk

STROUD BUDDHIST GROUP
Tradition: Theravada
Affiliated to: Amaravati Buddhist Monastery, UK National Organisations
Postal Address: Stroud Buddhist Group, c/o The Grange, Bussage, Stroud, GL6 8AT
Telephone Contact: 0796 7777742 (John Groves)

Meets on Thursdays from 7 to 9pm for sitting meditation. Although affiliated to Amaravati, the group is non-denominational and welcomes all traditions.

STROUD CH'AN GROUP
Tradition: Chinese
School: Ch'an
Affiliated to: Western Ch'an Fellowship, UK National Organisations
Telephone Contact: 01453 873877
Email: stroud@westernchanfellowship.org
Website(s):
www.westernchanfellowship.org/stroud

Refer to entry for the Western Ch'an Fellowship under UK National Organisations.

We are a small friendly group that welcomes new members irrespective of age, experience or beliefs. We meet on Wednesday evenings when we have two half-hour sits with some liturgy and chanting. This is followed by tea and a reading with some Dharma discussion. We also have some one day practice sessions and occasional weekend retreats. Meditation instruction is available for beginners. Please contact for more details and directions.

GREATER MANCHESTER

BOLTON

BOLTON MEDITATION GROUP
Tradition: Theravada
School: Variable
Affiliated to: Samatha Trust, UK National Organisations
Postal Address: Les Callow, 3 Nuneham Avenue, Withington, Manchester M20 9PZ
Telephone Contact: 0161 445 9746 (Les Callow)
Email: lescallow@hotmail.com
Website(s): www.samatha.org

ROCHDALE ZEN RETREAT
Tradition: Zen
School: Soto
Meetings: Rochdale Zen Retreat, 11 Trevarrick Court, Horwich, Bolton BL6 6TF
Affiliated to: The Order Of Buddhists Contemplatives, UK National Organisations
Charity No.: 1091415
Postal Address: Rev. Peter Bonati, 11 Trevarrick Court, Horwich, Bolton BL6 6TF
Telephone Contact: 01204 669951

We offer monastic and lay training. Our current weekly schedule includes; Dharma nights on Wednesdays and Fridays and Sunday morning meditation. We usually have a meditation sesshin the first weekend of every month and day retreats on a Saturday later in the month. The Temple is also open to congregation by appointment.

MANCHESTER

COMMUNITY OF INTERBEING - NORTHWEST SANGHA, MANCHESTER
Tradition: Vietnamese
School: Thich Nhat Hanh
Affiliated to: The Community Of Interbeing, UK, UK National Organisations
Telephone Contact: 0161 448 2715 (Dene Donalds)
Email: d.donald@btinternet.com
Website(s): www.interbeing.org.uk

Contact for information about local and regional activities for meditation and Days of Mindfulness. See UK National Orgaisations for details of The Community of Interbeing.

DZOGCHEN MANCHESTER
Tradition: Tibetan
School: Dzogchen
Affiliated to: Dzogchen Community UK, UK National Organisations
Email: marcfranks@btinternet.com
Website(s): www.dzogchencommunity.org

See UK NATIONAL ORGANISATIONS

FO GUANG SHAN (MANCHESTER)
Tradition: Chinese
School: Ch'an
Meetings: 540 Stretford Road, Old Stafford, Manchester M16 9AF
Affiliated to: London Fo Guang Temple, England, London, W 1
Postal Address: Fo Guang Shan (Manchester), 540 Stretford Road, Old Stafford, Manchester M16 9AF
Telephone Contact: 0161 872 3338
Fax: 0161 872 3334
Email: ibps_man_uk@hotmail.com

See BLIA London W1 for information about this organisation's objectives.

KAGYU LING
Tradition: Tibetan
School: Kagyu-Sakya
Affiliated to: Dechen Community, UK National Organisations
Charity No.: 1055813
Postal Address: Kagyu Ling, 20 Macefin Avenue, West Didsbury, Manchester M21 7QQ
Telephone Contact: 0161 445 3044
Email: manchester@dechen.org
Website(s): www.dechen.org

Kagyu Ling, the first Buddhist centre to be founded in Manchester, was established in 1975 by Karma Thinley Rinpoche and Lama Jampa Thaye. It has served as a centre of Buddhist study and practice ever since.

The centre exists to facilitate study and practice of the teachings of the Karma Kagyu tradition, a lineage of Tibetan Buddhism whose spiritual head is the Karmapa lama, incarnation of the Buddha of Compassion, Chenrezik.

Situated in West Didsbury in South Manchester, Kagyu Ling comprises a traditional shrine room as well as a refreshments area, dharma shop and office, all within a detached house. The Centre is

run by volunteers and funded by donations.

MANCHESTER BUDDHIST CENTRE (FWBO)
Tradition: FWBO
Meetings: 16-20 Turner Street, Northern Quarter, Manchester M4 1DZ
Affiliated to: Friends Of The Western Buddhist Order, UK National Organisations
Charity No.: 514937
Postal Address: Manchester Buddhist Centre, 16-20 Turner Street, Northern Quarter, Manchester M4 1DZ
Telephone Contact: 0161 834 9232
Or 0870 134 7356
Email: info@manchesterbuddhistcentre.org.uk
Website(s):
www.manchesterbuddhistcentre.org.uk

The Centre holds regular drop-in meditation classes as well as courses in meditation and Buddhism for newcomers. A Buddhist gift- and book-shop is open from Monday to Saturday and there is a vegetarian cafe in the basement open from Tuesday to Saturday

MANCHESTER CENTRE FOR BUDDHIST MEDITATION
Tradition: Theravada
Meetings: 21 High Lane, Chorlton, Manchester M21 9DJ
Affiliated to: Samatha Trust, UK National Organisations
Postal Address: The Secretary, Manchester Centre for Buddhist Meditation, 21 High Lane, Chorlton, Manchester M21 9DJ
Telephone Contact: 0161 861 7878 (Roger Barnes)
Or 0161 861 0276 (Pam Stanier)
Fax: pam@pstanier.freeserve.co.uk
Website(s): www.samatha.org

Meditation classes and other activities held Monday to Thursday at 8pm and there is a drop in class for all traditions and all abilities on Saturday morning at 11am. Meditation instruction for beginners is available at these times.

Activities for those who have completed the introductory meditation course include classes and groups in meditation, sutta study, abhidhamma study, chanting practice, festivals, physical work and periodically a programme of visiting speakers. Residential retreats are held at the Samatha Trust centre in Powys, Wales.

MANCHESTER CH'AN GROUP
Tradition: Chinese
School: Ch'an
Meetings: Friends Meeting House, Mount Street, Manchester M2 5NS
Affiliated to: Western Ch'an Fellowship, UK National Organisations
Postal Address: Manchester Chan Group, c/o Simon Child, 24 Woodgate Avenue, Bury, Lancashire BL9 7RU
Telephone Contact: 0161 761 1945 (Simon Child)
Email: manchester@WesternChanFellowship.org
Website(s): www.westernchanfellowship.org/manchester/

The Manchester Chan formed by merging the groups which formerly met in Bury (North Manchester) and Cheadle (South Manchester).

Meets Thursdays at 7pm. Day retreats held in Bury approximately bi-monthly.

Meditation Instructor: Simon Child, Chuan-fa Jing-hong, Dharma heir of Ch'an Master Sheng-yen.

For further details refer to the entry for Western Ch'an Fellowship (UK National Organisations)

MANCHESTER DIAMOND WAY BUDDHIST CENTRE
Tradition: Tibetan

School: Karma-Kagyu
Meetings: Building no. 29, Conference Room 1, Third Floor, MMU Student's Union Building, Oxford Road, Manchester.
Affiliated to: Diamond Way Buddhism UK, UK National Organisations
Charity No.: 1093406
Telephone Contact: 0161 660 7822
Email: manchester@dwbuk.org
Website(s): www.diamondway-buddhism.co.uk

We are a small, friendly, recently formed group. We meet every Thursday at 7.00 pm in Conference Room 1 on the 3rd floor of the Manchester Metropolitan University Students' Union. This is easily accessible by public transport and is only 3 - 5 minutes from Oxford Road train station, 5 - 10 minutes from St Peters Square metro stop and busses stop right outside the Student's Union building.

There is usually an introductory talk followed by a guided meditation on the 16th Karmapa. The meditation session is finished by 9.00 pm.

If you are new and before coming you are worried what it will be like, what to wear or indeed have any other question then please give us a call and we will do our best to answer your questions and explain what to expect.

MANCHESTER SHAMBHALA STUDY GROUP
Tradition: Tibetan
School: Kagyu-Nyingma
Meetings: London Shambhala Meditation Centre, England, London, SW 4
Charity No.: 1073977
Postal Address: Manchester Shambhala Study Group, 10 Albert Road, Stockport, SK4 4EQ
Telephone Contact: 0161 443 1664
Email: rachel@rachelodowd.co.uk
Website(s): www.manchester.shambhala-europe.org

England

MANCHESTER ZEN DOJO
Tradition: Zen
School: Soto
Meetings: Mill Street Venture Centre, 491 Mill Street, Openshaw, Manchester M11 2AD
Affiliated to: International Zen Association UK, UK National Organisations
Charity No.: 1069941
Telephone Contact: 0161 231 2040 (Alan Smith)
Email: nala.smith@virgin.net
Website(s): www.izauk.org

Zazen Timetable:

Half Day: 1st Saturday of each month (07.30 start)

Tuesday: 19.30, Thursday: 07.00, Saturday: 09.30, Sunday: 10.00

Introduction: Tuesday 19.00, Saturday 09.00

MEDICINE BUDDHA GOMPA
Meetings: Healing Heart Centre, 17 Woodstock Road, Old Trafford, Manchester, M16 0HR
Telephone Contact: 0161 881 7147 (Edmund Ho-Yuen To)

Remi movement practice. Please telephone for times of meetings.

PADMA LING

See UK NATIONAL ORGANISATIONS

OLDHAM

KETUMATI BUDDHIST VIHARA
Tradition: Theravada
Meetings: 3 Pretoria Road, Hollins, Oldham, Greater Manchester OL8 4NH
Charity No.: 1078173
Postal Address: Ketumati Buddhist Vihara, 3

Pretoria Road, Hollins, Oldham, Greater Manchester OL8 4NH
Sarath Yapa, 6 Hasguard Close, Bolton BL1 5FE
0161 678 9726 (Ven Pidiville Piyatissa Thero)
01204 494732 (Sarath Yapa)
ketumatibv@tiscali.co.uk

The Ketumati Buddhist Vihara was inaugurated on 17th April 1999 under the direction of the Ven Pidiville Piyatissa Thero. The Vihara follows the Theravada tradition as practised in Sri Lanka. There are two resident monks: Ven Pidiville Piyatissa Thero (Chief Incumbent) and Ven Nagama Hemaloka.

Current activities: Weekly Buddha Puja, Vandana and Meditation on Wednesdays and Sundays. Monthly programmes to mark the full moon poya days. All other traditional services such as Paritta Chanting, Sanghika Dana etc. Please contact for details of the current programme.

SALE

BUDDHIST SOCIETY OF MANCHESTER
Tradition: Theravada
Meetings: 3 Grosvenor Square, Sale, Cheshire, M33 1RW   1072411
Affiliated to: Buddhist Society of Manchester, 3 Grosvenor Square, Sale, Cheshire, M33 1RW
Telephone Contact: 01457 876372 Or 0161 973 7588
Email: dave@dajoo1.force9.co.uk

Open meetings Monday and Wednesday 8.00 - 10.00pm. Nearest Metro station: Brooklands.

SALFORD

SARANIYA DHAMMA MEDITATION CENTRE
Tradition: Theravada
School: Vipassana
Meetings: 420 Lower Broughton Road, Salford, Manchester M7 2GD

58

England

Charity No.: 328302
Postal Address: Saraniya Dhamma
Meditation Centre, 420 Lower Broughton Road,
Salford, Manchester, M7 2GD
Telephone Contact: 0161 281 6242
Or 0161 339 3900
Or 0161 794 7363
Email: admin@saraniya.com
Website(s): www.saraniya.com

Five and nine day retreats held from time to time.

Resident monks: Sayadaw U Pannasami and
Sayadaw U Nanojjota

STOCKPORT

STOCKPORT SAMATHA MEDITATION GROUP
Tradition: Theravada
Meetings: Friends Meeting House, Longshut
Lane, Stockport
Affiliated to: Samatha Trust, UK National
Organisations
Telephone Contact: 0161 303 8100 (Peter
Needham)
Email: petersati@btinternet.com
Website(s): www.samatha.org

The Stockport Samatha group meets on Monday
evenings during term time at 7:45pm at the
Friends' Meeting House, Cooper St. (Junction
Higher Hillgate & Longshut Lane). The class is
suitable for beginners and more experienced
meditators.

Members of the original Stockport group, which
was founded in 1990, also continue to meet
regularly with their teacher.

HAMPSHIRE

PORTSMOUTH
PORTSMOUTH BUDDHIST GROUP
Tradition: Theravada

Affiliated to: Cittaviveka, Chithurst Buddhist
Monastery, England, West Sussex, Chithurst
Postal Address: The Portsmouth Buddhist
Group, c/o Medhavi and Anuttara, 42 Crofton
Road, Milton, Portsmouth PO4 8NY
Telephone Contact: 023 9273 2280

The Group follows the Theravadan tradition.
Regular meetings on the 1st Monday of the month
for meditation, discussion etc. Monks or nuns from
Cittaviveka visit frequently to give talks and there
are regular trips to the monastery.

All are welcome.

PORTSMOUTH CH'AN GROUP
Tradition: Chinese
School: Ch'an
Meetings: The Quiet Mind Centre, 32 Lorne
Road, Southsea, Hampshire, PO5 1RR
Affiliated to: Western Ch'an Fellowship, UK
National Organisations
Postal Address: Flat 33 St Martin's House,
Clarence Parade, Southsea PO5 2E2
Telephone Contact: 023 9235 7783
(George Marsh)
Email: portsmouth@westernchanfellowship.org
Website(s):
www.westernchanfellowship.org/portsmouth

We meet fortnightly on Wednesdays at 7.30pm -
for dates see the website of the Western Ch'an
Fellowship.

PORTSMOUTH SERENE REFLECTION
MEDITATION GROUP
Tradition: Zen
School: Soto
Meetings: Howard Road Community Centre,
Hilsea, Portsmouth PO2 9PR
Affiliated to: The Order Of Buddhists
Contemplatives, UK National Organisations
Telephone Contact: 02392 648163 (John
Mallon)

Entry continued on the following page.

59

Website(s): john.mallon2@ntlworld.com

The group meets on the third Saturday of each month from 10am - 1pm. It receives visits from the Prior of Reading Buddhist Priory. Meditation instruction is available. Everyone welcome, please phone for details.

ROMSEY

ROMSEY BUDDHIST GROUP
Tradition: All
Meetings: 44 Alma Road, Romsey, Hants
Postal Address: Ganshin Rock, 44 Alma Road, Romsey, Hants SO51 8ED
Telephone Contact: 01794 512735
Website(s): yakushi-do.romsey@ntlworld.com

The Romsey Buddhist Group meets every Wednesday at 7.30pm. Ganshin E Rock, a priest of the Japanese Tendai tradition, who is also the representative in the United Kingdom of the Bukkyo Dendo Kyokai (Buddhist Promoting Foundation) of Japan, arranges the meetings in his home.

The meetings generally take the form of a short Buddhist service conducted by Ganshin Rock, meditation, text reading and study, followed by discussion and refreshments, ending about 9.30pm.

The group is non-denominational, and all, Buddhists and non-Buddhists, are welcome to attend.

SOUTHAMPTON

COMMUNITY OF INTERBEING - SOUTHAMPTON SANGHA
Tradition: Vietnamese
School: Thich Nhat Hanh
Affiliated to: The Community Of Interbeing, UK, UK National Organisations

Telephone Contact: 023 8058 3749 (Jillian)
Email: sirdar80@yahoo.co.uk
Website(s): www.interbeing.org.uk

Contact for information about local and regional activities for meditation and Days of Mindfulness. See UK National Orgaisations for details of The Community of Interbeing.

Meetings are generally held on the second and fourth Wednesdays of the month at 7.45pm. A Morning of Mindfulness is held on the first Sunday of the month in Stockbridge.

HAMPSHIRE BUDDHIST SOCIETY
Tradition: All
Meetings: The Friends Meeting House, Ordnance Road, Off London Road, Southampton also 32 Norfolk Road, Shirley, Southampton
Affiliated to: Cittaviveka, Chithurst Buddhist Monastery, England, West Sussex, Chithurst
Postal Address: The Secretary, Hampshire Buddhist Society, 15 St Anne's Gardens, Woolston, Southampton SO19 9FJ
Telephone Contact: 02380 612838 (Robert Elliot)
Email: robert_elliot@lineone.net

The aim of the Society is to provide information on Buddhism and to encourage its practice. The Theravadan group is under the direction of the senior monastics of Cittaviveka and the Zen group takes its reference from the Venerable Myokyo-ni of the Zen Centre, London.

The Theravadan group meets on the first and third Thursdays each month and the Zen group on Wednesdays.

SOUTHAMPTON BUDDHIST GROUP (FWBO)
Tradition: FWBO
Meetings: 163 Northumberland Road, Newtown, Southampton SO14 0EP

Affiliated to: Friends Of The Western Buddhist Order, UK National Organisations
Charity No.: 1059688
Postal Address: Southampton Buddhist Group, 163 Northumberland Road, Newtown, Southampton SO14 0EP
Telephone Contact: 023 8057 6134 Or 07758 834545
Email: contact-us@southampton.fwbo.net or fwbosouthampton@onetel.com
Website(s): www.southampton.fwbo.net

Please contact for details of the current programme.

Also Beginners Classes in Winchester.

SOUTHAMPTON SHIN SANGHA
Tradition: Pure Land
School: Jodo Shin Shu
Meetings: 6 Southcliff Road, Southampton SO14 6FH
Postal Address: Gary Robinson, 6 Southcliff Road, Southampton SO14 6FH
Telephone Contact: 02380 837145
Email: wheels.net@btinternet.com
Website(s): www.purelandnotes.com

Meets on Thursday evening at 7.30pm.

HEREFORDSHIRE

HEREFORD

SHEN PHEN THUBTEN CHOELING (Centre for socially and ecologically engaged Buddhism)
Tradition: Tibetan
School: Gelugpa
Meetings: Golden Valley Herefordshire
Affiliated to: Foundation For The Preservation Of The Mahayana Tradition, UK National Organisations
Postal Address: Elaine Brook, Nurses Cottage, Long Lane, Peterchurch, Hereford HR2 0TE
Telephone Contact: 0845 458 4718 Or 01981 550246
Fax: 01981 550030
Email: elaine@gaiacooperative.org

The centre is a member of FPMT (Foundation for the Preservation of the Mahayana Tradition) founded by Lama Thubten Yeshe and Lama Zopa Rinpoche. Classes are held in meditation and the principles of Mahayana Buddhism, closely following the teachings of His Holiness the Dalai Lama. Weekend retreats are held at intervals throughout the spring and summer.

Individual retreat accommodation is also available.

Director Elaine Brook

VIPASSANA TRUST
Tradition: Theravada
School: Vipassana
Charity No.: 327798
Postal Address: The Manager, Dhamma Dipa, The Marches, Harewood End, Hereford HR2 8JS
Telephone Contact: 01989 730234
Fax: 01989 730450
Email: info@dipa.dhamma.org
Website(s): www.dhamma.org or www.dipa.dhamma.org

Dhamma Dipa was established in 1991 by the Vipassana Trust, an educational charity. The centre offers courses in Vipassana meditation in the tradition of Sayagyi U Ba Khin as taught by S.N. Goenka and his assistant teachers.

Regular residential 10-day silent retreats are held throughout the year. Vipassana as taught by S.N.Goenka is a universal practice open to everyone regardless of background or belief. On the course the students learn to develop their capacity for ethical living, mastery over the mind,

Entry continued on the following page.

insight and the sharing of selfless love and compassion with others. The purpose is to acquire a practical technique which one can apply to everyday life.

Courses are run solely on a donation basis; teachers and centre staff all volunteer their time. Vipassana courses in this tradition are also held at rented sites in Britain and at centres throughout Europe and world-wide.

HERTFORDSHIRE

HEMEL HEMPSTEAD

AMARAVATI BUDDHIST MONASTERY

See UK National Organisations.

AMARAVATI BUDDHIST RETREAT CENTRE
Tradition: Theravada
Meetings: Great Gaddesden, Hemel Hempstead, Hertfordshire HP1 3BZ
Affiliated to: Amaravati Buddhist Monastery, UK National Organisations
Postal Address: The Manager, Amaravati Buddhist Retreat Centre, St Margaret's Lane Great Gaddesden, Hemel Hempstead, Hertfordshire HP1 3BZ
Telephone Contact: 01442 843239
Email: retreats@amaravati.org
Website(s): www.amaravati.org

We have accommodation for some 45 people who come to investigate, learn and practice meditation. Experienced meditators and newcomers are welcome - we also have special retreat programmes, e.g. for young persons, Death & Dying etc. Members of our monastic community offer 2/5/10 day meditation retreats throughout the year except for the months of January, February and March.

For retreat schedule and booking information, send

SAE to the Retreat Manager. Please note that retreats are often fully booked well in advance.

Public activities are suspended during January, February and March when the monastic community is in silent retreat.

BODHINYANA GROUP
Tradition: Theravada
Meetings: Amaravati Buddhist Monastery Great Gaddesden, Hemel Hempstead, Hertfordshire HP1 3BZ
Postal Address: Amaravati Buddhist Monastery, UK National Organisations Bodhinyana Group, c/o Amaravati Buddhist Monastery, Great Gaddesden, Hemel Hempstead, Hertfordshire HP1 3BZ
Telephone Contact: 01442 890034 (Chris Ward)
Email: c.ward@btinternet.com
Website(s): www.buddhacommunity.org

A group for lay supporters of the monastery. We meet in the Bodhinyana Hall on Wednesdays at 7.30pm for a half-hour of meditation followed by a dhamma talk and discussion.

LETCHWORTH

LETCHWORTH BUDDHIST CENTRE
Tradition: Theravada
Meetings: Letchworth Buddhist Centre, 32 High Avenue, Letchworth Garden City, Hertfordshire SG6 3QS
Postal Address: Letchworth Buddhist Centre, 32 High Avenue, Letchworth Garden City, Hertfordshire SG6 3QS
Telephone Contact: 01462 641326
Email: info@letchworthtemple.com
Website(s):www.letchworthtemple.com

Spiritual Director: Rev. Nahalle Rahula Thero

Meditation sessions followed by discussions: On every

Wednesday & Sunday from 6:30 pm to 8:00 pm

LETCHWORTH FWBO GROUP
Tradition: FWBO
Meetings: Seminar 2, The Letchworth Centre For Healthy Living, Rosehill Hospital, Hitchin Road, Letchworth, Herts SG6 3NA.
Affiliated to: Friends Of The Western Buddhist Order, UK National Organisations
Telephone Contact: 01462 621882 (Martin)
Or 01462 630428 (Sam)
Fax: 01462 678804
Email: martin.p@ntlworld.com or samc@windhorse.biz
Website(s): www.fwboletchworth.co.uk

We are an outreach group run with the help of Cambridge Buddhist Centre. The group started in May 2001 as a drop in meditation class. Since then, it has grown and offers a range of Buddhist practices.

Meeting every Thursday from 7.30pm - 9.45pm.

For more information on meditation please see www.fwbo.org/meditation.html

POTTERS BAR

POTTERS BAR DIAMOND WAY BUDDHIST CENTRE
Tradition: Tibetan
School: Karma-Kagyu
Meetings: 13 Swanley Crescent, Little Heath, Potters Bar, Herts EN6 1NQ
Affiliated to: Diamond Way Buddhism UK, UK National Organisations
Charity No.: 1093406
Potters Bar Diamond Way Buddhist Centre, 13 Swanley Crescent, Little Heath, Potters Bar, Herts EN6 1NQ
Telephone Contact: 01707 645273
Email: pottersbar@dwbuk.org

Website(s): www.diamondway-buddhism.co.uk

Regular Meditation Times

Tuesday 8:00pm:

Introductory talk and guided 16th Karmapa meditation, for people who are new to Buddhism and those who have been practising for many years. There is plenty of time to answer any questions you may have.

HUMBERSIDE

BEVERLEY

HULL BUDDHIST FORUM
Meetings: Beverley
Postal Address: Hull Buddhist Forum, 220 Park Avenue, Hull HU5 3EY
Telephone Contact: 01482 342033 (Christopher Cook)

The Forum meets every third Sunday afternoon 2.30 to 5.00pm. It does not adhere strictly to any particular school of Buddhism, but current members are largely interested in Theravada and (Soto) Zen. Meetings are informal and centre around a period of meditation, talk, discussion, tea and biscuits. The group has been in existence for about 12 years; usually about 8 people attend meetings.

HULL

HULL SERENE REFLECTION MEDITATION GROUP
Tradition: Zen
School: Soto
Meetings: Various
Affiliated to: The Order Of Buddhists Contemplatives, UK National Organisations
Postal Address: Mike Horne, 28 Salisbury Street, Hull HU5 3HA
Telephone Contact: 01482 346784 (Mike Horne)

Entry continued on the following page.

Email: m.j.horne@chem.hull.ac.uk

Weekly meditation meetings. Occasional retreats. Visits by a monk from Throssel Hole Buddhist Abbey. Phone for details.

ZEN PRACTICE CENTRE TRUST
Tradition: Zen
School: Soto/Rinzai
Affiliated to: Zen Practice Centre Trust, UK National Organisations
Postal Address: John Oldham, 32 Baxter Gate, Hedon, Hull HU12 8JN
Telephone Contact: 01482 898382
Email: johngold@johngold.karoo.co.uk

Sitting group most Thursdays at 7.15 pm (please ring to check)

ISLE OF WIGHT

COMMUNITY OF INTERBEING - ISLE OF WIGHT SANGHA
Tradition: Zen
School: Thich Nhat Hanh
Affiliated to: The Community Of Interbeing, UK, UK National Organisations
Telephone Contact: 01983 404740 (Angie & Mark)
Website(s): www.interbeing.org.uk

Contact for information about local and regional activities for meditation and Days of Mindfulness. See UK National Orgaisations for details of The Community of Interbeing.

NEWPORT

ISLE OF WIGHT BUDDHIST GROUP
Tradition: All
Meetings: Informally at Watergate Road
Postal Address: Dave Downer, 19 Watergate Road, Newport, Isle of Wight PO30 1XN
Telephone Contact: 01983 520795
Email: David@dvdowner.demon.co.uk

A group where people of various Buddhist traditions meet for meditation, tapes, video and discussion. Library facility. Meeting 7.45pm on Thursdays.

VENTNOR

ISLE OF WIGHT BUDDHIST GROUP (FWBO)
Tradition: FWBO
Affiliated to: Friends Of The Western Buddhist Order, UK National Organisations
Postal Address: Isle of Wight Buddhist Group. 51 St Catherine Street, Ventnor, Isle of Wight, PO38 1HG
Telephone Contact: 01983 855217 (Andrew Trotman)
Email: andrew_trotman@yahoo.com or fwbo.isleofwight@mac.com
Website(s): www.isleofwight.fwbo.net

Wednesdays - Practice night.

Monthly celebration of Buddhist festival days

KENT

PADMA LING

See UK NATIONAL ORGANISATIONS

SANG-NGAK-CHO-DZONG
Tradition: Tibetan
School: Nyingma
Meetings: Please contact Kgakpa Ga-wang for details.
Affiliated to: Sang-Ngak-Cho-Dzong, UK National Organisations
Charity No.: 1019886

Telephone Contact: 01227 728379
Email: gawang@nagakpa.com
Website(s): www.aroter.org

See UK National Organisations.

ASHFORD

ASHFORD MEDITATION GROUP
Tradition: Theravada
Affiliated to: Amaravati Buddhist Monastery, UK National Organisations
Telephone Contact: 01233 643848
(Bernie Oxland)
Email: bernardoxland@yahoo.co.uk

CANTERBURY

CANTERBURY BUDDHIST MEDITATION GROUP
Tradition: Theravada
Meetings: Darwin College, University of Kent at Canterbury
Affiliated to: Amaravati Buddhist Monastery, UK National Organisations
Telephone Contact: 01227 463342
(Charles Watters)
Email: C.Watters@kent.ac.uk

Meets on Wednesdays at 6.30pm during term time.

CANTERBURY DIAMOND WAY BUDDHIST CENTRE
Tradition: Tibetan
School: Karma-Kagyu
Meetings: Canterbury Christ Church University, Rhodaus Town, Canterbury in the Augustine House room AH 1.13 (first floor)
Affiliated to: Diamond Way Buddhism UK, UK National Organisations
Postal Address: Canterbury Christ Church University, c/o Dr. Burkhard Scherer, Theology and Religious Studies, North Holmes Road, Kent CT1 1QU

Telephone Contact: 01304 205157
Email: canterbury@dwbuk.org
Website(s): www.diamondway-buddhism.co.uk

The Canterbury group meets for meditation in the University every Thursday at 7:30pm. Please contact us if you have any questions.

Regular Meditation Times

Thursday 7:30pm: Introduction and 16th Karmapa guided meditation: for people who are new to Buddhism and those who have been practicing for many years. There is plenty of time to answer any questions you may have.

CANTERBURY TIBET LINK
Tradition: Tibetan
Affiliated to: Maitrikara, England, East Sussex, Brighton
Postal Address: Canterbury-Tibet Link, c/o Caroline Latham, 55 Havelock Street, Canterbury CT1 1NP
Telephone Contact: 01227 763505
Email: carolinetibetlink@yahoo.co.uk
Website(s): www.canterburytibetlink.org.uk

The group meets on Thursdays at 7.00pm during term time for an hour and a half of meditation. We practise Tibetan Buddhism. Monthly teachings, retreats and regular visits from leading Tibetan lamas.

OGYAN CHOKHOR LING
Tradition: Tibetan
School: Nyingma
Meetings: Initially contact Ngakpa Ga'wang
Affiliated to: Ogyan Chokhor Ling, UK National Organisations
Telephone Contact: 01227 728379
Email: gawang@nyingma.com
Website(s):
www.nyingma.com/ogyan-cho-khor-ling
Members of the sangha who live in Kent meet on practice days eg for Vajrakilaya, Troma Nagmo,

Entry continued on the following page.

England

Guru Rinpoche Days and Dakini Days. We also have a Ngondro Group. (See our UK National Organisations entry)

GILLINGHAM

MEDWAY CH'AN GROUP
Tradition: Chinese
School: Ch'an
Meetings: 195 Gillingham Road, Gillingham, Kent. ME7 4EP
Affiliated to: Western Ch'an Fellowship, UK National Organisations
Postal Address: Gillingham Ch'an Group. 195 Gillingham Road, Gillingham. Kent ME7 4EP
Telephone Contact: 01634 571659
Email: medwaytowns@westernchanfellowship.org
Website(s): www.westernchanfellowship.org/medway

A group meets on Thursday evenings for meditation and discussion.

For further details, refer to Western Ch'an Fellowship (UK National Organisations)

MAIDSTONE

MAIDSTONE MEDITATION GROUP
Tradition: Theravada
Affiliated to: Amaravati Buddhist Monastery, UK National Organisations
Telephone Contact: 01622 203751 (Shirley McDonald)
Email: shirleymed@blueyonder.co.uk

MAIDSTONE MEDITATION GROUP (LONGCHEN FOUNDATION)
Tradition: Tibetan
School: Kagyu-Nyingma
Meetings: Maidstone.
Affiliated to: Longchen Foundation, UK

National Organisations
Telephone Contact: 01622 670587 (Andrew Patching or Barbara Hussong)
Email: andrewpatching@btinternet.com.
Website(s): www.longchenfoundation.com

The Longchen Foundation is a circle of Mahayana Buddhist teachers and students under the spiritual direction of Rigdzin Shikpo (see National section). The main study and practice programmes are the Heart Essence course and the Mahayana Vision programme. Both programmes are designed to integrate the vision of Mahayana Buddhism with your everyday life.

Meetings are held on Mondays at 7:30pm for meditation, talk and discussion. Suitable for new students and experienced practitioners. Full meditation instruction is given. Regular meditation and practice days are held at weekends throughout the year.

Meditation instructor is Andrew Patching.

MID-KENT AND MEDWAY BUDDHIST GROUP
Tradition: Theravada
Meetings: Presently at home of group members.
Postal Address: Mr B Oxland, 15 Old Orchard, Ashford, Kent TN23 2PY
Telephone Contact: 01233 643848 (Mr B Oxland)
Email: bernardoxland@yahoo.co.uk

The Group which follows the Theravada tradition was formed some twenty years ago, and meets on alternate Mondays starting promptly at 8.00pm. Meetings consist of puja, meditation and discussion upon some aspect of the Buddha Dhamma. Guest speakers are invited from time to time.

As close a contact as possible is maintained with the Sangha at all the nearest Buddhist Viharas, visits especially being made by the Group to these temples on important days in the Buddhist Calendar.

Newcomers are particularly welcome, provision being made for individual instruction in both Dhamma and Meditation. There is a library from which books may be borrowed.

ZEN PRACTICE CENTRE TRUST
Tradition: Zen
School: Soto/Rinzai
Affiliated to: Zen Practice Centre Trust, UK National Organisations
Postal Address: Barbara Tetsuzen Hussong, 26 Milford Close, Maidstone ME16 OEY
Telephone Contact: 01622 670587 (Barbara Hussong)
Email: b.hussong@lineone.net

Sittings on Wednesdays plus one Sunday every month 10.00am - 5.00pm. Please phone for details.

WHITSTABLE

RISSHO KOSEI-KAI

See UK National Organisations

LANCASHIRE

BLACKBURN

BLACKBURN BUDDHIST CENTRE (FWBO)
Tradition: FWBO
Meetings: Maitri House, 16 Strawberry Bank, Blackburn, Lancashire, BB2 6AA
Affiliated to: Friends Of The Western Buddhist Order, UK National Organisations
Postal Address: Maitri House, 16 Strawberry Bank, Blackburn, Lancashire, BB2 6AA
Telephone Contact: 01254 261 270 (Vidusi)

Or 01254 722 551 (Adiccabandhu)
Email: blackburnbuddhistcentre.org

The Blackburn Centre is established to make available the teachings of Buddhism, and to invite people to join us in the practice of an ethical life based on compassion.

COLNE

KAGYU DZONG
Tradition: Tibetan
School: Kagyu-Sakya
Meetings: Primet Community Centre, Primet Hill, Colne, BB8 9NF
Affiliated to: Dechen Community, UK National Organisations
Charity No.: 1055813
Telephone Contact: 01282 866445
Email: colne@dechen.org
Website(s): www.dechen.org

Kagyu Dzong was established in 1988 to provide a centre for the Kagyu tradition in Northeast Lancashire. In addition to hosting periodic teachings by Lama Jampa Thaye it offers a continuing programme of meditation classes.

Introductory Classes, every Tuesday at 8.00pm

Introductory classes consist of a short talk on different aspects of Buddhism and an introduction to Buddhist meditation, and are designed for those who are new to Buddhism and the Kagyu tradition.

DARWEN

BLACKBURN & DARWEN SAMATHA GROUP
Tradition: Theravada
Meetings: Bolton Road United Reform Church, Ashleigh Street, Darwen BB3 2JS
Affiliated to: Samatha Trust, UK National Organisations
Telephone Contact: 01254 775158

Entry continued on the following page.

Email: grahamcatterall@hotmail.com
Website(s):www.samatha.org

The Blackburn and Darwen Samatha group meets on Thursday at 7:00pm

Note: The day of the class may change to a Wednesday so please contact Graham Catterall to confirm the day.

The class is suitable for beginners and more experienced meditators. Everyone is welcome.

LANCASTER

LANCASTER FWBO GROUP
Tradition: FWBO
Affiliated to: Friends Of The Western Buddhist Order, UK National Organisations
Charity No.: 1037404
Postal Address: 79, Green Lane, Lancaster LA1 2EZ
Telephone Contact: 01254 389705 (Samagita)
Website(s): www.fwbo.org

Please write or phone for details of current programme.

LANCASTER SERENE REFLECTION MEDITATION GROUP
Tradition: Zen
School: Soto
Meetings: The Friends Meeting House, Lancaster
Affiliated to: The Order Of Buddhists Contemplatives, UK National Organisations
Telephone Contact: 01524 593621 (Paul Taylor - daytime only)
Or 01524 39918 (Kate Shirra-Gibb)

Our weekly meetings on Monday evenings include periods of sitting and walking meditation. Meditation instruction is available and newcomers

are very welcome. Members of the monastic community Throssel Hole Buddhist Abbey regularly visit the group and also lead local day retreats. Each month transport is often available for those who wish to visit the Abbey for the monthly festival . Occasional social events are also held.

MORECAMBE BAY

COMMUNITY OF INTERBEING - LANCASHIRE SANGHA
Tradition: Zen
School: Thich Nhat Hanh
Affiliated to: The Community Of Interbeing, UK, UK National Organisations
Telephone Contact: 01524 762396 (Marion)
Website(s): www.interbeing.org.uk

Contact for information about local and regional activities for meditation and Days of Mindfulness. See UK National Orgaisations for details of The Community of Interbeing.

OLDHAM

OLDHAM SAMATHA MEDITATION GROUP
Tradition: Theravada
Meetings: Oldham Samatha Meditation Group, Unitarian Chapel, One World Centre, off King Street, Oldham
Affiliated to: Samatha Trust, UK National Organisations
Telephone Contact: 0161 628 2150 (Gil)
Email: info@samatha.org
Website(s): www.samatha.org

A small group offering practical instruction in samatha (mindfulness of breathing) meditation. Beginners are welcome.

PRESTON

CHAM TSE LING BUDDHIST GROUP
Tradition: Tibetan
School: Gelugpa / Kagyu
Meetings: University of Central Lancashire, Multi-faith Centre, 33 St. Peters Square, Preston PR1 2HE
Charity No.: 1091065
Postal Address: Eileen Maher, 13 Hawthorn Crescent, Lea, Preston PR2 1RD
Or Anne Walmsley, 18 Church Street, Churchtown, Garstang PR3 0HT
Telephone Contact: 01772 726481 (Eileen Maher)
Or 01995 602660
Or 01253 766901 (David Chadwick)
Email: ae.walmsley@gmail.com
Website(s):www.cham-tse-ling.co.uk

The group was formed in 1998 and meets Thursdays at 7:30pm at the University of Central Lancashire, Multi-faith Centre, 33, St. Peter's Sq., Preston. The meetings consist of Dharma readings, prayers, and discussions on integrating the teachings into everyday life. The group primarily follows the Gelug tradition, but has strong links with the Kagyu tradition. Members of any Buddhist tradition, and people of all faiths or none, are always very welcome.

As well as our weekly meetings, other events include evening talks, one-day and three-day courses and weekend retreats held by visiting teachers. The retreats are usually held at a Quaker retreat house in Carnforth.

PRESTON DIAMOND WAY BUDDHIST CENTRE
Tradition: Tibetan
School: Karma-Kagyu
Meetings: 2 Trower Street, Frenchwood, Preston PR1 4LY
Affiliated to: Diamond Way Buddhism UK, UK National Organisations
Charity No.: 1093406
Postal Address: Preston Diamond Way

Buddhist Centre, 2 Trower Street, Frenchwood, Preston PR1 4LY
Telephone Contact: 07856 328676 (Magdalena)
Or 07833 988913 (Tom)
Email: preston@dwbuk.org
Website(s): www.diamondway-buddhism.co.uk

We are a newly established group consisting of people who have been meditating for a while in other towns. If you wish to learn something about Buddhism and meditation do not hesitate to ask!

Regular Meditation Times

Tuesday 8:00pm:

Introductory talk and guided 16th Karmapa meditation, for people who are new to Buddhism and those who have been practising for many years. There is plenty of time to answer any questions you may have.

PRESTON SERENE REFLECTION MEDITATION GROUP
Tradition: Zen
School: Soto
Meetings: The Multifaith Centre, 33 St. Peters Square. Preston
Affiliated to: The Order Of Buddhists Contemplatives, UK National Organisations
Postal Address: 13 Broadfield, Broughton, Preston PR3 5LB
Telephone Contact: 01772 863232 (Chris Richardson)
Or 01772 732921 (Lyn Pyatt)
Email: candlrich@hotmail.com

This group meets every Thursday at 7.30pm. Meditation instruction is available and newcomers are welcome.

ZEN PRACTICE CENTRE TRUST
Tradition: Zen
School: Soto/Rinzai

Entry continued on the following page.

England

Affiliated to: Zen Practice Centre Trust, UK National Organisations
Postal Address: Jenny & Stef Grabysch, Hollinwood, Myerscough Hall Drive, Bilsborrow, nr Preston PR3 0RE
Telephone Contact: 01995 640189

Please telephone for details of sittings.

ROSSENDALE

ROSSENDALE SAMATHA GROUP
Tradition: Theravada
Affiliated to: Samatha Trust, UK National Organisations
Postal Address: The Secretary of the Samatha Association, The Samatha Centre, Greenstreete, Llangunllo (nr Knighton), Powys LD7 1PS
Telephone Contact: 01706 220375 (Andrew Hudson)
Email: info@samatha.org
Website(s): www.samatha.org

LEICESTERSHIRE

HINCKLEY

ZEN PRACTICE CENTRE TRUST
Tradition: Zen
School: Soto/Rinzai
Meetings: 34 Laneside Drive, Hinckley, Leicestershire LE10 1TG
Affiliated to: Zen Practice Centre Trust, UK National Organisations
Telephone Contact: 01455 619767

LEICESTER

LEICESTER BUDDHIST SOCIETY
Tradition: All
Meetings: 6 Half Moon Crescent, Oadby

Telephone Contact: 0116 271 2339

Meets on Fridays 8.00pm for Meditation and Dhamma Study. All traditions. Group Leader: David Russell.

LEICESTER BUDDHIST VIHARA (East Midlands Buddhist Association)
Tradition: Theravada
Meetings: 9 Una Avenue, Narborough Road South, Leicester LE3 2GS
Charity No.: 519860
Postal Address: Ven M.Sumana (Acting) Head of the Vihara, 9 Una Avenue, Narborough Road South, Leicester LE3 2GS
Or Ven D Ratanajothi, 9 Una Avenue, Narborough Road South, Leicester LE3 2GS
Telephone Contact: 0116 282 5003

The Leicester Buddhist Vihara is the leading Theravada Buddhist Vihara in the area. The activities are conducted by resident monks. The Vihara is open to all those who are interested in Buddhism. A monk will be present to give any additional information or assistance to newcomers or to devotees. The Vihara is open daily from 9.00am to 9.00pm. A shrine room, Library and collection of books are available for free distribution. Quarterly newsletter The Wisdom is published regularly.

Programme of Events:

Sunday: 6.00am - 7.00am - Chanting and meditation; 6.00pm - 7.30pm - Puja, Chanting and meditation.

Saturday: 9.00am - 11.30am - Sinhala & Buddhism classes for children. 5.30pm - 7.30pm - Puja, Dhamma talk and Meditation.

First Sunday of every month: Day retreat 9.00 am - 5.00 pm
Friday: 7.00 pm - 9.00 pm Meditation and Dhamma Discussion

70

LEICESTER SERENE REFLECTION MEDITATION GROUP

Tradition: Zen
School: Soto
Meetings: Leicester Buddhist Vihara, East Midlands Buddhist Association, 9 Una Avenue, off Narborough Road, Leicester LE3 2GS
Affiliated to: The Order Of Buddhists Contemplatives, UK National Organisations
Telephone Contact: 0116 292 8654 (Kevin Commons)

The group meets every Wednesday evening at 7.30pm, including a meeting at the Vihara on alternate weeks. Phone for details.

LEICESTER SHAMBHALA STUDY GROUP

Tradition: Tibetan
School: Kagyu-Nyingma
Meetings: London Shambhala Meditation Centre, England, London, SW 4
Charity No.: 1073977
Postal Address: Leicester Shambhala Study Group c/o 86 Peter's Drive, Leicester, LE5 2AP
Telephone Contact: 0116 292 9019 Or 0116 254 4495
Email: geep86@hotmail.com

A small group of practitioners following the Kagyu/Nyingma tradition as propagated by Chogyam Trunpa Rinpoche, i.e. Tibetan Buddhism / Shambhala Buddhism. See London Shambhala Centre, London SW4 for further details.

MAITRI PROJECT

Tradition: Pure Land
School: Amida Buddhism
Meetings: The Buddhist House, 12 Coventry Road, Narborough, Leicester LE19 2GB
Affiliated to: Amida Trust, UK National Organisations
Charity No.: 1060589
Postal Address: Maitri Project, The Buddhist House, 12 Coventry Road, Narborough, Leicester LE19 2GB

Telephone Contact: 0116 286 7476
Email: maitri@amidatrust.com
Website(s): amidatrust.typepad.com/maitri

A community chaplaincy project involved in offering help in the field of spiritual need, mental health, asylum, counselling, pastoral care and interfaith relations.

NARBOROUGH

BUDDHIST HOUSE

Tradition: Pure Land
School: Amida-Shu
Meetings: The Buddhist House, 12 Coventry Road, Narborough, Leicester LE19 2GB
Affiliated to: Amida Trust, UK National Organisations
Charity No.: 1060589
Postal Address: The Buddhist House, 12 Coventry Road, Narborough, Leicester LE19 2GB
Telephone Contact: 0116 286 7476
Email: amida@amidatrust.com
Website(s): www.amidatrust.com

Residential religious community of the Order of Amida Buddha, headquarters of the Amida Trust (see UK National Organisations) & congregation of Amida-Shu.

Full time Buddhist training. Retreats. Courses in Pure Land Buddhism, Socially Engaged Buddhism, and Buddhist Psychology. Weekly meetings and classes. Inter-faith and engaged Buddhist activities. Ceremonies. Chaplaincy. Pastoral care.

Visitors welcome.

LINCOLNSHIRE

NORTH SOMERCOTES

COMMUNITY OF INTERBEING - LINCOLNSHIRE SANGHA

Entry continrued on the following page.

Tradition: Vietnamese
School: Thich Nhat Hanh
Affiliated to: The Community Of Interbeing, UK, UK National Organisations
Telephone Contact: 01507 358543 (Tony and Jenni Weedon)
Website(s): www.interbeing.org.uk

Contact for information about local and regional activities for meditation and Days of Mindfulness. See UK National Orgaisations for details of The Community of Interbeing.

LONDON

DZOGCHEN LONDON
Tradition: Tibetan
School: Dzogchen
Affiliated to: Dzogchen Community UK, UK National Organisations
Email: juditta@macunlimited.net
Website(s): www.dzogchencommunity.org
See UK NATIONAL ORGANISATIONS

E 13

BUDDHA VIHARA
Tradition: Theravada
Meetings: 84 Dacre Road, Plaistow, London E13 0PR
Charity No.: 275170
Postal Address: Buddha Vihara, 84 Dacre Road, Plaistow, London E13 0PR
Telephone Contact: 020 8257 2740

The Vihara is run by the Ambedkar International Mission. The Head of the Vihara is Ven. Dr. Siri Sumana Mahathera and the tradition followed is Theravada.

Programme:

Daily puja: 6.00pm to 7.00pm

Daily meditation class: 7.00pm to 10.00pm

Sunday puja 6.00pm to 8.00pm

Monks are available to discuss the Dhamma at all times at the vihara and will go anywhere on invitation to give talks.

Tube: Upton Park (District Line)   Busses: 58, 104, 238, 330, 376

E 2

AMRITA DZONG
Tradition: Tibetan
School: Karma-Kagyu
Meetings: Unit 21F, Perseverance Works, 38 Kingsland Road, London E2 8DD
Affiliated to: Marpa House - Chos Khor Ling, England, Essex, Ashdon
Charity No.: 1004520
Postal Address: Amrita Dzong, Unit 21F, Perseverance Works, 38 Kingsland Road, London E2 8DD
Or Ross McCleary, 8 Pickard Close, London N14 6JG
Telephone Contact: 0208 882 3883 (Ross McCleary)
Email: ross.mccleary@zen.co.uk

Amrita Dzong is a Tibetan Buddhist centre of the Karma Kagyu school, though it is in no way restrictive with respect to those who wish to attend, being open to members of all schools of Buddhism, and also to non-Buddhists.

Although an independent charity, it is very closely linked to Marpa House (see Essex, Saffron Walden) and in many respects operates as the London Branch of that centre. It is used mainly by students of the Venerable Lama Chime Rinpoche.

On Wednesday evenings there is a regular Chenrezi Puja held from 7.00pm till 8.00pm followed by tea and biscuits and an opportunity to ask questions.

Occasional teachings are given by various Rinpoches. Details are given in the newsletters from Amrita Dzong.

The centre can be contacted in writing, email or by telephoning any of the trustees listed below.

FEDERATION OF AMBEDKARITE BUDDHIST ORGANISATIONS UK

See UK National Organisations.

LONDON BUDDHIST ARTS CENTRE (FWBO)
Tradition: FWBO
Meetings: Eastbourne House, Bullards Place, London E2 0PT
Affiliated to: Friends Of The Western Buddhist Order, UK National Organisations
Postal Address: London Buddhist Centre, 51 Roman Road, Bethnal Green, London E2 0HU
Telephone Contact: 020 8983 6134 Or 0845 458 4716
Fax: 020 8980 1960
Website(s): www.fwbo.org

FWBO Arts organises arts activities within the FWBO including arts events and arts studios.

Provides studio space for local Buddhist artists and musicians. Rehearsal space to let for dance, theatre and workshops linked with the Buddhist movement, other charities and the local community.

LONDON BUDDHIST CENTRE (FWBO)
Tradition: FWBO
Meetings: 51 Roman Road, Bethnal Green, London E2 0HU
Affiliated to: Friends Of The Western Buddhist Order, UK National Organisations
Charity No.: 255420
Postal Address: The Centre Manager, London Buddhist Centre, 51 Roman Road, Bethnal Green, London E2 0HU

Telephone Contact: 0845 458 4716 Or 020 8981 1225
Fax: 020 8980 1960
Email: info@lbc.org.uk
Website(s):www.lbc.org.uk

The LBC is one of the largest urban Buddhist Centres in the West, and perhaps the best established Centre run by the Friends of the Western Buddhist Order (FWBO). It opened in 1978, in a building that was once a Victorian fire station, and it has become a well-known landmark in the East End of London. Today it is at the heart of a 'Buddhist Village' comprising a number of residential communities and several 'right livelihood businesses'.

E 6

EAST LONDON BUDDHIST CULTURAL CENTRE
Tradition: Theravada
Meetings: 33 Maybury Road, Plaistow, LONDON E13 8RZ
Postal Address: East London Buddhist Cultural Centre, 33 Maybury Road, Plaistow, LONDON E13 8RZ
Telephone Contact: 020 7476 0681
Website(s): www.btinternet.com/~asankawebdesigns/srilankanetuk

A Sri Lankan vihara. Please contact for details of current programme. The Head of the vihara is Ven M Mangala.

Nearest Tube: Plaistow DLR: Prince Regent.

EC4

SAKYA DECHEN LING - CITY OF LONDON
Tradition: Tibetan
School: Kagyu-Sakya
Meetings: St Bride Foundation, Bride Lane Fleet Street, London EC4Y 8EQ - Directions: Please

Entry continued on the following page.

enter the building via St Bride Foundation's main entrance and follow signs to the Photographic Studio. See www.stbridefoundation.org/reachus.html
Affiliated to: Dechen Community, UK National Organisations
Charity No.: 282717
Telephone Contact: 020 7586 5234
Email: london@dechen.org
Website(s):www.dechen.org

There has been a Dechen presence in London since the early 1980's, principally consisting of regular Vajrayana meditation sessions run by experienced Buddhist practitioners.

However, with an increasing number of Lama Jampa Thaye's students living in London, and following Lama Jampa's own move to London in 2005, a more extensive programme of activities was established. This includes hosting major teachings and public talks in London by Lama Jampa Thaye, running weekly meditation classes for newcomers and organising meditation days.

Sakya Dechen Ling now runs weekly meditation classes in Notting Hill, St John's Wood and the City of London.

Introductory Classes and Courses are held every Tuesday 6.30pm - 7.30pm. These classes are for those who have an interest in Buddhist meditation and who would like to practise meditation in a supportive environment. Each session comprises guided meditation and a short talk drawn from the Tibetan Buddhist tradition? Classes are led by experienced instructors.

N 1

LONDON SERENE REFLECTION MEDITATION GROUP
Tradition: Zen
School: Soto
Meetings: Yoga Therapy Centre, 90-92

Pentonville Road, (entrance on Penton Street) Islington, N1
Affiliated to: The Order Of Buddhists Contemplatives, UK National Organisations
Postal Address: James Donegan, 24 Burke House, Maysoule Road, London SW11 2BY
Helen Spark, 23 Chiswick Court, Moss Lane, Pinner HA5 3AP
Telephone Contact: 020 7585 1901
(Jamie Donegan)
Or 020 7373 9574 (Basia Janowska)
Website(s): www.lsrmg.org

The Prior of Reading Buddhist Priory attends the group periodically. We offer meditation instruction to newcomers and an opportunity for questions on Buddhist teachings and practice. We find that coming together for meditation helps to clarify and deepen our practice.

Please contact us for details of current meetings.

PALYUL CENTRE UK

See UK National Organisations.

RIGPA FELLOWSHIP

See Rigpa Fellowship, UK National Organisations.

N 11

BUDDHIST REALISTS' VIHARA
Tradition: All
Meetings: 85 Highworth Road, New Southgate, London N11 2SN
Postal Address: The Religious Director, Buddhist Realists' Vihara, 85 Highworth Road, New Southgate, London N11 2SN
Telephone Contact: 020 8361 6394
Fax: 020 8361 6394
Although we deal mostly with concepts from the Pali Tipataka, our approach is non-traditional and

England

non-sectarian. We advocate integration of Buddhism with Culture and ethics.

Please contact for details of current programme.

Executive Director: Rev. Sumana Siri, D.B.S., B.A. (Hons), D. Hom (Med.) MHMA (U.K.) N.M.D., D.H.M (USA), F.B.I.H (UK). (Founder).

N 12

OGYAN CHOKHOR LING
Tradition: Tibetan
School: Nyingma
Meetings: Initially contact Ngakpa Ga'wang
Affiliated to: Ogyan Chokhor Ling, UK National Organisations
Telephone Contact: 01227 728379
Email: gawang@nyingma.com
Website(s): www.nyingma.com/ogyan-cho-khor-ling

A Ngondro Group meets monthly to practice and to provide an introduction to the Dudjom Lineage of the Nyingma school of Tibetan Buddhism (See our UK National Organisations entry).

N 15

LINH SONH PHAT DUONG TEMPLE
Tradition: Vietnamese Mahayana
Postal Address: Linh Sonh Phat Duong Temple, 11 Ermine Road, Tottenham, London N15
Telephone Contact: 020 8809 1566

Contact: Bhikshuni Thich Nu Tri Phuong

N 3

NICHIREN BUDDHIST TEMPLE OF LONDON
Tradition: Nichiren
School: Nichiren Shu

Postal Address: Nichiren Buddhist Temple of London, 47 Wentworth Avenue, London N3 1YN
Telephone Contact: 020 8349 1433
Email: mail@nichiren-shu.org.uk
Website(s): www.nichiren-shu.org.uk

The Nichiren Buddhist Temple of London belongs to Nichiren Shu, which is the true, original and main school of Nichiren Buddhism. Nichiren Shu is one of the world-wide organisations of Mahayana Buddhism. The purposes of this Temple are to promote and practice the teaching of the Lotus Sutra and to support and serve through teaching the people and communities of the UK.

For more information, please feel free to contact the resident priest of the Temple.

N 4

ZEN LONDON
Tradition: Zen
School: Kwan Um School
Meetings: Contact for details
Postal Address: Zen London, c/o Bogumila Malinowska, 9B Crouch Hill, London N4 4AP
Telephone Contact: 020 7263 5579 (Bogusia)
Or 07742 979050
Email: bogumila108@yahoo.co.uk
Website(s): www.kwanumzen.com or zen.kwanumeurope.org/group/london/

Regular Practice Times:

Mornings: Weekdays 5.50 to 7.20

Weekends: 6.45 to 8.15 or 9.00

Midday: Sunday 11.00 to 12.40

Evening: Friday 19.00 to 21.00

If you wish to attend morning practice, please call one day in advance.

Entry continued on the following page.

N 5

NORTH LONDON ZEN DOJO
Tradition: Zen
School: Soto
Meetings: Highbury Roundhouse, Community Centre, 71, Ronalds Road, London N5 1XB
Affiliated to: International Zen Association UK, UK National Organisations
Charity No.: 1069941
Telephone Contact: 0207 732 3287 (Anette Fajardo)
Email: anettefajardo@yahoo.co.uk
Website(s): www.izauk.org

Zazen: Wednesday 7.00am, Thursday 7.30pm, Friday 7.00am, Sunday 9.00am.

Introduction: Thursday 7.00pm.

N 7

COMMUNITY OF INTERBEING - NORTH LONDON SANGHA
Tradition: Zen
School: Thich Nhat Hanh
Affiliated to: The Community Of Interbeing, UK, UK National Organisations
Telephone Contact: 020 7700 7615
Website(s): www.interbeing.org.uk

Contact for information about local and regional activities for meditation and Days of Mindfulness. See UK National Orgaisations for details of The Community of Interbeing.

NORTH LONDON BUDDHIST CENTRE (FWBO)
Tradition: FWBO
Meetings: 72 Holloway Road, London N7 8JQ
Affiliated to: Friends Of The Western Buddhist Order, UK National Organisations
Charity No.: 801632
Postal Address: North London Buddhist Centre 72 Holloway Road, London N7 8JQ

Telephone Contact: 020 7700 3075
Or 020 7700 1177
Email: info@northlondonbuddhistcentre.com
Website(s):
www.northlondonbuddhistcentre.com

The Centre holds regular drop-in meditation classes as well as courses in meditation and Buddhism for newcomers. It also holds regular drop-in yoga classes and yoga courses.

SUKHAVATI BUDDHIST TEMPLE
Tradition: Pure Land
School: Amida-Shu
Meetings: Sukhavati, 21 Sussex Way, Finsbury Park, London N7 6RT
Affiliated to: Amida Trust, UK National Organisations
Charity No.: 1060589
Postal Address: Sukhavati, 21 Sussex Way, Finsbury Park, London N7 6RT
Telephone Contact: 020 7263 2183
Email: amita-madrakara@hotmail.co.uk
Website(s): www.amidalondon.org.uk

London Temple of the Amida Trust (see Related Organisations) and the Order of Amida Buddha.

Retreats. Courses in Pure Land Buddhism, Socially Engaged Buddhism, and Buddhist Psychology. Weekly meetings. Ceremonies. Inter-faith and engaged Buddhist activities.

Visitors by arrangement.

N 9

SAMADHI MEDITATION CENTRE
Tradition: Theravada
Meetings: Samadhi Meditation Centre, 1 Oxford Road, Edmonton, London N9 0LY
Postal Address: Samadhi Meditation Centre, 1 Oxford Road, Edmonton, London N9 0LY
Telephone Contact: 020 8803 7194

Email: samadhiorganisation@yahoo.co.uk
geocities.com/samadhi_edmonton

Samadhi Meditation Centre was established on 22nd February in 2004 by a handful of buddhist devotees coming together with the Ven. Gunnepana Sumanarama as its incumbent priest. The main purpose behind establishing a Buddhist centre in Edmonton was to fill the vacuum left in North London at that time for the vast number of Sri Lankan, Indian as well as Western Buddhists who live in this area.

Although the number of pioneering devotees added up to only single figures, their devotion and dedication seem to have surpassed all barriers and obstacles. This was evidently proven by the fact that within two months of finding temporary accomodation, the altruistic Dayaka Committee has been able to raise a mortgage and purchase the present premises at No.1 Oxford Road on 10th September 2004.

The centre offers classes in Buddhism, Meditation, Sinhalese and Pali. Talks are given and pujas and festivals celebrated. There is a library and the centre publishes a magazine along with others material.

NW 11

LONDON RETREATS
Meetings: King Alfred School, 149 North End Road, London NW11
Affiliated to: Gaia House, Newton Abbot, Devon, England
Postal Address: London Retreats, London Retreats, 1 Thackeray Avenue, London N17 9DT
Telephone Contact: 020 8892 2324 (Anita Courtman)
Email:
enquiries@londoninsightmeditation.org.uk
Website(s):
www.londoninsightmeditation.org.uk

London Insight Meditation offers a programme of

monthly retreats, teaching and other events in the Insight meditation tradition. The retreats are suitable for both beginners and experienced meditators, and provide an opportunity to spend a day in quiet contemplation and reflection. All retreats are led by an experienced teacher, normally associated with the long-established Gaia House retreat centre in Devon.

The one-day retreats offer an opportunity to explore and develop serenity, wisdom and compassion through meditation and mindfulness practice, in a supportive environment. Periods of sitting meditation alternate with those of walking meditation. The teachers normally provide guidance through meditation instruction, a dharma (teaching) talk and a question and answer session.

Beginners are offered additional instructions and assistance, while for experienced meditators the day is an opportunity to refresh and deepen their practice. The retreats also serve as a time for us to connect with others who share an interest in wisdom, compassion and freedom.

Apart from the set times of communication, the retreats are normally held in silence. At the end of the day there is the opportunity to get to know each other over a cup of tea.

The practices focused on are mainly those of Insight (Vipassana) and Loving Kindness meditation.

NW 3

HAMPSTEAD BUDDHIST GROUP
Tradition: Theravada
Meetings: The Constable Room, Burgh House, New End Square, London NW3 1LT
Affiliated to: Amaravati Buddhist Monastery, UK National Organisations
Postal Address: Susan Jordan, 181C Fordwych Road, London NW2 3NG
Telephone Contact: 020 8452 4174 (Susan Jordan)
Or 020 8444 4685 (Adrienne Jeffrey)

Entry continued on the following page.

Or 020 8348 0537 (Caroline Randall)
Email: susan@jordan9333.freeserve.co.uk
Website(s): www.amaravati.org

Sitting meditation, discussion and teaching visits from the Sangha of Amaravati and Chithurst Monasteries (Theravada), the spiritual head of which is Venerable Ajahn Sumedho. Please contact for details of current venue and timetable.

KANZEON ZEN PRACTICE TRUST
Tradition: Zen
School: Soto/Rinzai
Meetings: Top Flat, 32 Shirlock Road, London NW3 2HS
Affiliated to: Zen Practice Centre Trust, UK National Organisations
Telephone Contact: 020 7267 6147
Email: hazymoon@onetel.com
Thursday Weekly Meditation Group in London NW3 at 7pm-9pm:

Zazen, open sharing, tea, reading from a Dharma text. Friendly, encouraging, informal. Open to all.

Hosted by Sarita Doveton and Manu Bazzano. Donation: £3

Last Saturday of each month: One Day of Zen lunch included 10am-4pm donation: £15-£25 depending on income.

No one will be turned away for lack of money.

Phone for more information.

NW 8

SAKYA DECHEN LING - ST. JOHN'S WOOD
Tradition: Tibetan
School: Kagyu-Sakya
Meetings: Kailash Centre, 7 Newcourt Street, St Johns Wood, NW8 7AA
Affiliated to: Dechen Community, UK National

Organisations
Charity No.: 282717
Telephone Contact: 020 7586 5234
Email: london@dechen.org
Website(s): www.dechen.org

Introductory Classes and Courses are held every Wednesday at 7.30pm. These classes are for those who are new to Buddhism or Dechen and wish to learn more. Each session comprises a short talk on an aspect of the Buddhist Path, given by an experienced Buddhist practitioner, followed by guided meditation, questions & answers, and refreshments. Classes are structured around a number of course themes, although it is not necessary to attend all classes in a single course.

NW 9

LONDON BURMESE BUDDHIST VIHARA (BRITAIN BURMA BUDDHIST TRUST)
Tradition: Theravada
Meetings: 1 Old Church Lane, Kingsbury, London NW9 8TG
Charity No.: 284619
Postal Address: The Senior Bhikkhu, The Britain Burma Buddhist Trust, 1 Old Church Lane, Kingsbury, London NW9 8TG
Telephone Contact: 020 8200 6898
Email: ucandobhasa@googlemail.com
Website(s): www.nibbana.com/london.htm

A Theravada Vihara. Please contact for details of the current programme.

SRI SADDHATISSA INTERNATIONAL BUDDHIST CENTRE
Tradition: Theravada
Meetings: 309-311 Kingsbury Road, Kingsbury, London NW9 9PE
Charity No.: 1008762
Postal Address: The Secretary, Sri Saddhatissa International Buddhist Centre, 309-311 Kingsbury Road, London NW9 9PE
Telephone Contact: 020 8204 3301

Fax: 020 8933 9395
Email: ssibc@ntlworld.com
Website(s): www.worldbuddhistfoundation.org

A Theravada Vihara affiliated to the World Buddhist Foundation catering for a wide range of Buddhist religious needs:

Propagating the Dhamma (according to the Theravada tradition), Buddhist meditation classes, Charitable works, Promoting cultural activities, Buddhist festival celebrations such as Vesak, Poson, Sanghamitta Day, Kathina Robe-Offering Ceremony, etc;

Regular talks on the Dhamma for the public. Dhamma classes for the young. Dhamma classes for adults leading to a diploma in Buddhist Studies from the World Buddhist Foundation.

Publications: Quarterly journal, Budumaga and books on Buddhism under the aegis of the World Buddhist Foundation.

The Spiritual Director of the Centre is Ven Galayaye Piyadassi.

NW10

PADMA LING

See UK NATIONAL ORGANISATIONS

SE 1

KAGYU SAMYE DZONG LONDON
Tradition: Tibetan
School: Karma-Kagyu
Meetings: Carlisle Lane, Off Royal Street, Lambeth, London SE1 7LG
Affiliated to: Kagyu Samye Ling Monastery And Tibetan Centre, UK National Organisations
Postal Address: Kagyu Samye Dzong London, Carlisle Lane, Off Royal Street, Lambeth, London SE1 7LG

Or Manor Place Samye Dzong, 33 Manor Place, Southwark, London SE17 3BD
Telephone Contact: 020 7928 5447
Or 020 7708 8969
Email: london@samye.org
Website(s): www.samye.org/london

This Centre is in the heart of London, near the Houses of Parliament. Within a few minutes walk from Westminster tube station and Waterloo tube and mainline stations, the Centre is next to the Archbishop's Park and opposite St Thomas's Hospital, where it provides an inner city oasis of peace and calm. Kagyu Samye Dzong London provides a venue for teachings from visiting lamas and also offers regular prayer sessions, meditation groups and comfortable, reasonably priced hostel accommodation for out of town guests, as well as a shop with a selection of beautiful statues, books and other Dharma objects. Inside the gates, guests enter a smoke, drug and alcohol free zone where they are welcome to meditate in the serene atmosphere of the beautiful shrine room.

Kagyu Samye Dzong London is run by Lama Zangmo, a well qualified nun who has completed eleven years of retreat and has taught at various Dharma centres both at home and abroad.

SOUTH LONDON ZEN DOJO
Tradition: Zen
School: Soto
Meetings: 4a Park Street, London Bridge, London SE1 9AB
Affiliated to: International Zen Association UK, UK National Organisations
Charity No.: 1069941
Telephone Contact: 020 7582 0794 (Alex)
Email: alex.lefevre@ntlworld.com
Website(s): www.izauk.org

Zazen: Mondays 7.30pm. Introduction: Mondays 7.00pm.
Tube: London Bridge. Allow 10 minutes to walk from the station.

Entry continued on the following page.

England

SE 11

JAMYANG BUDDHIST CENTRE
Tradition: Tibetan
School: Gelugpa
Meetings: The Old Courthouse, Renfrew Road, Kennington, LONDON SE11 4WA
Affiliated to: Foundation For The Preservation Of The Mahayana Tradition, UK National Organisations
Charity No.: 1106802
Postal Address: Jamyang Buddhist Centre, The Old Courthouse, 43 Renfrew Road, Kennington, London SE11 4NA
Telephone Contact: 020 7820 8787
Fax: 020 7820 8605
Email: admin@jamyang.co.uk
Website(s): www.jamyang.co.uk or www.buddhistthought.org

Jamyang Buddhist Centre is the London centre of the Foundation for the Preservation of the Mahayana Tradition (FPMT). Founded by Lama Thubten Yeshe and Lama Thubten Zopa Rinpoche, it is a Gelugpa Tibetan Buddhist Centre situated in a Grade II listed Victorian Courthouse and offers a full range of teachings and courses in the Lama Tsong Khapa tradition.

The resident geshe is Geshe Tashi Tsering, who gives weekly teachings in English. There are also regular visits from Lama Thubten Zopa Rinpoche, the Spiritual Director of the FPMT, and from other distinguished Tibetan Lamas such as Kirti Tsenshab Rinpoche and Khensur Lobsang Tenzin Rinpoche. Classes and teachings at all levels are open to everyone.

The regular weekly programme includes introductory courses about Buddhism, in-depth study of Tibetan Buddhist philosophy and simple relaxation and meditation classes, as well as retreats and pujas. Jamyang also runs a 2 year study programme called The Foundation Of Buddhist Thought, which is available as either a campus or a correspondence course. Jamyang's cultural programme includes weekend workshops on traditional thangka painting. Please see our website or phone for the current programme.

SE 13

BUDDHIST INTERHELP AND COMMUNITY OF INTERBEING VIETNAMESE CONTACT
Tradition: Vietnamese Thich Nhat Hanh
Affiliated to: The Community Of Interbeing, UK, UK National Organisations
Charity No.: 1070380
Postal Address: Buddhist Interhelp, c/o Mai Nguyen, 12 Shell Road, Lewisham, London SE13 7TW
Or Buddhist Interhelp, 12 Radegund Road, Cambridge CB1 3RL
Telephone Contact: 020 8692 1737 (Mai Nguyen)
Or 01223 242824
Email: cm90@supanet.com
Website(s): www.interbeing.org.uk

Buddhist Interhelp began practising in London early in 1982. By 1986, Thay, Thich Nhat Hanh named us with an English equivalent to the Vietnamese 'Hoi Tuong Te Phat Giao' - the Sangha of lay Buddhists who assist the Abbot or Abbess in daily tasks to maintain the Temple, to support the teaching and practice of Buddhism and to share practices with the family and help each other. These lay Sanghas exist in every district, neighbourhood or village where there is a Buddhist Temple and are an integral part of Vietnamese culture and way of life.

Abbreviated, Buddhist Interhelp is BI, which is the Vietnamese equivalent of karuna (compassion). The term beautifully expresses our Sangha's philosophy, objectives and action. Our activities embrace three principal aspects of practice: mindfulness training and practice, preserving and enriching Vietnamese culture and working to help others in need.

England

Regularly we hold days of mindfulness: reciting the sutras and precepts and engaging in Dharma discussion. We also receive Dharma talks from Thay and have retreats with him and other Buddhist masters of both Mahayana and Theravada traditions.

LONGCHEN FOUNDATION
Tradition: Tibetan
School: Kagyu-Nyingma
Meetings: South London
Affiliated to: Longchen Foundation, UK National Organisations
Telephone Contact: 020 8690 8778 (David Hutchens)
Website(s): www.longchenfoundation.com

The Longchen Foundation was established by Chögyam Trungpa Rinpoche and Dilgo Khyentse Rinpoche, two of the great Tibetan teachers of the 20th century, to pass on the authentic Mahayana MahaAti (Dzogchen) teachings of the Nyingma lineage to the west. The spiritual director and principal teacher, Rigdzin Shikpo, one of Trungpa Rinpoche's earliest western students and a qualified lama of the Nyingma tradition, was entrusted by them to teach in direct response to the needs of westerners and is among the most experienced and inspiring Buddhist teachers in Britain.

The Foundation is a community of Buddhist teachers, meditation instructors and students practising these teachings with the vision of liberating the hearts of beings. For details of weekend courses, retreats, publications, newsletters, please visit our website.

The Lions Roar is a course that introduces the view and innermost teachings of the Longchen tradition and offers a deep and authentic grounding in the practice of meditation. It is suitable for total beginners and experienced meditators. The course is available in Britain and in Germany.

SE 17

MANOR PLACE SAMYE DZONG
Tradition: Tibetan
School: Karma-Kagyu
Meetings: 33 Manor Place, London SE17 3BD
Affiliated to: Kagyu Samye Ling Monastery And Tibetan Centre, UK National Organisations
Postal Address: Kagyu Samye Dzong London, 33 Manor Place, London SE17 3BD Manor Place Samye Dzong, 33 Manor Place, Southwark, London SE17 3BD
Telephone Contact: 020 7708 8969 020 7928 5447
Email: manorplace@samye.org
Website(s): www.samye.org/london

This Centre is in the heart of London. Manor Place Samye Dzong provides a venue for teachings from visiting lamas and also offers regular prayer sessions, meditation groups and a shop with a selection of books and other Dharma objects.

Manor Place Samye Dzong is run by Lama Zangmo, a well qualified nun who has completed eleven years of retreat and has taught at various Dharma centres both at home and abroad.

SE 18

LEI ZANG SI TEMPLE LONDON
Tradition: Chinese
School: True Buddha School
Meetings: 40 Glyndon Road, Plumstead, London SE18
Charity No.:1056407
Postal Address: Ms Hayley Poon, 40 Glyndon Road, Plumstead, London SE18 7PB Mayriet Loh Temple Co-ordinator 40 Glyndon Road, Plumstead, London SE18 7PB
Telephone Contact: 020 8854 7054 (Temple)
Or 07941 519631(Mayriet Loh)
Fax: 020 7700 7881
Email: ceeannamay@hotmail.com or

England

tbs_lond_lzs_temple@hotmail.com
Website(s): www.tbsn.org

Lei Zang Si Temple London is one of the temples of the True Buddha School. Our Guru is Grand Master Lian Sheng, his teaching is called 'True Buddha Tantric Dharma' and includes Tantric Buddhism and meditation. The Temple is open on Sunday from 1.00pm to 5.30pm. At present Dharma Practice is in Chinese only, but we plan to have English practice in the future. However if you should require any information about the True Buddha School's teachings in English please refer to our website, or call the Temple Co-ordinator for enquiries.

SE 19

LINH SON TEMPLE AND MEDITATION CENTRE
(Vietnamese Buddhist Society in the UK.)
Tradition: Vietnamese
Meetings: The Linh Son Temple, 76 Beulah Hill, Upper Norwood, London SE19 3EW
Charity No.: 287922
Postal Address: The Secretary, The Linh Son Temple, 76 Beulah Hill, Upper Norwood, London SE19 3EW
Telephone Contact: 020 8771 5933
Or 07762 071365
Fax: 020 8771 5484
Email: linhson_uk@yahoo.co.uk
Website(s): www.geocities.com/linhsonuk

Primarily for the Vietnamese expatriate community. Please contact for details of the current programme.

SE 21

COMMUNITY OF INTERBEING - DULWICH SANGHA
Tradition: Vietnamese
School: Thich Nhat Hanh
Affiliated to: The Community Of Interbeing,

UK, UK National Organisations
Telephone Contact: 020 869 3251 (Stella)
Website(s): www.interbeing.org.uk

Established group meets on Tuesday evening each week.

Contact for information about local and regional activities for meditation and Days of Mindfulness. See UK National Orgaisations for details of The Community of Interbeing.

SE 24

LONDON-SOUTH DIAMOND WAY BUDDHIST CENTRE
Tradition: Tibetan
School: Karma-Kagyu
Meetings: 54 Danecroft Road, Herne Hill, London SE24 9NZ
Affiliated to: Diamond Way Buddhism UK, UK National Organisations
Charity No.: 1093406
Postal Address: London-South Diamond Way Buddhist Centre, 54 Danecroft Road, Herne Hill, London SE24 9NZ
Telephone Contact: 020 7326 1682
Email: southlondon@dwbuk.org
Website(s): www.diamondway-buddhism.co.uk

The new centre in Herne Hill, South London was started in January 2005. We are within walking distance of Herne Hill and North Dulwich stations as well as various bus routes. If you are coming by car, parking is free on the street.

We offer regular guided meditation evenings that include a short introduction to Buddhism for newcomers every Tuesday at 8pm. All are welcome and there is no charge for coming along. There is a small library at the centre, offering a selection of books, magazines, videos and other Buddhist bits and pieces!

If you are new to Buddhism and would like to find out more, please feel free to come over one Tuesday, give us a call or send us an email. We look forward to seeing you there.

Regular Meditation Times:

Tuesday 8:00pm and Friday 8:00pm

16th Karmapa guided meditation.

For people who are new to Buddhism and those who have been practicing for many years. There is plenty of time to answer any questions you may have.

SOUTH LONDON BUDDHIST GROUP (FWBO)
Tradition: FWBO
Affiliated to: Friends Of The Western Buddhist Order, UK National Organisations
Postal Address: FWBO Brixton c/o 24 Guernsey Grove, Herne Hill, London SE24 9YZ
Telephone Contact: 020 8766 8505
Website(s): www.fwbo.org

SW 1

BUDDHIST SOCIETY

See UK National Organisations.

SW 11

NIPPONZAN MYOHOJI PEACE PAGODA
Tradition: Nichiren
School: Myohoji shu
Meetings: Battersea Park, London
Postal Address: Rev Nagase, Nipponzan Myohoji Peace Pagoda, c/o The Park Office, Albert Bridge Road, Battersea, London SW11 4NJ
Telephone Contact: 020 7228 9620
Fax: 020 7228 9620

The London Peace Pagoda is one of many worldwide, built by monks and nuns of Nipponzan Myohoji, which was founded by the most Ven. Nichidatsu Fujii in order to promote peace. The movement is part of Nichiren Hokke-shu, but the Pagoda is aimed at the general promotion of Peace.

An annual Peace Pagoda celebration takes place on Saturday afternoon in mid-June, with all traditions of Buddhists being represented, along with interfaith prayers for peace and a cultural programme. On Nagasaki Day (9th August) each year, an interfaith Peace Pilgrimage takes place from Westminster Cathedral, usually leaving around 7:30 pm and arriving at the Pagoda about 8:15pm when prayers are given and floating lanterns offered to the River Thames. Throughout the year, smaller ceremonies take place in the little temple close to the Pagoda in the Park. Daily prayers are taken from 5-6 am and 5-6 pm. All are welcome to participate in all events and help is always very welcome and much appreciated in keeping the Pagoda clean.

Rev Nagase, the resident monk, looks after the Pagoda and temple, which are situated in a public park.

SW 19

BUDDHAPADIPA TEMPLE
Tradition: Theravada
Meetings: 14 Calonne Road, Wimbledon, London SW19 5HJ
Postal Address: The Secretary, Buddhapadipa Temple, 14 Calonne Road, Wimbledon, London SW19 5HJ
Telephone Contact: 020 8946 1357
Fax: 020 8944 5788
Email: dhammacaro@yahoo.co.uk
Website(s): www.buddhapadipa.org

The Buddhapadipa Temple, also known as the Thai Temple or Wat Buddhapadipa was so named by

Entry continued on the following page.

His Majesty the King of Thailand. The area of the Temple covers approximately four acres, in which is situated an ornamental lake, a grove and flower garden.

The Uposatha or Shrine Hall was built in the Thai architectural style and officially inaugurated on 30th October 1982 in the presence of HRH Princess Galyani Vaddana, the sister of the King of Thailand, as well as HRH Princess Alexandra and many distinguished Buddhists and non-Buddhists. As the Uposatha Hall has been located on such an excellent site surrounded by woodland, it has become famous in Wimbledon, as both a beauty spot and an historical landmark since its inauguration.

The Temple is run by resident Dhammaduta bhikkhus, or Buddhist missionary monks with the assistance of three lay communities.

These bhikkhus are selected by the Supreme Council of The Buddhist Order (the Sangha) in Thailand to go abroad and disseminate Theravada Buddhism or the Dhamma-teachings of the Buddha. A senior incumbent is also selected by the Supreme Council to take charge of the Temple.

COMMUNITY OF INTERBEING - WIMBLEDON SANGHA
Tradition: Zen
School: Thich Nhat Hanh
Affiliated to: The Community Of Interbeing, UK, UK National Organisations
Telephone Contact: 020 8541 1530 (Colin)
Website(s): www.interbeing.org.uk

Contact for information about local and regional activities for meditation and Days of Mindfulness. See UK National Orgaisations for details of The Community of Interbeing.

WIMBLEDON SAMATHA MEDITATION GROUP
Tradition: Theravada

Meetings: 40 Spencer Hill Road, Wimbledon, London SW19 4EL
Affiliated to: Samatha Trust, UK National Organisations
Telephone Contact: 020 7381 5288
Email: info@samatha.org
Website(s): www.samatha.org

There is a beginners class at the Friends Meeting House in Wimbledon. The class will meet every Wednesday at 7:45pm except for break periods over Christmas, Easter and during the summer holidays.

As a beginners class it is suitable both for those who have some experience of meditation and for those who have no previous experience.

There will usually be some group instruction in mindfulness of breathing and a group practice together and then an opportunity to report to the teacher individually, and also refreshments.

Email for more details. All welcome.

SW 3
COMMUNITY OF INTERBEING - HEART OF LONDON SANGHA
Tradition: Vietnamese
School: Thich Nhat Hanh
Affiliated to: The Community Of Interbeing, UK, UK National Organisations
Telephone Contact: 020 8771 2175 (Zofia Hockin)
Email: zofia.hockin@talktalk.net
Website(s): www.geocities.com/heartoflondon

Contact for information about local and regional activities for meditation and Days of Mindfulness. See UK National Orgaisations for details of The Community of Interbeing.

Underground: Sloane Square. About 20 minutes walk down Kings Road. Buses: 11, 19, 22, 319.

England

SW 4

LONDON SHAMBHALA MEDITATION CENTRE
Tradition: Tibetan
School: Kagyu-Nyingma
Meetings: 27 Belmont Close, London SW4 (5 minutes from Clapham Common underground station)
Charity No.: 1073977
Postal Address: London Shambhala Meditation Centre, 27 Belmont Close, London SW4 6AY
Telephone Contact: 020 7720 3207
Fax: 020 7627 4224
Email: info@shambhala.org.uk
Website(s): www.shambhala.org.uk
London Shambhala

Meditation Centre (formerly Dharmadhatu London) is part of Shambhala International, a world-wide organisation of meditation centres founded by the late Chögyam Trungpa Rinpoche (1939-1987) and now under the guidance of Sakyong Mipham Rinpoche.

Trungpa Rinpoche's teachings emphasise the importance of mindfulness-awareness sitting meditation and Mahayana lojong compassion practices, both in their own right and as a prerequisite foundation for the Mahamudra and Ati (Dzogchen) paths of Vajrayana Buddhism.

Regular public meditation sessions with individual meditation instruction are held at the centre free of charge. Buddhist study includes talks, evening classes and weekend programmes combining study with meditation. All liturgies are practised in English. Small meditation intensives are held at the centre from time to time. Larger programmes, including dathün (a month-long meditation intensive practice) are held at Dechen Chöling in France and at centres world-wide. Ivy Bank, a retreat house near the South Coast, is available for individual retreats.

The centre's activities also include Shambhala Training, a non-religious path of meditation in everyday life, and Nalanda Contemplative Arts, in which meditative awareness is fostered through disciplines such as Kyudo (Zen archery) and Ikebana (Japanese flower-arranging).

Public Opening Times: Monday and Wednesday: 7.30 to 9.30pm.

W 1

BUDDHA'S LIGHT INTERNATIONAL ASSOCIATION LONDON (B.L.I.A. LONDON)
Tradition: Chinese
School: Ch'an
Meetings: 84 Margaret Street, London W1W 8TD
Affiliated to: London Fo Guang Temple, London, W 1 England
Charity No.: 1023575
Postal Address: BLIA London, 84 Margaret Street, London W1W 8TD
Telephone Contact: 020 7636 8394
Fax: 020 7580 6220

BLIA is an International Buddhist organisation which was founded by Venerable Master Hsing Yun and was inaugurated at the Hsi Lai Temple, Los Angeles, on 16th may 1992. Its objectives are:

1) to encourage the study of and research into Buddhism;

2) to support related cultural and educational programmes;

3) to serve community, society and humanity;

4) to develop and implement educational programmes for all Buddhists;

5) to promote Dharma propagation internationally.

There are many branches of BLIA functioning in over 80 countries in the world. Membership is open to all Buddhists irrespective of nationality or

Entry continued on the following page.

age. The activities of the London branch include meditation, chanting, meditation retreats, Dharma talks/discussions, classes in Chinese language, Chinese vegetarian cookery and flower arrangement. In conjunction with the London Fo Guang Temple, BLIA, London publishes Buddha's Light Newsletter reporting events of interest to Buddhists. The members meet frequently for various activities.

LONDON FO GUANG TEMPLE
Tradition: Chinese
School: Ch'an
Meetings: 84 Margaret Street, London W1W 8TD
Charity No.: 1023575
Postal Address: Ven Man Jang, Abbess, IBPS UK, 84 Margaret Street, London W1N 7HD.
Telephone Contact: 020 7636 8394
Fax: 020 7580 6220
Email: london@ibps.org.uk
Website(s): www.ibps.org.uk

The Temple is a branch of Fo Guang Shan, Taiwan. Fo Guang Shan was founded by Venerable Master Hsing Yun in 1967 for the purpose of propagating Humanitarian Buddhism. It is now one of the largest monasteries in the world, with branch centres in many parts of the world.

London Fo Guang Temple, just as the mother institution, belongs to the Ch'an school of Mahayana Buddhism. The Temple was officially opened in September, 1992. Services at the Temple are held every Sunday. On Moon days, a Light Offering Service is held. All services start at 10.30am. and at the conclusion of the service, the congregation is served with a vegetarian lunch. Traditional Chinese Buddhist festivals are also celebrated. Classes in meditation and Buddhist teachings are also held.

There is also a programme of classes in cultural subjects, exhibitions, charitable performances etc.

The Temple publishes its monthly newsletter, Buddha's Light Newsletter, which is distributed free of charge to all.

The library has a collection of Dharma books, cassettes and videos in both Chinese and English and these items are available for loan.

W 11

HOLLAND PARK GROUP Theravada
Affiliated to: Amaravati Buddhist Monastery, UK National Organisations
Telephone Contact: 020 7221 9330 (Jeffrey Craig)

Please contact for time and place of meetings.

W 2

LONDON ZAZEN GROUP
Tradition: Zen
School: Soto
Meetings: Centre for Counselling and Psychotherapy Education. Beauchamp Lodge, 2 Warwick Crescent, London. W2 6NE
Postal Address: Ray Menezes. London Zazen Group. CCPE, Beauchamp Lodge, 2 Warwick Crescent, London W2 6NE
Telephone Contact: 07957 934047
Email: raymond@menez.fsnet.co.uk
Website(s):www.raymenezes.com

The London Zazen Group meets every Friday from 7:30pm to 9:00pm. The group is run by Ray Menezes who is a UKCP registered psychotherapist working from a Zen Buddhist perspective. Ray Menezes also runs retreats throughout the year, both residential and non-residential; he is author of the book Blood Washing Blood - a Zen perspective of Psychotherapy. Contact Ray Memezes for all details.

WEST LONDON BUDDHIST CENTRE (FWBO)
Tradition: FWBO
Meetings: 94 Westbourne Park Villas, London W2 5EB
Affiliated to: Friends Of The Western Buddhist Order, UK National Organisations
Charity No.: 721591
Postal Address: The Centre Manager, West London Buddhist Centre, 94 Westbourne Park Villas, London W2 5EB
Telephone Contact: 020 7727 9382
Email: info@westlondonbuddhistcentre.com
Website(s):
www.westlondonbuddhistcentre.com

Here at the West London Buddhist Centre we run a programme of different classes to support our individual practice.

If you are looking for beginners meditation classes then come along to our: Wednesday Lunchtime Meditation Taster. Alternatively a meditation class open for all levels is our: Saturday Morning Drop in Class. Or you could consider booking a Meditation Course.

We also run classes in Buddhism and mark Buddhist festivals throughout the year with dedicated evenings.

Nearest Underground: Royal Oak, Bayswater.

W 3

THREE WHEELS
Tradition: Pure Land
School: Jodo Shin Shu
Meetings: 55 Carbery Avenue, Acton Town, London W3 9AB
Charity No.: 1076610
Postal Address: Three Wheels, 55 Carbery Avenue, Acton Town, London W3 9AB
Telephone Contact: 020 8248 2542
Fax: 020 8248 2578
Email: threewheels@threewheels.org

Website(s): www.threewheels.org

'Promoting Harmony in Diversity'

Three Wheels is a temple in the Jodo Shinshu tradition of Pure Land Buddhism; a school also known in the West as 'Shin Buddhism'.

Shin Buddhism is especially effective at transforming the challenges faced by lay-people into the development of faith, wisdom and compassion. As the emphasis is placed upon the 'activity of the Infinite Dharmakaya' ('Tariki' - the power of Amida Buddha) no person is excluded from awakening on the basis of their personal conditions or circumstances. Jodo Shinshu is therefore a universal Dharma-gate well suited to people from all walks of life and of different natures. For this reason the great Rinzai Zen scholar D.T.Suzuki described Shin Buddhism as 'Japan's greatest gift to the West'.

Regular activities include:

Daily: 6.30am and 6.30pm. Chanting sutras in gratitude to Amida Buddha. The morning service is followed by a short meeting.

Weekly: Meditation Classes.

Monthly: Meetings to read 'The Letters' (Ofumi).

Eza Meetings held once every two months where a formal talk is delivered to the whole Samgha and their guests.

For information about any of our activities please contact Rev. Prof. Kemmyo Taira Sato.

Rev. Prof. Kemmyo Taira Sato also gives monthly lectures at The Buddhist Society on the Letters (Ofumi) by Rennyo Shonin (1415-1499), Restorer of Shin Buddhism (Jodo Shinshu). Professor Sato will give lectures on those letters that Rennyo Shonin gave to his followers to clarify the Shin Buddhist faith. In their daily service Shin Buddhist

Entry continued on the following page.

England

followers read out the Letters one after another.

W 4

LONDON BUDDHIST VIHARA
Tradition: Theravada
Meetings: Dharmapala Building, The Avenue, Bedford Park, Chiswick, London W4 1UD
Postal Address: The London Buddhist Vihara, Dharmapala Building, The Avenue, Chiswick, London W4 1UD
Telephone Contact: 020 8995 9493 Or 020 8994 8130
Email: london.vihara@virgin.net
Website(s): www.londonbuddhistvihara.org

The tradition followed is Theravadin. The regular programme is as follows:

Sunday puja with sermon/lecture weekly at 5.00pm.-7.00pm.

Dhamma classes for children: Sundays 2.30pm.-4.15pm.

Meditation classes: Wednesdays 7.00pm.-8.30pm.

Classes on Buddhist Doctrine: Mondays: 7.00pm-9.00pm; Tuesdays: 7.00pm.-9.00pm; Thursdays: 7.00pm - 9.00pm (in conjunction with the University of London); Fridays 7.30pm.-9.00pm.

Full Moon puja 5.00pm.

Monthly meditation retreat: last Saturday of each month except August and December (half day).

A large reference library is available for registered supporters of the Vihara. A comprehensive stock of Buddhist literature is available at the Vihara's bookstall.
Venerable Seelawimala will arrange for a monk speaker to be sent to schools and colleges on request.

ZEN LONDON
Tradition: Zen
School: Kwan Um School
Meetings: Crouch Hill, London W4 please telephone for details
Telephone Contact: 077429 79050
Email: londonzen@szm.com
Website(s): www.kwanumzen.org

Introduction to Zen Practice

Regular Meetings with Zen Group

Kong-ans Interviews with Zen Masters

Informal Interview with Senior Dharma Teacher

Public Talks and Monthly Retreats

The Kwan Um School of Zen is an international organization of more than a hundred centers and groups founded by Zen Master Seung Sahn, the first Korean Zen Master to live and teach in the West. The School's purpose is to make this practice of Zen Buddhism available to an ever-growing number of students throughout the world.

The founding teacher of our School is Zen Master Seung Sahn, the 78th Patriarch in his line of transmission in the Chogye order of Korean Buddhism. In 1972 he came to the United States and started the Providence Zen Center, the first center in what is now the Kwan Um School. He and his students have founded over a hundred temples, centers, and groups around the world. His books include Ten Gates, The Compass of Zen, Dropping Ashes on the Buddha, Only Don't Know and The Whole World is a Single Flower -- 365 Kong-ans for Everyday Life.

W 8

SAKYA DECHEN LING - NOTTING HILL
Tradition: Tibetan
School: Kagyu-Sakya
Meetings: Essex Unitarian Church, 112 Palace

88

Gardens Terrace, Notting Hill Gate, London W8 4RT
Affiliated to: Dechen Community, UK National Organisations
Charity No.: 282717
Telephone Contact: 020 7706 2425
Email: london@dechen.org
Website(s): www.dechen.org

Introductory Classes and Courses are held every Tuesday 7.30pm. These classes are for those who are new to Buddhism or Dechen and wish to learn more. Each session comprises a short talk on an aspect of the Buddhist Path, given by an experienced Buddhist practitioner, followed by guided meditation, questions & answers, and refreshments.

W 9

BRITISH BUDDHIST ASSOCIATION
Tradition: All
Meetings: London, Kent, Sussex
Postal Address: A Haviland-Nye, British Buddhist Association, 11 Biddulph Road, London W9 1JA
Telephone Contact: 020 7286 5575

The British Buddhist Association promotes educational, religious and meditation aspects of the Buddha's teaching at evening and weekend sessions both in London and at country retreats, to augment private study and practice. Activities are generally ordered to a structured form both for those who have a professional interest in the Buddha's teaching and interested members of the public who are able to give systematic attention and radical reflection to it. The BBA is non-sectarian and seeks to express religious devotion in ways suitable to Western practitioners.

WC 1

LONDON DIAMOND WAY BUDDHIST CENTRE
Tradition: Tibetan

School: Karma-Kagyu
Meetings: 27 Johns Mews, London, WC1N 2NS
Affiliated to: Diamond Way Buddhism UK, UK National Organisations
Charity No.: 1093406
Postal Address: Buddhist Centre London, 27 Johns Mews, London, WC1N 2NS
Telephone Contact: 020 7916 2282
Email: london@dwbuk.org
Website(s): www.diamondway-buddhism.co.uk

The London centre is the longest established Diamond Way Buddhist centre in the UK. It has been at its present location in the heart of London since 1998, close to both Holborn and Chancery Lane tube stations. Our popular meditation classes have proved highly effective for Londoners who want to integrate meditation into their busy lives.

The London centre offers broad access to the Buddha's highest methods for developing freedom and joy in every situation. These methods were practiced in Tibet and India for centuries in an unbroken transmission lineage.

We have a small library of Buddhist books and a selection of Diamond Way Buddhist magazines and meditation booklets.

Please email us your address if you would like to be notified of forthcoming events.

Regular Meditation Times

Monday 7:00pm: 16th Karmapa guided meditation.

Suitable for those who are new to Buddhism or wish to learn more. Each session starts with a 30-minute talk on an key Buddhist topic, given by an experienced Buddhist practitioner, and a chance for questions and answers. This is followed by a guided 16th Karmapa Meditation. You are most welcome to come a little earlier for a cup of tea and a chat before the session.

Entry continued on the following page.

Thursday 8:00pm: 16th Karmapa guided meditation.

Thursdays are our busiest sessions which usually start with a 10-minute talk on a Buddhist topic, given by a member of the group. This is follwed by a 16th Karmapa Meditation, guided by an experienced Buddhist practitioner. There is also always plenty of time to answer any questions you may have.

All sessions are free of charge.

SCHOOL OF ORIENTAL AND AFRICAN STUDIES (SOAS) MEDITATION SOCIETY, THE
Tradition: Theravada
Meetings: School for Oriental and African Studies (SOAS), Malet St WC1
Affiliated to: Samatha Trust, UK National Organisations
Telephone Contact: 020 7381 5288
Email: stefaniamenin@hotmail.com
Website(s): www.samatha.org

The meditation classes are held every Wednesday at 6.00pm to 8pm during term time. Please telephone for further details.

SOAS (The School of Oriental and African Studies), is part of the University of London. The meditation class takes place in the Vernon Square campus. The nearest tubes are King's Cross and Angel.

LONDON: ESSEX

ILFORD

ASSOCIATION FOR INSIGHT MEDITATION
Tradition: Theravada
School: Vipassana
Meetings: 34B Cambridge Road, Seven Kings, Essex IG3 8LU

Postal Address: Association for Insight Meditation. c/o T Shine, 3 Clifton Way, Alperton, Middlesex, HA0 4PQ
Telephone Contact: 020 8902 4644
Email: tshine@onetel.net.uk or pesala@aimwell.org
Website(s): www.aimwell.org

The aim of the Association for Insight Meditation is to publish books and organise meditation retreats in the Burmese Insight Meditation tradition, especially that of Venerable Mahasi Sayadaw.

REDBRIDGE BUDDHIST CULTURAL CENTRE
Tradition: Theravada
Meetings: 9 Balfour Road, Ilford, Essex
Charity No.: 1075351
Postal Address: R C Wimalasundera (Secretary), Redbridge Cultural Centre, 9 Balfour Road, Ilford, Essex IG1 4HP
Telephone Contact: 020 8478 8286
Venerable Sumanarama
Email: bhikkhupesala@clara.co.uk
Website(s): www.redbridgerenet.co.uk/redbridgebuddhistcentre.html

Description: Sri Lankan Buddhist Centre with traditional cultural activities plus regular Dhamma teaching and meditation classes conducted mostly in English. There is currently one Sri Lankan and one English resident bhikkhu.

Weekly Programme:

Sunday: Sinhala and Dhamma classes for children 2:30 pm to 4:30 pm. Puja with Dhamma discussion from 6:30 to 8:00 pm.

Thursday: Meditation classes for beginners 7:30 to 9:00 pm.

Friday: Meditation Classes for experienced meditators 7:30 (walking), 8:00 (sitting), 9:00

(walking), 9:30 (sitting). Join or leave quietly at 7:30, 8:00, 9:00 or 9:30 pm.

Resident monks: Bhikkhu Pesala and Venerable Sumanarama.

LONDON: MIDDLESEX

EDGWARE

EDGWARE MEDITATION GROUP
Tradition: All
Postal Address: Josephine Doorley, 5 Shelley Close, Edgware, Middlesex HA8 8DX
Telephone Contact: 020 8958 4056

A newly relaunched open sitting group which meets on the last Wednesday of each month and is anxious to recruit new members. The primary form of practice is vipassana meditation as taught at Gaia House, but other forms of practice and all religious affiliations are welcome.

HARROW

HARROW ZAZENKAI
Tradition: Zen
School: Soto
Meetings: Flat 3, 4 Stuart Avenue, South Harrow, Middlesex HA2 9BB
Postal Address: Frank Tettsu Woods, Flat 3, 4 Stuart Avenue, South Harrow, Middlesex HA2 9BB
Telephone Contact: 020 8422 9757 (Frank Tettsu Woods)
Email: Franktettsu@onetel.com
Website(s): www.wwzc.org

Harrow Zazenkai - a White Wind Zen Community Branch Centre - provides the environment in which students may gather together to practice Zen. The Head Monastery is Honzan Dainen-ji in Ottawa,

which is under the direction and teaching of the Abbot, Ven. Anzan Hoshin roshi and is in the Hakukaze Soto Zen stream.

The main activity at Harrow Zazenkai is sitting - Zazen. In this context we unfold the forms of chanting, listening to teisho tapes by Anzan Hoshin roshi, Daruma kata - a movement practice - and oryoki. Practice interviews are regularly available with Senior Practice Advisors and at Dainen-ji - by telephone and email. We also have the opportunity for face to face interviews with visiting Practice Advisors when we also hold Introductory Zen Workshops. Formal students travel regularly to Dainen-ji and this helps keep the practice environment fresh.

The practice schedule at Harrow Zazenkai is:

Weekday mornings 7.00 - 8.00am.

Monday and Friday 7.30 - 9.00 pm.

Sunday 7.30 - 9.00am.

One-day sittings are held monthly. Other sitting times and instruction in sitting posture are available by appointment.

For further information on the White Wind Zen Community consult http://www.wwzc.org or email info@wwzc.org.

HESTON

SANTISUKHA VIHARA
Tradition: Theravada
Meetings: 269 Vicarage Farm Road, Heston, Middlesex TW5 0DR
Postal Address: Santisukha Vihara 269 Vicarage Farm Road, Heston, Middlesex TW5 0DR
Telephone Contact: 020 8570 2097
Website(s): web.ukonline.co.uk/buddhism/santi.htm

Entry continued on the following page.

England

The Vihara is open to all and the resident monks will be more than happy to help. There is a full range of daily activities, courses and talks. Please contact for more details.

HOUNSLOW

SLSCO-FLAME
Tradition: Theravada
Meetings: The Sri Lanka Community Centre, 25, Springwell Road, Heston, Hounslow, Middx TW5 9ED
Charity No.: 1076765
Telephone Contact: 01462-686075
Email: slsco.flame1@ntlworld.com

Latha Gunatunga - Secretary SLSCO-FLAME

SOUTHALL

BUDDHA VIHARA
Tradition: Theravada
School: Ambedkarite
Meetings: 12 Featherstone Road, Southall, Middlesex UB2 5AA
Affiliated to: Federation Of Ambedkarite Buddhist Organisations UK, UK National Organisations
Postal Address: Buddha Vihara, 12 Featherstone Road, Southall, Middlesex UB2 5AA
Telephone Contact: 020 8571 5131 Or 01871 433 1032

Caters primarily for the needs of the local community. Please contact for details of the current programme.

TWICKENHAM

TISARANA VIHARA
Tradition: Theravada
Meetings: 357 Nelson Road, Whitton, Twickenham, Middx, TW2 7AG

Postal Address: Tisarana Vihara, 357 Nelson Road, Whitton, Twickenham, Middx, TW2 7AG
Telephone Contact: 0208 898 6965

Website(s): www.nibbana.com/tisarana.htm

The Theravada tradition is followed under the spiritual direction of the Abbots, Venerable Sayadaw U Abhayalankara and Venerable Sayadaw Waiponeka.

Please contact for details of the current programme and facilities.

UXBRIDGE

UXBRIDGE SAMATHA MEDITATION GROUP
Tradition: Theravada
Meetings: Quaker Meeting House, Uxbridge (entrance along Friends Walk, from York Road or Belmont Road)
Affiliated to: Samatha Trust, UK National Organisations
Telephone Contact: 020 7381 5288
Email: vijaykhuttan@hotmail.com
Website(s): www.samatha.org

Classes start at 8pm on Thursdays at the Uxbridge Quaker Meeting House, Uxbridge UB8 1QW (entrance along Friends walk, from York Road or Belmont Road), near Uxbridge tube station, which is on the Metropolitan and the Piccadilly line.

Cost is £3 to cover room hire (there is no charge for the teaching).

All welcome. Please send e-mail for more details.

LONDON: SURREY

CROYDON

CROYDON BUDDHIST CENTRE
Tradition: FWBO
Meetings: 96-98 High Street, Croydon, Surrey CRO 1ND   Friends Of The Western Buddhist Order, UK National Organisations
Charity No.: 270460
Postal Address: The Buddhist Centre, 96-98 High Street, Croydon, Surrey CRO 1ND
Telephone Contact: 020 8688 8624
Fax: 020 8649 9375
Email: info@croydonbuddhistcentre.com
Website(s):www.croydonbuddhistcentre.com

The centre comprises a large shrine room, reception area, and bookshop. The complex also houses a Right Livelihood business, Oasis Natural Products and there are two men's communities and one women's community linked to the centre.

Beginners meditation sessions are held regularly. We also offer introductory Buddhism courses, yoga classes, some holistic therapies, study groups, celebration of Buddhist festivals, schools visits, plus occasional public talks and arts events.

The Buddhist Centre and shop are open six days a week.

Monday - Friday 11.30am - 5.30pm & Saturday 10am - 1.30pm

Retreats are held at Rivendell our retreat centre in Sussex.

HAM

COMMUNITY OF INTERBEING - HAM / RICHMOND SANGHA
Tradition: Vietnamese

School: Thich Nhat Hanh
Affiliated to: The Community Of Interbeing, UK, UK National Organisations
Telephone Contact: 020 8546 5525 (Geraldine Worthington)
Website(s): www.interbeing.org.uk

Contact for information about local and regional activities for meditation and Days of Mindfulness. See UK National Orgaisations for details of The Community of Interbeing.

KINGSTON UPON THAMES

YOUN-HWA-SA (LOTUS HOUSE)
Tradition: Korean
Postal Address: 5 Waters Road, KINGSTON-ON-THAMES Surrey KT1 3LW
Telephone Contact: 020 8977 6963 (Lewis)

Yon-Hwa-Sa is a Korean temple serving both the local Korean community and others interested in learning about Korean Zen. The temple is of the Chogye lineage whose main practice is based around a deep questioning on the fundamental mysteries of life. There are open meetings every Thursday at 7.30pm with the resident monk where, as well as formal meditation, there is opportunity for tea and discussion. The meetings are conducted in English and are suitable for people of all levels of experience. There is no charge for the class and all are welcome to drop in.

RICHMOND

RICHMOND SAMATHA MEDITATION GROUP
Tradition: Theravada
Meetings: The Friends Meeting House, 1 Retreat Road, Richmond-Upon-Thames, Surrey TW9 1NN.
Affiliated to: Samatha Trust, UK National Organisations
Telephone Contact: 020 7381 5288

Entry continued on the following page.

Email: richmond_samatha@yahoo.co.uk
Website(s): www.samatha.org

Classes are open to all. No previous experience of meditation is required - beginners are welcome. Please feel free to join the class any week.

There is no charge for teaching, but we welcome donations to cover the cost of the room hire. During the class, there is usually a talk and a group meditation practice. Please bring a cushion which you are comfortable sitting on. Because everybody's experience of meditation is different, there is an opportunity each week to speak to the teacher one-to-one, before or after the class.

The class is every Thursday night at 8pm.

For more information about the class, please send an email.

SELSDON

THAMES BUDDHIST VIHARA
Tradition: Theravada
Meetings: 49 Dulverton Road, Selsdon, Surrey CR2 8PJ
Charity No.: 289655
Postal Address: Ven Somaratana, 49 Dulverton Road, Selsdon, Surrey, CR2 8PJ
Telephone Contact: 020 8657 7120
020 8405 6833   020 8651 3776
Email: thamesvihara@btinternet.com
Website(s):
www.geocities.com/thamesbuddhistvihara

The Vihara follows the Theravada tradition providing a shrine room for Puja, meditation, sermons and Pirith chanting.

Daily Puja and Pirith chanting is from 6.00pm to 7.30pm.

Sunday evening special Puja and Meditation takes place from 6.00pm to 7.30pm.

There is a Sunday school for Sinhalese language and Dhamma for children from 4.00pm.

Dhamma discussion on the last Saturday of the month 6pm - 8pm.

A Buddhist bookshop and lending library are available and a quarterly newsletter is published.

The Vihara is open to all.

Monks in residence: Ven Somaratana (Head of the Vihara), Ven H Pannasekara (Spiritual Director), Ven Nagasena.

The Vihara is maintained by the Thames Meditation Society.

SUTTON

RICHARD HUNN ASSOCIATION FOR CH'AN STUDY
Tradition: Chinese
School: Ch'an
Telephone Contact: 0208 405 9874
Email: chandao@fastmail.fm
Website(s):
chanbuddhismuk.proboards34.com

Richard Hunn, the inspiration behind the association, passed away this year, in Kyoto, Japan. He was our former spiritual director, and the association he helped found, now bears his name, in respectful memory.

Our new spiritual director, is the Ch'an monk Shih Ying-Fa, the Abbot of the Dragon Flower Ch'an Temple, to which we are officially affiliated. See Cloud Water Zendo - www.cloudwater.org

We offer written guidance and support for all those embarking upon the Ch'an path.

MERSEYSIDE

LIVERPOOL

KAGYU SHEDRUP LING
Tradition: Tibetan
School: Kagyu-Sakya
Meetings: Blackburne House, Blackburne Place, Off Hope Street, Liverpool L8 7PE
Affiliated to: Dechen Community, UK National Organisations
Charity No.: 1055813
Telephone Contact: 07762 010529
Email: merseyside@dechen.org
Website(s): www.dechen.org

Kagyu Shedrup Ling was established in 1983. Numerous teachings have been bestowed at the centre by Karma Thinley Rinpoche and Lama Jampa Thaye and a continuing programme of classes is offered to the public.

Introductory Classes consist of a short talk on different aspects of Buddhism and an introduction to Buddhist meditation. Please phone for details.

LIVERPOOL AMARAVATI GROUP
Tradition: Theravada
Affiliated to: Amaravati Buddhist Monastery, UK National Organisations
Postal Address: Liverpool Amaravati Group, c/o Ursula Haeckel, 5 Glenluce Road, Liverpool, L19 9BX
Telephone Contact: 0151 427 6668 (Ursula Haeckel)

Please contact for details of current activities. All traditions welcome.

LIVERPOOL DIAMOND WAY BUDDHIST CENTRE
Tradition: Tibetan
School: Karma-Kagyu
Meetings: 61 Newsham Drive, Liverpool, (Tuebrook/Newsham Park), L6 7UQ
Affiliated to: Diamond Way Buddhism UK, UK National Organisations
Charity No.: 1093406
Postal Address: Liverpool Diamond Way Buddhist Centre, 61 Newsham Drive, Liverpool, (Tuebrook/Newsham Park), L6 7UQ
Telephone Contact: 0151 222 3543
Email: liverpool@dwbuk.org
Website(s): www.diamondway-buddhism.co.uk

The Liverpool Centre is situated in a beautiful location, overlooking Newsham Park. The house is an old Victorian town house, built in the 1880s. The centre was established in 2001 and has been at Newsham Park since 2003.

The main purpose of the Centre is to provide access to the living tradition of Diamond Way Buddhism of the Karma Kagyu Lineage, free of confusing cultural baggage. It is a place for those interested in meditation practise, learning about the nature of mind, and combining these with modern active lives.

We offer regular guided meditation evenings that include a short introduction to Buddhism for newcomers. All are welcome and there is no charge for coming along.

In-depth knowledge is provided at frequent courses and talks with authorised teachers from our tradition. Furthermore, the centre hosts a growing library, offering a selection of Buddhist books, Diamond Way Buddhist magazines, videos, audio-recordings and meditation booklets!

If you are new to Buddhism and would like to find out more, please feel free to come along, give us a call or send us an email. We look forward to seeing you there.

Regular Meditation Times

Wednesday 8:00pm: Introduction and 16th Karmapa guided meditation: for people who are

Entry continued on the following page.

new to Buddhism and those who have been practicing for many years. There is plenty of time to answer any questions you may have.

Sunday 6:00pm: 16th Karmapa guided meditation.

LIVERPOOL MEDITATION CENTRE (FWBO)
Tradition: FWBO
Meetings: Floor 7, Gostin Building, 32/36 Hanover St, Liverpool L1 9EA
Affiliated to: Friends Of The Western Buddhist Order, UK National Organisations
Charity No.: 1044466
Telephone Contact: 0161 281 2291 (Buddhashanti)
Or 0151 709 6561
Email: buddhashanti@supanet.com
Website(s):
www.liverpoolbuddhistcentre.co.uk

The Centre holds regular courses in meditation and Buddhism for newcomers.

LIVERPOOL SERENE REFLECTION MEDITATION GROUP
Tradition: Zen
School: Soto
Affiliated to: The Order Of Buddhists Contemplatives, UK National Organisations
Telephone Contact: 0151 353 1692 (Lynne Heidi Stumpe)

This group meets on Thursdays at 7.30pm and all are welcome. Phone for details.

LIVERPOOL ZEN GROUP
Tradition: Zen
School: Soto/Rinzai
Meetings: 1 Blackburne Terrace, Blackburne Place (off Hope Street), Liverpool L8 7PE
Telephone Contact: 0151 706 0125
Email: dl.scott@virgin.net
Website(s): www.liverpool-zen.org.uk

We previously met at The Dojo, a rented space at 13 Hope Street, but have been at the above address since 19 March 2007. The new property is a full-time Zen centre accommodating a small number of lay practitioners. Please note that the 'sangha space' comprises the ground and lower floors, the upper floors are private.

The Liverpool Zen Group meets for zazen literally, 'sitting meditation' regularly at our centre in Blackburne Terrace, and we always welcome practitioners old and new. If you're coming for the first time, we suggest that you try to come to one of our brief introductions to zazen and the 'form' we follow during the evening ceremony (please see our website or telephone for more details).

It is best to wear loose, dark clothing that will be comfortable to sit in and won't be a distraction to others. Once the ceremony is over, we will break for tea and biscuits, which will be followed by a 'dharma talk' (a talk on Zen practice), usually led by our teacher, Dave Scott. If you have any questions, please don't hesitate to ask any of the people you'll meet at the Zen centre.

SOUTHPORT

KAGYU OSEL CHOLING
Tradition: Tibetan
School: Kagyu-Sakya
Meetings: Central Southport
Affiliated to: Dechen Community, UK National Organisations
Charity No.: 1055813
Postal Address: Kagyu Osel Choling, c/o 24 Birkey Lane, Formby L37 4BU
Telephone Contact: 01704 872169
Email: southport@dechen.org
Website(s): www.dechen.org

Kagyu Osel Choling was founded in 1996 to provide a programme of classes and meditation in West Lancashire.

If you are interested in finding out about the Buddhist Path you are welcome to attend any of our meetings where we offer an informal introduction to Buddhism and Buddhist meditation. Meetings are held in Central Southport on Thursday evenings at 7:30. Please phone for details.

WIRRAL

KARME CHOLING
Tradition: Tibetan
School: Kagyu-Sakya
Meetings: Friends Meeting House, 83 Park Road, Birkenhead CH43 4UU
Affiliated to: Dechen Community, UK National Organisations
Charity No.: 1055813
Postal Address: Karme Choling, c/o Flat 2, 9 Dudley Road, New Brighton, Wirral CH45 9JP
Telephone Contact: 0151 638 2568
Email: wirral@dechen.org
Website(s): www.dechen.org

Karme Choling was established in 1992. It has hosted various initiations and teachings given by Lama Jampa Thaye and provides a programme of classes and meditation for the general public.

Introductory classes consist of a short talk on different aspects of Buddhism and an introduction to Buddhist meditation, and are designed for those who are new to Buddhism and the Kagyu tradition. Please phone for details.

MONMOUTHSHIRE

CHEPSTOW

SANG-NGAK-CHO-DZONG
Tradition: Tibetan
School: Nyingma
Meetings: Please contact Ngakma She'-z'er

and Ngakpa Namgyal for details.
Affiliated to: Sang-Ngak-Cho-Dzong, UK National Organisations
Charity No.: 1019886
Telephone Contact: 07969 112541
Email: bristolmeditation@arobuddhism.org
Website(s): www.aroter.org

See UK National Organisations.

NORFOLK

MUNDESLEY

TARA ROKPA NORFOLK
Tradition: Tibetan
School: Karma-Kagyu
Meetings: The Maisonette, St Cecilias, 13 Sea View Road, Mundesley, Norfolk NR11 8DH
Affiliated to: Kagyu Samye Ling Monastery And Tibetan Centre, UK National Organisations
Telephone Contact: 01263 721493
Website(s): www.rokpa.org

NORWICH

COMMUNITY OF INTERBEING - NORFOLK SANGHA
Tradition: Vietnamese
School: Thich Nhat Hanh
Affiliated to: The Community Of Interbeing, UK, UK National Organisations
Telephone Contact: 01603 438059 (Noreen)
Email: dianajcooper@onetel.com
Website(s): www.interbeing.org.uk

Contact for information about local and regional activities for meditation and Days of Mindfulness. See UK National Orgaisations for details of The Community of Interbeing.

NORWICH AMARAVATI MEDITATION GROUP
Tradition: Theravada
Affiliated to: Amaravati Buddhist Monastery, UK National Organisations
Meetings: E Tattersall, 53 The Street, Ringland, Norwich NR8 6JD
Postal Address: J Wilde, 5 Bacon Road, Norwich NR2 3QX
Telephone Contact: 01603 260717 (Elaine Tattersall)
Or 01603 465189 (Julian Wilde)
Or 01603 629129 (Jan Thompson)

A regular friendly group which meets on the second Thursday of each month for meditation and discussion.

NORWICH BUDDHIST CENTRE (FWBO)
Tradition: FWBO
Meetings: Norwich Buddhist Centre, 14 Bank Street, Norwich NR2 4SE
Affiliated to: Friends Of The Western Buddhist Order, UK National Organisations
Charity No.: 272024
Telephone Contact: 01603 627034
Email: norwich-buddhistcentre@zen.co.uk
Website(s): www.norwichbuddhistcentre.com

We welcome visits to the centre and our team provides workshops or courses for schools, community groups or professional bodies. We can also visit your group or organisation.

Our bookshop and daytime reception are open from Monday to Friday between 12 and 3pm.

Courses and classes are open to everyone and all charges go towards running the centre. Book in advance for all events, except open days and drop-in classes.

Please write or telephone for details of the current programme.

NORWICH SERENE REFLECTION MEDITATION GROUP
Tradition: Zen
School: Soto
Affiliated to: The Order Of Buddhists Contemplatives, UK National Organisations
Telephone Contact: 01263 577661 (Faith Broadbent)
Or 01692 538537 (Chris Loukes)
Email: contact@norwichserenereflection.org
Website(s): www.norwichserenereflection.org

The Group meets in central Norwich every Wednesday evening for meditation, scripture recitation and taped lectures, and on Sunday mornings for meditation and scripture recitation. Periodically the Group also organises retreats and social events. Newcomers are welcome and meditation instruction is available. The Group has a small journal, book and tape lending library.

NORWICH ZEN DOJO
Tradition: Zen
School: Soto
Meetings: Elements of Health, 64 Bethel Street, Norwich. NR2 1NR
Affiliated to: International Zen Association UK, UK National Organisations
Charity No.: 1069941
Telephone Contact: 01263 768206 (Jon Ball)
Email: jonhball@hotmail.com
Website(s): www.izauk.org   Zazen Timetable: Wednesday, 20.00;

Half Day, 3rd Sunday of each month; Introduction by arrangement.

REIYUKAI CENTRE
Tradition: Nichiren
School: Reiyukai
Meetings: Saint Mary's Works, Duke Street, Norwich NR3 1QA
Charity No.: 274781

England

Postal Address: UK Secretary, Reiyukai, Saint Mary's Works, Duke Street, Norwich NR3 1QA.
Telephone Contact: 01603 630857
Fax: 01603 760749

We are a martial arts facility sponsored by the Reiyukai. The Reiyukai is an international movement, originating in Japan after World War 1. Its teachings spring from the twin sources of the then existing forms of ancestor remembrance and from the Lotus Sutra. The basic practices are to better oneself by reciting key passages of the Lotus Sutra, compiled by the founders of The Reiyukai into a book called The Blue Sutra, remembering one's ancestors (the act of recital is a form of offering) and the practice of Michibiki. Michibiki literally translated means to guide someone along the path. It involves trying to get the individual to accept responsibility for their own actions, to perceive how these actions are determined by personal karma and by karma inherited from one's ancestors and family upbringing and of course hopefully to further promote the teachings of the Reiyukai.

The Reiyukai, a registered charity in the UK, has always worked to present an open, accessible and non-confrontational profile in this country and is actively involved in many interfaith projects. We do not believe that a person has to forcefully or prematurely reject previously held beliefs in order to become a practising member.

RIGPA NORWICH
Tradition: Tibetan
School: Nyingma
Affiliated to: Rigpa Fellowship, UK National Organisations
Postal Address: Rigpa Fellowship, 4 Girton Road, Norwich, Norfolk NR1 1BB
Telephone Contact: 07860 938993
Email: r.pumer@rigpa.org.uk
Website(s): www.rigpa.org.uk

See UK National Organisations.

SURLINGHAM

PADMALOKA MEN'S RETREAT CENTRE (FWBO)
Tradition: FWBO
Lesingham House, Covey Lane, Surlingham, Norfolk NR14 7AL
Affiliated to: Friends Of The Western Buddhist Order, UK National Organisations
Charity No.: 273850
Postal Address: Padmaloka, Lesingham House, Covey Lane, Surlingham, Norfolk NR14 7AL
Telephone Contact: 01508 538112
Email: info@padmaloka.org.uk
Website(s): www.padmaloka.org

Padmaloka holds retreats for men involved with the FWBO at all levels of experience, but more especially for those who are preparing for ordination into the Western Buddhist Order.

Ordination Team Email
ordinationteam@padmaloka.org.uk

Office hours: Mon - Fri, 9.30 am - 1.00 pm and 2.30 pm - 5 pm.

WELLS-NEXT-THE-SEA

WELLS-NEXT-THE-SEA ZEN GROUP (IZAUK)
Tradition: Zen
School: Soto
Meetings: Friends Meeting House, Quaker Yard, Church Street, Wells-next-the-sea, Norfolk NA23 1HZ
Affiliated to: International Zen Association UK, UK National Organisations
Charity No.: 1069941
Telephone Contact: 01328 712067
Email: jan.pearse@ntlworld.com
Website(s): www.izauk.co.uk

Zazen: Wednesday 7.30 pm.

Introduction Wednesday by arrangement.

NORTH YORKSHIRE

HARROGATE

KAGYU DECHEN DZONG
Tradition: Tibetan
School: Kagyu-Sakya
Meetings: 2b Chudleigh Road, Harrogate HG1 5NP
Affiliated to: Dechen Community, UK National Organisations
Charity No.: 1064198
Postal Address: Kagyu Dechen Dzong Buddhist Centre, 2b Chudleigh Road, Harrogate HG1 5NP
Telephone Contact: 01423 536915
Email: harrogate@dechen.org
Website(s): www.dechen.org

Kagyu Dechen Dzong was established by Lama Jampa Thaye in the early 1990s following his visits to Yorkshire at the request of his students living in the area. A programme of activities by the group was established which included the hosting of several major teachings and public talks in Harrogate by Lama Jampa-la.

SKIPTON

DECHEN IN SKIPTON
Tradition: Tibetan
School: Kagyu-Sakya
Meetings: Friends Meeting House, The Ginnel (off Newmarket Street), Skipton BD23 2JA
Affiliated to: Dechen Community, UK National Organisations
Charity No.: 1064198
Postal Address: Kagyu Dechen Dzong Buddhist Centre, 2b Chudleigh Road, Harrogate HG1 5NP
Telephone Contact: 01423 536915
Email: harrogate@dechen.org
Website(s): www.dechen.org

Introductory Classes are on the 1st and 3rd Friday of the month at 7.30pm. The sessions consist of a short talk followed by guided meditation, and cover the understanding and motivation that underpin the Buddhist path, giving newcomers a gentle and relaxed opportunity to meet the sangha and contemplate the teachings of Lord Buddha.

COMMUNITY OF INTERBEING - YORKSHIRE SANGHA
Tradition: Zen
School: Thich Nhat Hanh
Affiliated to: The Community Of Interbeing, UK, UK National Organisations
Telephone Contact: 01904 653504 (Katherine)
Website(s): www.interbeing.org.uk
Contact for information about local and regional activities for meditation and Days of Mindfulness. See UK National Orgaisations for details of The Community of Interbeing.

YORK

DECHEN IN YORK
Tradition: Tibetan
School: Kagyu-Sakya
Meetings: The Library Room, Friends Meeting House, Friargate, York YO1 9RL
Affiliated to: Dechen Community, UK National Organisations
Charity No.: 1064198
Postal Address: Kagyu Dechen Dzong Buddhist Centre, 2b Chudleigh Road, Harrogate HG1 5NP
Telephone Contact: 01423 536915
Email: harrogate@dechen.org
Website(s): www.dechen.org

Introductory Classes in York are held monthly, every second thursday of the month at 7.30 pm. The sessions consist of a short talk followed by guided meditation, and cover the understanding and motivation that underpin the Buddhist path, giving newcomers a gentle and relaxed opportunity to meet the sangha and contemplate the teachings of Lord Buddha.

SANG-NGAK-CHO-DZONG
Tradition: Tibetan
School: Nyingma
Meetings: Please contact Naljorma Thrinl'e for details.
Affiliated to: Sang-Ngak-Cho-Dzong, UK National Organisations
Charity No.: 1019886
Telephone Contact: 01904 415047
Email: thrinle@msn.com
Website(s): www.aroter.org

See UK National Organisations.

YORK CH'AN BUDDHIST GROUP
Tradition: Chinese
School: Ch'an
Meetings: York
Affiliated to: Western Ch'an Fellowship, UK National Organisations
Telephone Contact: 01904 628536 (Jannie Mead or Jake Lyne)
Email: york@westernchanfellowship.org
Website(s): www.westernchanfellowship.org/york

For details see under Western Ch'an Fellowship, UK National Organisations.

Meets Mondays 7.30 - 10pm and Thursday 6.45 - 7.50am near the centre of York, for meditation and discussion. Meditation Instruction is available. We also hold regular day retreats and residential weekend Ch'an reteats to provide extended periods of practice, suitable for experienced practitioners and beginners.

Meditation Instructors: Jake Lyne.

YORK DIAMOND WAY BUDDHIST CENTRE
Tradition: Tibetan
School: Karma-Kagyu
Meetings: Clementhorpe Community Centre, 2 Lower Ebor Street, York, YO23 1AY
Affiliated to: Diamond Way Buddhism UK, UK National Organisations
Charity No.: 1093406
Postal Address: York Diamond Way Buddhist Centre, Clementhorpe Community Centre, 2 Lower Ebor Street, York, YO23 1AY
Telephone Contact: 07855 340628 (Bartek)
Email: york@dwbuk.org
Website(s): www.diamondway-buddhism.co.uk

We are a small and friendly group. We meet once a week on Saturdays at 1pm in Clementhorpe Community Centre, on Lower Ebor Street, ten minutes walking distance from the Railway Station. Each week we give a short talk on a Buddhist topic and are always able to give an introduction to Buddhism and how to meditate. Please give us a call beforehand if you would like to join us. We have some Buddhist books and a selection of meditation booklets. Newcomers are always welcome.

Regular Meditation Times

Saturday 1:00pm:

Introduction and 16th Karmapa guided meditation: for people who are new to Buddhism as well as those who have been practicing for many years. There is plenty of time to answer any questions you may have. The sessions are free.

NORTHAMPTONSHIRE

KETTERING

KAGYU SAMYE DZONG NORTHAMPTONSHIRE
Tradition: Tibetan
School: Karma-Kagyu

Entry continued on the following page.

England

Meetings: Friends Meeting House, Northall Street, Northants NN16 8DS
Affiliated to: Kagyu Samye Ling Monastery And Tibetan Centre, UK National Organisations
Charity No.: 3260031
Postal Address: c/o 4 Whitehill Road, Desborough, Kettering NN14 2JZ
Telephone Contact: 07812 567496
Email: kettsamyedzong@aol.com

Kettering Samye Dzong offers a varied programme, ranging from 'Taming the Tiger' therapy groups to meditation classes as well as teaching from visiting lamas.

NORTHAMPTON

COMMUNITY OF INTERBEING - THE PATH HOME SANGHA, NORTHAMPTON
Tradition: Zen
School: Thich Nhat Hanh
Affiliated to: The Community Of Interbeing, UK, UK National Organisations
Telephone Contact: 01473 421096 (Ann)
Website(s): www.interbeing.org.uk

Contact for information about local and regional activities for meditation and Days of Mindfulness. See UK National Orgaisations for details of The Community of Interbeing.

BELSAY

ARUNA RATANAGIRI, HARNHAM BUDDHIST MONASTERY
Tradition: Theravada
Meetings: 2 Harnham Hall Cottages, Belsay, Northumberland NE20 0HF
Affiliated to: Amaravati Buddhist Monastery, UK National Organisations
Charity No.: 326695
Postal Address: Harnham Buddhist Monastery, 2 Harnham Hall Cottages, Belsay, Northumberland NE20 0HF

Telephone Contact: 01661 881612
Fax: 01661 881019
Website(s): www.ratanagiri.org.uk

A small monastery in the Theravada tradition, established in 1981.

The monastic community comprises about six monks and two postulants. Senior monks from the monastery visit associated Buddhist groups in the north of England and in Scotland. Occasional meditation retreats are held. Visitors are welcome and short-stay guest accomodation is available by prior arrangement. Guests are expected to live by the eight precepts and follow the monastic routine. Pujas and meditations are held on most days at 7.30pm and on Sunday evenings there is often a Dhamma talk.

Senior Incumbent: Venerable Ajahn Munindo.

HEXHAM

HEXHAM BUDDHIST GROUP
Tradition: Theravada
Postal Address: c/o Robert Bluck, 10 Tynedale Terrace, Hexham, Northumberland NE46 3JE
Telephone Contact: 01434 602759

HEXHAM SERENE REFLECTION MEDITATION GROUP
Tradition: Zen
School: Soto
Affiliated to: The Order Of Buddhists Contemplatives, UK National Organisations
Telephone Contact: 01434 601928 (Jan and Alex Reed)
Email: hexham@northeastserenereflection.org.uk
Website(s): www.northeastserenereflection.org.uk

The group meets weekly. There are regular visits

from a monk from Throssel Hole Buddhist Abbey.

THROSSEL HOLE BUDDHIST ABBEY
Tradition: Zen
School: Soto
Meetings: Throssel Hole Buddhist Abbey,
Carrshield, Hexham, Northumberland NE47 8AL
Affiliated to: The Order Of Buddhists
Contemplatives, UK National Organisations
Charity No.: 506094
Postal Address: The Guestmaster, Throssel
Hole Buddhist Abbey, Carrshield, Hexham,
Northumberland NE47 8AL
Telephone Contact: 01434 345204
(9.30am - 11.30am and 2.30pm - 4.30pm)
Fax: 01434 345216
Email: gd@throssel.org.uk
Website(s): www.throssel.org.uk

A training monastery and retreat centre following
the Serene Reflection Meditation tradition (Soto
Zen). Soto Zen is a tradition within Mahayana
Buddhism which was introduced from China to
Japan in the 13th century by Great Master Dogen.
The main emphasis is on meditation, the Buddhist
Precepts, the heart of compassion, and the
teaching that all beings have Buddha Nature.

The monastery was founded in 1972 by the late
Rev Master Jiyu-Kennett, and it has about 30
ordained monastics. Men and women have equal
status within the order and train together. The
monastic order is celibate.

There is a programme of retreats for lay guests
throughout the year, with the laity training
alongside the monks. Guests are welcome to come
for the regular scheduled retreats or for stays
outside of retreat times, provided they have
attended one of the introductory retreats
beforehand. The centrally heated facilities include
a large meditation and ceremony hall, a dining
hall, a common room, a number of bedrooms, and
wash rooms with showers. Guests usually sleep in
the lay meditation hall in the tradition of Soto Zen

monasteries. Traditional Buddhist festivals are
celebrated and the Abbey conducts memorials,
funerals, naming ceremonies for children, and
other ceremonies for individuals.

Senior priests provide spiritual guidance and by
phone or mail. The Abbey has a bookshop with
mail order service providing a small range of
Buddhist supplies.

NOTTINGHAMSHIRE

NORTH CLIFTON, NEWARK

**PURELAND RELAXATION AND MEDITATION
CENTRE**
Meetings: North Clifton, Nr Newark,
Nottinghamshire
Postal Address: Pureland Relaxation and
Meditation Centre, Pureland, North Clifton, Nr
Newark, Nottinghamshire
Telephone Contact: 01777 228567
Fax: 01777 228567

A Relaxation and Meditation Centre with a
Japanese Garden.

**COMMUNITY OF INTERBEING - EAST MIDLANDS
SANGHA**
Tradition: Zen
School: Thich Nhat Hanh
Affiliated to: The Community Of Interbeing,
UK, UK National Organisations
Telephone Contact: 0115 933 5582 (Tony)
Website(s): www.interbeing.org.uk

Contact for information about local and regional
activities for meditation and Days of Mindfulness.
See UK National Orgaisations for details of The
Community of Interbeing.

NOTTINGHAM

NOTTINGHAM BUDDHIST CENTRE (FWBO)
Tradition: FWBO
Meetings: 9 St Mary's Place, St Mary's Gate, Nottingham NG1 1PH
Affiliated to: Friends Of The Western Buddhist Order, UK National Organisations
Postal Address: Nottingham Buddhist Centre, 9 St Mary's Place, St Mary's Gate, Nottingham NG1 1PH
Telephone Contact: 0115 956 1008
Email: info@nottinghambuddhistcentre.org
Website(s): www.nottinghambuddhistcentre.org

Please contact the Centre for details of the current programme.

NOTTINGHAM CH'AN GROUP
Tradition: Chinese
School: Ch'an
Meetings: Theosophical Lodge, Maid Marion Way, Nottingham N61 6AJ
Affiliated to: Western Ch'an Fellowship, UK National Organisations
Postal Address: 8 Park Terrace, Nottingham, N61 5DN
Telephone Contact: 0115 924 2075 (Hillary Richards)
Email: nottingham@westernchanfellowship.org
Website(s):
www.westernchanfellowship.org/nottingham

Refer to entry under Western Ch'an Fellowship under UK National Organisations.

We are a small group of mixed experience, welcoming new members of any level. We meet on Tuesday evenings from 7.30 till 10.00pm, in the centre of Nottingham, for sitting and walking meditation and discussion.

We also run occasional day retreats to provide an extended period of practice, spending the day in silence, and including several sessions of meditation. Our day retreats are suitable for beginners and those who already have experience of meditation.

NOTTINGHAM SERENE REFLECTION MEDITATION GROUP
Tradition: Zen
School: Soto
Meetings: The Friends' Meeting House, Clarendon Street, Nottingham
Affiliated to: The Order Of Buddhists Contemplatives, UK National Organisations
Postal Address: Ted Fullick, Flat 10, Windsor House, Redcliffe Gardens, Mapperley Park, Nottingham NG3 5AX
Telephone Contact: 0115 960 3450 (Ted Fullick)
Or 0115 916 4997 (Tom Kirwan)
Or 01332 864673 (Brian Hermeston)
Email: tom.kirwan@ntlworld.com

This group meets on Mondays at 7.30pm. The group receives regular visits from a senior monk from Throssel Hole Buddhist Abbey.

BANBURY

BANBURY BUDDHIST GROUP
Meetings: Forest Hermitage, England, Warwickshire, Sherbourne
Postal Address: The Banbury Buddhist Group. 106 Bath Road, Banbury, Oxon
Telephone Contact: 01295 278744(Sarah Wallis)
Email: sarah.wallis@virgin.net

OXFORDSHIRE

OXFORD

COMMUNITY OF INTERBEING - OXFORD SANGHA

Tradition: Vietnamese
School: Thich Nhat Hanh
Affiliated to: The Community Of Interbeing, UK, UK National Organisations
Telephone Contact: 01865 552833 (Ruth and James)
Website(s): www.interbeing.org.uk

Contact for information about local and regional activities for meditation and Days of Mindfulness. See UK National Orgaisations for details of The Community of Interbeing.

DRUK THEKCHEN CHOEKOR LING
Tradition: Tibetan
School: Kagyu
Telephone Contact: 01491 838345
Fax: 01491 833577
Email: oxford@drukpa-kargyud.org

LONGCHEN FOUNDATION
Tradition: Tibetan
School: Kagyu-Nyingma
Meetings: Oxford
Affiliated to: Longchen Foundation, UK National Organisations
Telephone Contact: 01865 725569 (Sally Sheldrake)
Email: ssheldrake@longchenfoundation.com
Website(s): www.longchenfoundation.com

The Longchen Foundation was established by Chögyam Trungpa Rinpoche and Dilgo Khyentse Rinpoche, two of the great Tibetan teachers of the 20th century, to pass on the authentic Mahayana MahaAti (Dzogchen) teachings of the Nyingma lineage to the west. The spiritual director and principal teacher, Rigdzin Shikpo, one of Trungpa Rinpoche's earliest western students and a qualified lama of the Nyingma tradition, was entrusted by them to teach in direct response to the needs of westerners and is among the most experienced and inspiring Buddhist teachers in Britain.

The Foundation is a community of Buddhist teachers, meditation instructors and students practising these teachings with the vision of liberating the hearts of beings. For details of weekend courses, retreats, publications, newsletters, please visit our website.

The Lions Roar is a course that introduces the view and innermost teachings of the Longchen tradition and offers a deep and authentic grounding in the practice of meditation. It is suitable for total beginners and experienced meditators. The course is available in Britain and in Germany.

OXFORD BUDDHIST GROUP (FWBO)
Tradition: FWBO
Meetings: Thrangu House Buddhist Centre, Magdalen Road, Oxford.
Affiliated to: Friends Of The Western Buddhist Order, UK National Organisations
Charity No.: 1025401
Postal Address: Oxford Buddhist Group. 18 Bhandari Close, Cricket Road, Oxford OX4 3DT
Telephone Contact: 01865 777297(Shantiprabha)
Email: fwbo.oxford@ecosse.net

Please phone or write for details of current activities.

OXFORD BUDDHIST VIHARA
Tradition: Theravada
Charity No.: 1099361
Postal Address: The Oxford Buddhist Vihara, 33 Cherwell Drive, Oxford OX3 0BN
Telephone Contact: 01865 791591
Fax: 01865 340604
Email: oxford_buddhavihara@yahoo.co.uk
Website(s): www.oxfordbuddhavihara.org.uk

The Oxford Buddha Vihara (OBV) is a newly established Buddhist centre in Oxford. The Vihara was founded in 2003 by Venerable Dhammasami,

Entry continued on the following page.

who did his doctoral study on Buddhist education at St. Anne's College, University of Oxford.

OXFORD CENTRE FOR BUDDHIST STUDIES
Affiliated to: Society For The Wider Understanding Of The Buddhist Tradition, England, Oxfordshire, Oxford
Postal Address: Wolfson College, Linton Road, Oxford OX2 6UD
Telephone Contact: 01865 274 0987
Fax: 01865 274125
Email: info@ocbs.org
Website(s): www.ocbs.org

The OCBS is a Recognised Independent Centre of Oxford University (RIC). The University has a great record in the study of Buddhist texts, social forms, theories and practices; the OCBS channels private funds to maintain and build on this scholarly activity. In the context of its relationship with So-Wide (which see), it is committed to the widespread diffusion of information about the Buddhist tradition that is at the same time academically sound and accessible to the non-expert.

The OCBS has funded Europe's first endowed Chair in Buddhist Studies (the new Numata Professor is due to take up his or here post in October 2007). Endowed Lecturerships are planned in: Pali Buddhist Studies; East Asian Buddhist Studies; Tibet and Himalayan Buddhist Studies; Buddhist Social History; and Buddhist Art.

The OCBS functions within the University by way of the Buddhist Studies Unit. Postgraduate students are invited to apply to undertake doctoral research. As from the academic year 2008/9 a one-year Master of Studies course will also be available.

OXFORD SAMATHA GROUP
Tradition: Theravada
Affiliated to: Samatha Trust, UK National

Organisations
Postal Address: Cary Mandel, 46 Norreys Avenue, Oxford OX1 4SS
Telephone Contact: 01865 343768 (Colin)
Email: oxford_enquires@samatha.org
Website(s): www.samatha.org/oxford

Classes held for students, during University terms, and for the general public. Please contact for details of current times and venues.

OXFORD ZEN DOJO
Tradition: Zen
School: Soto
Meetings: Friends Meeting House, 43 St Giles, Oxford OX1 3LW and Thrangu House, Magdalen Road, East Oxford
Affiliated to: International Zen Association UK, UK National Organisations
Charity No.: 1069941
Telephone Contact: 01865 240196 (Rosemary Cottis)
Email: rose@magic40.fsnet.co.uk
Website(s): www.izauk.org

Zazen Timetable at Friends Meeting House:

Wednesday 19.30. Introduction Wednesday - by arrangement 19.00.

Zazen Timetable at Thrangu House: Monday 6.30am

SOCIETY FOR THE WIDER UNDERSTANDING OF THE BUDDHIST TRADITION ('SO-WIDE')
Tradition: All
Postal Address: Wolfson College, Linton Road, Oxford OX2 6UD
Telephone Contact: 01865 274 0987
Fax: 01865 274125
Email: info@ocbs.org
Website(s): www.so-wide.org

So-Wide aims to promote the study of the

Buddhist tradition from its origins to the present day; and, on that basis, to diffuse as widely as possible an accurate and sympathetic understanding of the tradition as a whole, in its diversity and underlying unity.

So-Wide's principal projects are currently based in Oxford University: the Oxford Centre for Buddhist Studies (which see) and soon the Oxford Mindfulness Centre ('OMC').

So-Wide's first role is to raise funds for these projects. It also coordinates their work outside the University. In this way, it offers a range of learning opportunities to individuals and institutions world-wide. An example is the Intensive Pali Programme, which can within a fortnight take beginners to the point where they can read the Pali Canon in the original.

So-Wide has links with Buddhist institutions across Asia, for instance in Thailand and Korea. A range of outreach activities in the UK are in prospect.

THRANGU HOUSE BUDDHIST CENTRE
Tradition: Tibetan
School: Karma-Kagyu
Meetings: Thrangu House, 42 Magdalen Road, Oxford OX4 1RB
Charity No.: 283921
Postal Address: The Secretary, Thrangu House, 42 Magdalen Road, Oxford OX4 1RB
Telephone Contact: 01865 241555 Or 01865 243841
Fax: 01865 241555
Email: secretary@thranguhouse.org.uk
Website(s): www.thranguhouse.org.uk

Thrangu House Buddhist Centre was founded in the early 1980's by disciples of the Venerable Khenchen Thrangu Rinpoche, the 9th incarnation of the Thrangu lineage, teacher of the Four Regents of the Karma Kagyu lineage, and personal tutor to His Holiness the 17th Gyalwa Karmapa

Ogyen Trinley Dorje. Thrangu Rinpoche visits Thrangu House once a year to give teachings. Thrangu House is managed by Rinpoche's representative; Lama Karma Wangyal. Lama Wangyal has completed a traditional three year meditation retreat, during which he was trained in the Six Yogas of Naropa. Upon successful completion of the retreat, Lama was sent to Oxford by Rinpoche in 2001, as spiritual head of the centre.

Lama teaches meditation classes, Mahamudra healing exercises, and leads pujas on a weekly basis. Please check the timetable on the website, or with the secretary. Lama is also available for advice, counselling, blessings for babies, weddings and funerals, and visits schools to give talks and teach meditation. He makes regular visits to patients in the local mental hospitals, as well as visiting regular hospitals to care and pray for patients. An interview with Lama can be arranged at any time; again please contact the secretary.

SHROPSHIRE

LUDLOW

LUDLOW SAMATHA BUDDHIST GROUP
Tradition: Theravada
Meetings: Friends Meeting House, St Mary's Lane, (off Lower Corve St), Ludlow
Affiliated to: Samatha Trust, UK National Organisations
Postal Address: Ludlow Samatha Buddhist Group, c/o Jeremy Bruce, Hill Cottage, Rhos-y-meirch, Knighton, Powys LD7 1PD
Telephone Contact: 07768 650106 (Jeremy Bruce)
Email: jeremy.bruce@virgin.net
Website(s): www.samatha.org

Meditation in the Samatha tradition meeting regularly, suitable for beginners as well as those with experience. Currently meeting Thursday evenings starting at 7.00pm.

Entry continued on the following page.

SHREWSBURY

SHREWSBURY BUDDHISM AND MEDITATION GROUP (FWBO)
Tradition: FWBO
Meetings: Friends Meeting House, Corporation Lane, Berwick Road, Shrewsbury
Affiliated to: Friends Of The Western Buddhist Order, UK National Organisations
Postal Address: Birmingham Buddhist Centre, 11 Park Road, Moseley, Birmingham B13 8AB
Telephone Contact: 0121 449 5279
Email: info@birminghambuddhistcentre.org.uk
Website(s): www.birminghambuddhistcentre.org.uk

This group meets weekly. There is a session of meditation (with full instruction for those who want), followed by talk and discussion on a particular aspect of Buddhism or meditation. Newcomers are welcome to join us on any week. For more details, or a map of the location, please contact the Birmingham Buddhist Centre.

TELFORD

TELFORD BUDDHIST PRIORY
Tradition: Zen
School: Soto
Meetings: 49 The Rock, Ketley, Telford
Affiliated to: The Order Of Buddhists Contemplatives, UK National Organisations
Charity No.: 1088942
Postal Address: Telford Buddhist Priory, 49 The Rock, Ketley, Telford TF3 5BH
Telephone Contact: 01952 615574
Fax: 01952 615574
Website(s): www.tbpriory.org.uk

An established Priory of the Order of Buddhist Contemplatives, offering a regular programme of Introductory Evenings, Services, Festivals, Dharma talks, Meditation and Day Retreats. Overnight accommodation may be available by prior arrangement for guests who have a long distance to travel.

Please contact by telephone or letter for details of the current programme.

WHITCHURCH

TARALOKA RETREAT CENTRE FOR WOMEN
Tradition: FWBO
Meetings: Cornhill Farm, Bettisfield, Nr. Whitchurch, Shropshire SY13 2LD
Affiliated to: Friends Of The Western Buddhist Order, UK National Organisations
Charity No.: 274500
Postal Address: The Secretary, Taraloka Retreat Centre, Bettisfield, Nr Whitchurch, Shropshire SY13 2LD
Telephone Contact: 01948 710646 Or 0845 3304063 (UK local call rate)
Fax: 01948 710646
Email: info@taraloka.org.uk
Website(s): www.taraloka.org.uk

Taraloka provides a varied year-round programme for women of all ages, nationalities, backgrounds and all levels of experience in Buddhism from beginner to fully committed practitioner. Retreats all include meditation instruction and practice. All aspects of Buddhism are taught by experienced and committed Buddhist practitioners.

A full time community also lives at Taraloka and follows a daily programme of meditation and puja.

SOMERSET

GLASTONBURY

GLASTONBURY CH'AN GROUP
Tradition: Chinese
School: Ch'an
Affiliated to: Western Ch'an Fellowship, UK

108

National Organisations
Telephone Contact: 01458 833663 (Ned Reiter)
Or 01458 832300 (Devin)
Email: glastonbury@westernchanfellowship.org
Website(s):
www.westernchanfellowship.org/glastonbury

We meet every Monday from 7pm to 9.30pm. All welcome. Meditation instruction available for beginners. For full details please telephone Ned Reiter.

SHIPHAM

WINTERHEAD RETREAT HOUSE
Tradition: Zen
Meetings: Winterhead Hill Farm, Shipham, Somerset, BS25 1RS
Affiliated to: Western Ch'an Fellowship, UK National Organisations
Postal Address: John Crook, Winterhead Hill Farm, Shipham, Somerset, BS25 1RS
Telephone Contact: 01934 842231
Fax: 01934 842231
Email: john@johcro.demon.co.uk
Website(s): www.westernchanfellowship.org

Dr John Crook, Dharma Heir to Master Sheng-yen and the Teacher of the Western Ch'an Fellowship has converted part of his farmhouse to provide a facility for solitary retreats.

Practitioners who would welcome solitary retreats under supervision in a small community of retreatants are invited to apply for periods of seclusion varying from one to eight weeks. The retreat schedule will be negotiated. Suitable methods of practice could be Chan mindfulness, Silent illumination, Koan work or Mahamudra/Dzogchen.

Three bed-sitters with modern conveniences, a kitchen, lounge and conservatory, meditation space and a Buddha Chapel. Self-catering basis

with self-provisioning. Two-hour work period on the property per day.

Applications with an account of personal training to date invited.

SOUTH PETHERTON

SARASWATI BUDDHIST GROUP
Tradition: Tibetan
School: Gelugpa
Meetings: The Market House, Market Sq., South Petherton, Somerset TA13 5BT
Postal Address: Andy Wistreich and Shan Tate, The Market House, Market Sq., South Petherton, Somerset TA13 5BT
Telephone Contact: 01460 241339
Or 01823 601527
Fax: 01460 249214
Email: andy.wistreich@btinternet.com or natkinsonco@btinternet.com

Meetings most Sundays 7:00-9:00pm. Newcomers are always welcome. Sessions include brief prayers, meditation, short talk and discussion with tea and biscuits. Also every two months we run a meditation day on a Saturday.

An introductory class also takes place on most Wednesday evenings in High Ham near Langport, Somerset.

The group was established and named with the permission from His Holiness the Dalai Lama. Shan Tate and Andy Wistreich, who lead the group have studied with lamas of the Gelug tradition of Tibetan Buddhism, some of whom visit occasionally but the group itself is non-sectarian.

TAUNTON

TAUNTON MEDITATION GROUP
Tradition: Theravada

Entry continued on the following page.

Meetings: Heathfield Community Centre,
Heathfield Drive, Taunton
Telephone Contact: 01278 455830 (Lindy)
Or 01278 457245 (Annie Fisher)
Email: lindy.booth1@virgin.net

Meets Monday evenings 7.45pm - 9.00pm. We
meditate and discuss spiritual matters inspired by
broadly Buddhist teachings.

SOUTH YORKSHIRE

DONCASTER

DONCASTER DIAMOND WAY BUDDHIST CENTRE
Tradition: Tibetan
School: Karma-Kagyu
Meetings: Doncaster Central Library,
Community Meeting Room, Doncaster, Waterdale,
DN1 1JE
Affiliated to: Diamond Way Buddhism UK, UK
National Organisations
Charity No.: 1093406
Telephone Contact: 07838 561322
(Andrzej)
Email: doncaster@dwbuk.org
Website(s): www.diamondway-buddhism.co.uk

We are a small and friendly group. We meet once
a week on Saturdays at 3pm in Doncaster Central
Library. We have a short talk on a Buddhist topic
and we are always able to give an introduction to
Buddhism and how to meditate. Please give us a
call beforehand if you would like to meet and join
us some time. We have Buddhist books and
magazines, lecture tapes and a selection of
meditation booklets. Newcomers are always
welcome.

Regular Meditation Times

Saturday 3pm:

Introduction and 16th Karmapa guided meditation:

for people who are new to Buddhism and those
who have been practicing for many years. There is
plenty of time to answer any questions you may
have. The sessions are free.

SHEFFIELD

AMIDA SHEFFIELD CONGREGATION
Tradition: Pure Land
School: Amida-Shu
Meetings: Rev. Bhaktika & Rev. Sundari, 118
Broomspring Lane, Sheffield, S.Yorkshire, S10 2ED
Amida Trust, UK National Organisations
Charity No.: 1060589
Postal Address: Rev. Bhaktika & Rev.
Sundari, 118 Broomspring Lane, Sheffield,
S.Yorkshire, S10 2ED
Telephone Contact: 0114 272 4290
Email: mike fitter@blueyonder.co.uk
Website(s): www.amidatrust.com &
www.groups.yahoo.com/group/a

A congregation affiliated to Amida-Shu (see Amida
Trust - UK National Organisations).

Meetings, services, rites of passage, engaged
Buddhist work, chaplaincy, interfaith activities

ARRIVING HOME
Tradition: Zen
School: Soto/Rinzai
Telephone Contact: 0114 263 0177
Email: alison.richard@btopenworld.com

COMMUNITY OF INTERBEING - BLUE LOTUS
SANGHA
Tradition: Zen
School: Thich Nhat Hanh
Affiliated to: The Community Of Interbeing,
UK, UK National Organisations
Telephone Contact: 0114 2511139 (Alan &
Nidge)
Email: Barken220@lineone.net

Website(s): www.interbeing.org.uk

Contact for information about local and regional activities for meditation and Days of Mindfulness. See UK National Orgaisations for details of The Community of Interbeing.

SHEFFIELD SAMATHA BUDDHIST GROUP
Tradition: Theravada
Meetings: Ranmoor Parish Centre, 5 Ranmoor Park Road, Sheffield S10 3GX
Affiliated to: Samatha Trust, UK National Organisations
Charity No.: 266367 Ian Rose, 6 Stanedge Road, Bakewell, Derbyshire DE45 1DG
Telephone Contact: 01629 814617 (Ian)
Email: rose@nascr.net
Website(s): www.samatha.org

Weekly meditation class - beginners are always welcome.

SHEFFIELD BUDDHIST CENTRE (FWBO)
Tradition: FWBO
Meetings: Howard Road, Sheffield. S6 3RT
Affiliated to: Friends Of The Western Buddhist Order, UK National Organisations
Charity No.: 1024087
Postal Address: Sheffield Buddhist Centre, Howard Road, Sheffield, S6 3RT
Telephone Contact: 0114 234 9994
Email: info@fwbosheffield.org
Website(s): www.fwbosheffield.org

The centre holds regular drop-in meditation classes as well as courses in meditation and Buddhism for newcomers.

Around the Centre is a thriving mandala of other activities.

SHEFFIELD DIAMOND WAY BUDDHIST CENTRE
Tradition: Tibetan

School: Karma-Kagyu
Meetings: 31 Lynmouth Road, Sheffield, S7 2DF
Affiliated to: Diamond Way Buddhism UK, UK National Organisations
Charity No.: 1093406
Postal Address: Sheffield Diamond Way Buddhist Centre, 31 Lynmouth Road, Sheffield, S7 2DF
Telephone Contact: 07756479455 (Eve) Or 07837193858 (Andy)
Email: sheffield@dwbuk.org
Website(s): www.diamondway-buddhism.co.uk

We are very happy to invite everyone to our meditation group. We have a guided meditation every week and we will give explainations on how to meditate if you haven't done so before and any information you want about Buddhism in general.

Regular Meditation Times

Sunday 7:00pm:

Introduction and 16th Karmapa guided meditation: for people who are new to Buddhism as well as those who have been practicing for many years. There is plenty of time to answer any questions you may have. The sessions are free.

SHEFFIELD SERENE REFLECTION MEDITATION GROUP
Tradition: Zen
School: Soto
Affiliated to: The Order Of Buddhists Contemplatives, UK National Organisations
Telephone Contact: 0114 296 6113 (Martin Jordan)
Or 0114 230 7134 (Neil Dunbar)
Website(s): www.zensheffield.org

This group meets weekly on Wednesday evening from 7.15 to 9.15. These are regular visits from a monk from Throssel Hole Buddhist Abbey. Please see website and phone for details.

Entry continued on the following page.

SHEFFIELD ZEN GROUP - WHITE PLUM
Tradition: Zen
School: Soto/Rinzai
Meetings: Quaker Sheffield Central Meeting House, 10 St James Street, Sheffield S1 2EW
Affiliated to: Zen Practice Centre Trust, UK National Organisations
Telephone Contact: 0114 258 2729 (Robert Bowles)
Or 01302 886580 (Scott Williams)
Email: enquiries@white-plum-zen-sheffield.org
Website(s): www.white-plum-zen-sheffield.org

Feel free to come along to a meeting. They are held at the Quaker Meeting House, near the Sheffield Cathedral and the Blue Moon vegetarian cafe. Thursday meetings start at 7.30pm and finish around 9pm, followed by tea.

STAFFORDSHIRE

STOKE-ON-TRENT

NORTH STAFFS ZAZEN GROUP
Meetings: 21 Longton Road, Trentham, Stoke-on-Trent, Staffordshire, ST4 8ND
Postal Address: North Staffs Zazen Group, 21 Longton Road, Trentham, Stoke-on-Trent, Staffordshire, ST4 8ND
Telephone Contact: 01782 657851

SUFFOLK

COMMUNITY OF INTERBEING - SUFFOLK SANGHA
Tradition: Vietnamese
School: Thich Nhat Hanh
Affiliated to: The Community Of Interbeing, UK, UK National Organisations
Telephone Contact: 01473 726825 (Isabelle)
Website(s): www.interbeing.org.uk

Contact for information about local and regional activities for meditation and Days of Mindfulness. See UK National Orgaisations for details of The Community of Interbeing.

BURY ST EDMUNDS

BURY ST EDMUNDS FWBO GROUP
Tradition: FWBO
Meetings: Friends Meeting House, St. John's Road, Bury St. Edmunds Suffolk
Affiliated to: Friends Of The Western Buddhist Order, UK National Organisations
Postal Address: Dhammapattiya c/o 21 St John's Street, Bury St. Edmunds, Suffolk IP33 1SJ
Telephone Contact: 01284 750 254 (Dhammapattiya)
Email: dhammapattiya@onetel.net.uk
Website(s): www.cambridgebuddhistcentre.com

Meets regularly for meditation, study and puja as well as holding activities for newcomers.

VAJRASANA RETREAT CENTRE (FWBO)
Tradition: FWBO
Meetings: Potash Farm. Walsham Le Willows, Bury St. Edmunds, Suffolk. IP31 3AR
Affiliated to: Friends Of The Western Buddhist Order, UK National Organisations
Postal Address: Vajrasana Retreat Centre, c/o London Buddhist Centre, 51 Roman Road, London, E2 0HU
Telephone Contact: 0845 458 4716
Or 01359 259 344
Fax: 020 8980 1960
Email: info@lbc.org.uk
Website(s): www.lbc.org.uk

The London Buddhist Centre's country retreat facility. Vajrasana regularly hold introductory weekend retreats as well as a variety of longer retreats for people at all levels of experience. Solitary retreat facilities are also available.

IPSWICH

IPSWICH BUDDHIST CENTRE (FWBO)
Tradition: FWBO
Meetings: First Floor, (above Evolution Shop),
5 The Thoroughfare, Ipswich, IP1 1BX
Affiliated to: Friends Of The Western
Buddhist Order, UK National Organisations
Charity No.: 1023335
Postal Address: Ipswich Buddhist Centre.
First Floor, 5 The Thoroughfare, Ipswich, IP1 1BX
Telephone Contact: 01473 211516
Email: enquiries@ipswichbuddhistcentre.org.uk
Website(s): www.ipswichbuddhistcentre.org uk

Offers a range of activities from beginners level to
advanced. Meditation and Buddhism courses every
term. Open sessions every Wednesday evening at
7pm. There is a bookshop and local weekend
retreats.

SOUTHWOLD

TREVOR LEGGETT ADHYATMA YOGA TRUST
Tradition: Zen
Postal Address: Peter Longcroft, 4 Lakeside
Close, Reydon, Southwold, Suffolk IP18 6YA
Telephone Contact: 01502 723902
Website(s): www.leggett.co.uk

Trevor Leggett had a long association with the
Buddhist Society for which he was a regular
speaker and contributor at the Summer School up
to his death on 2nd August 2000. His articles
continue to appear in The Middle Way.

He studied Zen in Japan and he studied Adhyatma
Yoga as a long-standing pupil of Hari Prasad
Shastri. His many books include A First Zen
Reader, The Tiger's Cave, Samurai Zen, Zen and
the Ways, The Old Zen Master, Realisation of the
Supreme Self, Chapter of The Self, and a
translation from Sanskrit of The Complete
Commentary by Shankara on the Patanjali Yoga
Sutras. He also produced collections of training

and teaching stories including Encounters in Yoga
and Zen and Lotus Lake, Dragon Pool. He was
expert in Judo (Kodokan sixth dan) and Shogi -
Japanese chess (fifth dan) and he was head of the
BBC Japanese Service for twenty years.

Trevor Leggett made provision in his will for a Trust
to promote the knowledge of Yoga, Buddhism, Zen,
Judo and Shogi and The Trevor Leggett Adhyatma
Yoga Trust was established after his death and
registered as a charity. A small group of Trust
members and guests meet regularly on a Tuesday
evening at the Buddhist Society.

Further details of Trevor Leggett's books and some
other training and teaching stories are included on
the Trust's website at www.leggett.co.uk. For
more information about the Trust please contact
the Trust Secretary, Peter Longcroft, at the postal
address.

SURREY

GUILDFORD

COMMUNITY OF INTERBEING - GUILDFORD SANGHA
Tradition: Vietnamese
School: Thich Nhat Hanh
Affiliated to: The Community Of Interbeing,
UK, UK National Organisations
Telephone Contact: 01252 323922 (Luan)
Email: dinhpostbox@yahoo.co.uk
Website(s): www.interbeing.org.uk

Contact for information about local and regional
activities for meditation and Days of Mindfulness.
See UK National Orgaisations for details of The
Community of Interbeing.

GUILDFORD CH'AN GROUP
Tradition: Chinese
School: Ch'an

Entry continued on the following page.

Meetings: Guildford
Affiliated to: Western Ch'an Fellowship, UK National Organisations
Telephone Contact: 01483 202422 (Roger Taylor)
Email: guildford@westernchanfellowship.org
Website(s):
www.westernchanfellowship.org/guildford

Refer to entry under Western Ch'an Fellowship under UK National Organisations.

Weekly meditation group in Guildford.

MODERN BUDDHA WAY
Tradition: All
Meetings: The Quiet Centre, University of Surrey campus, Stag Hill, Guildford, Surrey
Postal Address: c/o Prof. Geoff Hunt. EIHMS, University of Surrey, Guildford, Surrey. GU2 7XH
Or 422 Hurst Road, West Molesey, Surrey KT8 1QS
Telephone Contact: 01483 689779
Or 020 8979 8616
Email: modernbuddhaway@aol.com or g.hunt@surrey.ac.uk
Website(s): www.modernbuddhaway.org

Weekly practice sessions (Sundays) and monthly beginners' class; one-day retreats; annual arts day; visits to Theravada temple; study sessions.

Modern Buddha Way is distinguished by these features: works in and with western culture and language; no abstractions or beliefs; not a membership group; practices Tranquility and Insight meditation; works with consistent message of the Buddha only; available to ordinary people; relates to everyday life and social issues; participatory and open style.

SURBITON

SHINNYO-EN UK
Tradition: Shingon

Postal Address: The Manor House, Woodstock, Lane North, Long Ditton, Surrey KT6 5HL
Telephone Contact: 020 8398 2221
Fax: 020 8398 8062
Email: thomas.yano@shinnyo-en.fr

Shinnyo-en is a Buddhist denomination originally established in Japan. Today it has temples and meeting places in various countries headquartered in Japan. Its name means a borderless garden of shinnyo. It is, first and foremost, a place for Buddhist training, in which all people regardless of age, gender, nationality, or religious background can cultivate their innate buddha nature, the kernel of enlightenment existing in all beings.

Founder Shinjo Ito, who became a monk of Shingon Buddhism (Japanese esoteric Buddhism), pursued and established a way for lay practitioners to grasp the essence of Buddhist teachings: liberation from the ignorance and craving that cause suffering in people's daily lives. Along with holding traditional Buddhist services, he developed an effective mentoring framework and sesshin meditative training based on concepts in the Nirvana Sutra.

WOKING

SURREY THERAVADA BUDDHIST GROUP
Tradition: Theravada
Meetings: 'Chelsfield' 143 York Road, Woking, Surrey GU22 7XS
Affiliated to: Cittaviveka, Chithurst Buddhist Monastery, England, West Sussex, Chithurst
Postal Address: Surrey Theravada Buddhist Group, 'Chelsfield' 143 York Road, Woking, Surrey GU22 7XS
Telephone Contact: 01483 761398 (Rocana)

The group meets on the 2nd and 4th Wednesday of each month at 7.45 for 8.00pm. Regular visits from a monk or nun.

TYNE AND WEAR

NEWCASTLE UPON TYNE

AMIDA SANCTUARY
Tradition: Pure Land
School: Amida-Shu
Meetings: 49 Linden Road, Gosforth,
Newcastle NE3 4HA
Affiliated to: Amida Trust, UK National
Organisations
Charity No.: 1060589
Postal Address: 49 Linden Road, Gosforth,
Newcastle NE3 4HA
Telephone Contact: 0191 213 2564
(Rev.Sujatin Johnson)
Email: elspeth@elspeth.freeserve.co.uk
Website(s): www.amidatrust.com

Shrine and meeting place of the Amida Trust (see
UK National Organisations) and the Order of Amida
Buddha.

Weekly meetings. Ceremonies. Inter-faith and
engaged Buddhist activities. Buddhist Chaplaincy.
Memorial Garden. Visitors by arrangement.

BLACK MOUNTAIN ZEN CENTRE
Tradition: Zen
School: Soto
Meetings: Public Library, 141/143 Main St.
Newcastle
See website for more details
Affiliated to: Black Mountain Zen Centre,
Ireland, Co Antrim, Belfast
Telephone Contact: 028 90244010
Or 07745 468995
Or 0790 5367611
Email: contact@blackmountainzencentre.org
Website(s): www.blackmountainzencentre.org

Originally known as Belfast Meditation Centre, we
came together in the year 2000, and launched
Black Mountain Zen Centre in 2004 .

The practice of Black Mountain Zen Centre is Soto
Zen in the lineage of Shunryu Suzuki Roshi, our
founder in the West, and we are affiliated to San
Francisco Zen Center.

We emphasize the practice of ZaZen (sitting Zen)
as the essence of Shakyamuni Buddha's practice,
together with the practice of Precepts (ethics) and
the cultivation of Compassion and Wisdom
(Prajna). In India this practice of meditation was
known as Dhyana (Sanskrit), later being
pronounced Ch'an in China, and Zen in Japan.

We also offer dharma discussion evenings, yoga
evenings, day long events and regular
retreats/sesshins.

Black Mountain Zen Centre has local affiliated
groups in Belfast, Larne, Coleraine, Ballymena,
and Newcastle, and is willing to give help and
advice to anyone wishing to set up a similar group
in their own area. Please see the 'Local Groups'
page on our website for details.

Newcastle Zen Group
Meets from 07:00 pm to 08:30 pm each
Wednesday evening.

NEWCASTLE BUDDHIST CENTRE (FWBO)
Tradition: FWBO
Meetings: 3rd Floor, 9-11 Carliol Square,
Newcastle upon Tyne NE1 6UF
Affiliated to: Friends Of The Western
Buddhist Order, UK National Organisations
Charity No.: 1044379
Postal Address: Newcastle Buddhist Centre,
3rd Floor, 9-11 Carliol Square,
Newcastle upon Tyne NE1 6UF
Telephone Contact: 0191 2611 722
Email: info@newcastlebuddhistcentre.org
Website(s):
www.newcastlebuddhistcentre.org

The Buddhist Centre is normally open Monday,
Tuesday and Friday afternoons between 2.30pm

Entry continued on the following page.

and 5pm though we recommend you ring to arrange to visit before making a special journey.

It is possible to come in to talk to a practising meditator/Buddhist, to browse the bookshop or library, or simply to have a look around.

NEWCASTLE DIAMOND WAY BUDDHIST CENTRE

Tradition: Tibetan
School: Karma-Kagyu
Meetings: 60 Wilton Avenue, Walker, Newcastle upon Tyne NE6 2TT
Affiliated to: Diamond Way Buddhism UK, UK National Organisations
Charity No.: 1093406
Postal Address: Newcastle Diamond Way Buddhist Centre, 60 Wilton Avenue, Walker, Newcastle upon Tyne NE6 2TT
Telephone Contact: 0191 276 0634
Or 07752 475473
Email: newcastle@dwbuk.org
Website(s):
www.diamondway-buddhism.co.uk

The Newcastle group is located in Walker, East of Newcastle town centre, not far from the Tyne river. We are a small family run group and hold a weekly meditation and every two months a public lecture or event (please contact for details). Anybody new to meditation can get instruction on how to meditate with tea all for free.

We are also able to provide general background information on Diamond Way Buddhism and also have a small collection of books that can be borrowed or bought.

Regular Meditation Times

Wednesday 7:30pm: Introduction and 16th Karmapa guided meditation: for people who are new to Buddhism and those who have been practicing for many years. There is plenty of time to answer any questions you may have.

Ngondro Sundays: On the first Sunday of every month we meet at 2.00pm for ngondro. Please come along and do your own practice.

NEWCASTLE SERENE REFLECTION MEDITATION GROUP

Tradition: Zen
School: Soto
Meetings: Jesmond Methodist Church Hall, St George's Terrace, Newcastle upon Tyne NE2
Affiliated to: The Order Of Buddhists Contemplatives, UK National Organisations
Telephone Contact: 01830 520760 (Steve Roberts)
Or 01912 812459 (Lillian Calder)
Email:
newcastle@northeastserenereflection.org.uk
Website(s):
www.northeastserenereflection.org.uk

The group meets on Thursday evenings from 7.30pm - 9.30pm. Meetings include serene reflection meditation, walking meditation, scripture recitation and ceremonies. Monks from Throssel Hole Buddhist Abbey visit the group on a regular basis and there are occasional day retreats held in Newcastle. The group usually visits Throssel Hole Buddhist Abbey for the day on the first Sunday in each month. Everyone is welcome to come along and meditation instruction is available.

SUNDERLAND

SUNDERLAND SAMATHA GROUP

Tradition: Theravada
Meetings: Room C.24, Priestman Building, University of Sunderland, Green Terrace (nr. bottom of Chester Rd), Sunderland, SR1 3PZ
Affiliated to: Samatha Trust, UK National Organisations
Postal Address: Peter Harvey, 10 Cedar Drive, Farewell Hall, Durham City, DH1 3TF
Telephone Contact: 0191 384 3913

Email: peter.harvey@sunderland.ac.uk
Website(s): www.samatha.org

Classes in Theravada Samatha meditation, based on mindfulness of breathing, are given by a member of the Samatha Trust. The classes begin in early October, but people are welcome to join at any time. The group meets on Thursdays at 5pm. A practice-oriented talk is followed by a guided meditation and then an opportunity for one-to-one discussion of people's practice. Information is provided on retreats at the Samatha Trust's centre in Powys, Wales. The meditation teacher is author of several books on Buddhism.

WARWICKSHIRE

LEAMINGTON SPA

COMMUNITY OF INTERBEING - LEAMINGTON SANGHA
Tradition: Vietnamese
School: Thich Nhat Hanh
Affiliated to: The Community Of Interbeing, UK, UK National Organisations
Telephone Contact: 01926 422694 (Jenifer)
Website(s): www.interbeing.org.uk

Contact for information about local and regional activities for meditation and Days of Mindfulness. See UK National Orgaisations for details of The Community of Interbeing.

SHERBOURNE

FOREST HERMITAGE (WAT PAH SANTIDHAMMA)
Tradition: Theravada
Meetings: The Forest Hermitage, Lower Fulbrook, nr Sherbourne, Warwickshire CV35 8AS
Charity No.: 289913
Postal Address: The Forest Hermitage, Lower Fulbrook, nr Sherbourne,

Warwickshire CV35 8AS
Telephone Contact: 01926 624564 Or 01926 624101
Email: enquiries@foresthermitage.org.uk
Website(s): www.foresthermitage.org.uk

A Theravada forest monastery and branch of Wat Nong Pah Pong in NE Thailand under the guidance of the British born bhikkhu, Venerable Chao Khun Bhavanaviteht (Luangpor Khemadhammo) OBE.

It is the home of the English Shwe Dagon Pagoda and the headquarters of ANGULIMALA, the Buddhist Prison Chaplaincy Organisation. For details of meditation groups, retreats, monthly Newsletter, library facilities, and the current programme of events, please write or telephone. The monastery depends on free-will offerings and makes no charges whatso ever. The supporting body is the Buddha-Dhamma Fellowship.

WARWICK

WARWICK BUDDHISM AND MEDITATION GROUP
Tradition: FWBO
Meetings: Gap Community Centre, 39 Oakwood Grove, Warwick, CV34 5TD
Affiliated to: Friends Of The Western Buddhist Order, UK National Organisations
Postal Address: Birmingham Buddhist Centre, 11 Park Road, Moseley, Birmingham, West Midlands B13 8AB
Telephone Contact: 0121 449 5279
Email: info@birminghambuddhistcentre.org.uk
Website(s): www.birminghambuddhistcentre.org.uk
Meeting Times: Tuesdays 7.30 - 9.30pm

We also run day retreats at the Birmingham Buddhist Centre and weekend retreats at various country locations.

For more information please contact Birmingham FWBO

117

WEST MIDLANDS

DZOGCHEN MIDLANDS
Tradition: Tibetan
School: Dzogchen
Affiliated to: Dzogchen Community UK, UK National Organisations
Email: barry@redsandstonehill.net
Website(s): www.dzogchencommunity.org
See UK

NATIONAL ORGANISATIONS

BIRMINGHAM

BIRMINGHAM BUDDHIST CENTRE (FWBO)
Tradition: FWBO
Meetings: 11 Park Road, Moseley, Birmingham B13 8AB
Affiliated to: Friends Of The Western Buddhist Order, UK National Organisations
Charity No.: 516568
Postal Address: Birmingham Buddhist Centre, 11 Park Road, Moseley, Birmingham B13 8AB
Telephone Contact: 0121 449 5279
Email: info@birminghambuddhistcentre.org.uk
Website(s):
www.birminghambuddhistcentre.org.uk

The Birmingham Buddhist Centre is part of the Friends of the Western Buddhist Order (FWBO) which was founded in 1967 by Sangharakshita. The FWBO makes Buddhism and meditation accessible as a living tradition in the modern world. The centre holds regular drop-in meditation classes as well as courses in meditation and Buddhism for newcomers.

We welcome visits from schools, colleges, interfaith groups and other interested parties. We can organise visiting speakers and meditation teachers.

Attached to the centre is a shop offering a range of Buddhist literature, meditation and yoga equipment, incense, cards, Buddhist figures, and more.

BIRMINGHAM BUDDHIST VIHARA
Tradition: Theravada
Meetings: 29 - 31 Osler St, Birmingham. B16 9EU
Charity No.: 513368
Postal Address: Birmingham Buddhist Vihara, 29 - 31 Osler St, Birmingham B16 9EU
Telephone Contact: 0121 454 6591
Fax: 0121 455 0650
Email: vihara@bbv.org or nagasena_bhikkhu@hotmail.com
Website(s):
www.birminghambuddhistvihara.org

A Theravada monastery with Myanmar affiliations, it has always catered for Westerners. It was under the spiritual direction of Aggamahapandita Rewata Dhamma until he passed away in 2004. There are four permanent resident monks - and often a number of visiting monks as well. In the grounds are the Dhamma Talaka Peace Pagoda, opened in June 1998, and the Sangharama Monastery, opened in August 2002. The next phase is to build a Dhamma Hall with living quarters for retreatants.

Originally set up as the West Midlands Buddhist Centre in nearby Carlyle Road in November 1978, it has always been the major Buddhist organisation in the West Midlands. It is therefore willing to provide space for activities of Buddhists of other schools. The beauty of its buildings combined with sensitive teaching draws students from schools and colleges all over Britain and abroad most weeks in term time. Ven. Dr. Rewata Dhamma works with those of other faiths in the city and encourages inter-faith dialogue. Several of its devotees are members of the Birmingham Council of Faiths.

It has a small press, Dhamma Talaka Publications, and since 2001 has also published The Lotus lay review.

BIRMINGHAM DIAMOND WAY BUDDHIST CENTRE

Tradition: Tibetan
School: Karma-Kagyu
Meetings: 25 Sunhouse, 9 Bennets Hill, Birmingham, B2 5RS
Affiliated to: Diamond Way Buddhism UK, UK National Organisations
Charity No.: 1093406
Postal Address: Birmingham Diamond Way Buddhist Centre, 25 Sunhouse, 9 Bennets Hill, Birmingham, B2 5RS
Telephone Contact: 07790 853491
Email: birmingham@dwbuk.org
Website(s):
www.diamondway-buddhism.co.uk

The Birmingham group is located 5 minutes walk from New Street railway station. Please call or email us for more information or join us for a free guided meditation.

Regular Meditation Times are on Sundays at 7:30pm: Introduction and 16th Karmapa guided meditation: for people who are new to Buddhism and those who have been practicing for many years. Please telephone us before coming for the first time.

BIRMINGHAM SAMATHA GROUP

Tradition: Theravada
Meetings: St Francis' Hall Chaplaincy, University of Birmingham
Affiliated to: Samatha Trust, UK National Organisations
Postal Address: Keith Munnings, 105 Middleton Hall Road, King's Norton, Birmingham B30 1AG
Telephone Contact: 0121 458 2353 (Keith)
Email: keith@eskola.freeserve.co.uk

Website(s): www.samatha.org

Beginners Samatha Meditation class and a group for more experienced meditators.

Talks form speakers from a variety of Buddhist traditions arranged by Birmingham University Buddhist Society. You do not need to be a member of the University to come along.

BIRMINGHAM SERENE REFLECTION MEDITATION GROUP

Tradition: Zen
School: Soto
Postal Address: Birmingham Buddhist Vihara, Osler St, Birmingham B16 9EU The Order Of Buddhists Contemplatives, UK National Organisations
Telephone Contact: 0121 351 2518 (Duncan Kennedy)

Please call for details of meetings. Newcomers are always welcomed and meditation instruction is given.

BUDDHAVIHARA TEMPLE

Tradition: Theravada
Meetings: Eastfield House, Alrewas Road, Kings Bromley, Staffordshire DE13 7HR
Charity No.: 1082096
Postal Address: The Buddhavihara Temple, Eastfield House, Alrewas Road, Kings Bromley, Staffordshire DE13 7HR
Telephone Contact: 01543 472315
Email: ajahn@watthaiuk.com
Website(s): www.watthaiuk.com

There are 2-5 Thai Bhikkhus resident at the vihara; the Head Monk is Dr. PK Panyasudhammawithet (formerly Dr Phramaha Laow Panyasiri). Most of the monks speak English; ceremonies are conducted in English and Thai.

Activities include:

Entry continued on the following page.

- Buddhist study and Dhamma talk

- School visits by appointment

- Public talks by invitation

- Buddhism for beginners

-Thai language classes

- Vipassana Meditation Classes

- Buddhist Festivals: Magha Puja Day (February), Wesak (May), Asalha Puja Day (July) and Kathina Ceremony (November)

- Some Thai festivals (Thai New Year, Loi Kratong)

- Meditation retreats (Weekend retreats are available upon request).

The Buddhavihara Temple is administered through the Thai-British Buddhist (Buddhavihara Temple) Trust.

COMMUNITY OF INTERBEING - BIRMINGHAM SANGHA
Tradition: Vietnamese
School: Thich Nhat Hanh
Affiliated to: The Community Of Interbeing, UK, UK National Organisations
Telephone Contact: 0121 449 3977 (John)

Website(s): www.interbeing.org.uk
Contact for information about local and regional activities for meditation and Days of Mindfulness. See UK National Orgaisations for details of The Community of Interbeing.

FWBO CENTRAL
Tradition: FWBO
Affiliated to: Friends Of The Western Buddhist Order, UK National Organisations
Charity No.: 1017329

Postal Address: FWBO Central, Madhyamaloka, 'Brackley Dene', 30 Chantry Road, Moseley, Birmingham B13 8HD
Telephone Contact: 0121 449 3700
Fax: 0121 449 3780
Email: liaison@fwbo.org
Website(s): www.fwbo.org

Houses the Preceptors College and Council of the FWBO. FWBO Central is the central source of information and liaison with other Buddhist Groups. For details of classes and courses at FWBO centres please contact The London Buddhist Centre, 51 Roman Road, E2 0HU. Tel: 020 8981 1225

JETAVANA BUDDHIST TEMPLE
Tradition: Theravada
School: Ambedkarite
Meetings: Jetavana Buddhist Temple 13 Booth Street, Handsworth, BIRMINGHAM B21 0NG
Affiliated to: Federation Of Ambedkarite Buddhist Organisations UK, UK National Organisations
Charity No.: 516598
Postal Address: The Secretary, Jetavana Buddhist Temple 13 Booth Street, Handsworth, Birmingham B21 0NG
Telephone Contact: 0121 554 1466

The activities of our association are conducted by annually-elected officers, while Puja and Meditation are conducted by Buddhist Monks who speak English, various Indian languages and Sinhala. Please contact us for details of our current programme.

MIDLANDS BUDDHIST ASSOCIATION [VIETNAMESE]
Tradition: Vietnamese
Meetings: 34 Holyhead Road, Handsworth, Birmingham
Charity No.: 1041845
Postal Address: Midlands Buddhist

Association, 34 Holyhead Road, Handsworth, Birmingham, B21 0LT
Telephone Contact: 0121 551 8614
Or 0121 551 7751
Fax: 0121 551 8614
Website(s): www.vdc.org.uk

This is the only Vietnamese Buddhist temple outside London. The resident monk, Ven Thich Phuoc Hue, travels to various cities to participate in Vietnamese Buddhist activities. Both the Mahayana and Theravada traditions are recognised, reflecting the situation in Vietnam itself.

The programme of the temple is as follows: Chanting and meditation (occasionally following the Theravada tradition) are held daily at 6.00am, 2.00pm and 7.00pm and on festival days additionally at 11.00am. Classes in Buddhism for adults and children are held on Saturdays and Sundays.

The main events in the Buddhist calendar are celebrated on a grand scale.

MIDLANDS INTERNATIONAL BUDDHIST ASSOCIATION IN THE UK

Tradition: Theravada
Affiliated to: MIBA/Birmingham Buddhist Maha Vihara (UK), 216 New John's Street, West Hockly, Birmingham B19 3WA
Charity No.: 1020543
Telephone Contact: 0121 523 6660
Fax: 0121-3827108
Email: mibauk86@hotmail.com
Website(s): www.buddhist-mahavihara.com

The Association was established in Derby in 1992 by a Sri Lankan monk, Ven W Kassapa in order to provide Dhamma in the Theravadin tradition but was later transferred to Birmingham.

The Birmingham centre provides meditation, Dhamma discussion classes and daily pujas

morning and evening. There are special programmes on full moon days. Once a week one of the monks visits local schools to teach Buddhism. The centre is open to people of all traditions and nationalities.

Venerable Witharandeniya Kassapa (Vihara Head Monk)

RIGPA BIRMINGHAM

Tradition: Tibetan
School: Nyingma
Affiliated to: Rigpa Fellowship, UK National Organisations
Postal Address: Rigpa Birmingham. 171 Pineapple Road, Stirchley, Birmingham B30 2SU
Telephone Contact: 0121 441 1698
Email: birmingham@rigpa.eclipse.co.uk
Website(s): www.rigpa.org.uk

See UK National Organisations.

SAKYA GOSHAK CHOLING

Tradition: Tibetan
School: Kagyu-Sakya
Meetings: 55 Russell Road, Moseley, Birmingham B13 8RB
Affiliated to: Dechen Community, UK National Organisations
Postal Address: Sakya Goshak Choling, 55 Russell Road, Moseley, Birmingham B13 8RB
Telephone Contact: 0121 449 3296
Email: birmingham@dechen.org
Website(s): www.dechen.org

Sakya Goshak Choling was founded in 1988 to provide an opportunity for people in the Midlands to make contact with the Sakya tradition and learn its systems of meditation and study. In addition to hosting teachings by Lama Jampa Thaye the centre has also been blessed by visits from His Holiness Sakya Trizin and Karma Thinley Rinpoche. Phone for details of activities.

UK FA YUE BUDDHIST MONASTERY
Meetings: UK Fa Yue Buddhist Monastery, Cottage Street, Brierley Hill, West Midlands DY5 1RE
Postal Address: UK Fa Yue Buddhist Monastery, Cottage Street, Brierley Hill, West Midlands DY5 1RE
Telephone Contact: 01384 484552
Fax: 01384 481209

WAT SANGHATHAN
Tradition: Theravada
Meetings: 107 Handsworth Wood Road, Handsworth Wood, Birmingham B20 2PH
Postal Address: Wat Sanghathan, 107 Handsworth Wood Road, Handsworth Wood, Birmingham B20 2PH
Telephone Contact: 0121 551 5729
Fax: 0121 515 2213
Email: wat@sanghathan.freeserve.co.uk
Website(s): www.sanghathan.co.uk

A Thai temple in Birmingham. The Abbot is Ajahn Chan Janthawanno. Please contact for details of our current programme.

COVENTRY

WARWICK UNIVERSITY BUDDHIST SOCIETY
Postal Address: Forest Hermitage, England, Warwickshire, Sherbourne
Email: buddsoc@sunion.warwick.ac.uk
Website(s): www.sunion.warwick.ac.uk/buddsoc

HALESOWEN

SMILING MOUNTAIN MEDITATION GROUP
Tradition: Zen
Postal Address: Smiling Mountain Meditation Group, 79 Midhurst Road, Kings Norton, Birmingham B30 3RA
Telephone Contact: 07816 5788 (Graham Paul)

Email: graham.email@btinternet.com

This group is for people who are already committed to a practice of daily meditation, of any religious background or none, or for beginners and those who really would like to commence such a practice.

The organisers of the group are not 'Gurus' and are not claiming any spiritual authority or achievement, although they do have sufficient experience to instruct beginners in the techniques and mechanics of meditation. Participation in the group is free except for the contributions necessary to meet the inevitable running expenses.

Please contact for details of the current programme.

SUTTON COLDFIELD

SUTTON COLDFIELD BUDDHISM AND MEDITATION GROUP (FWBO)
Tradition: FWBO
Meetings: Friends Meeting House, Kenelm Road, off Manor Hill, Sutton Coldfield
Affiliated to: Friends Of The Western Buddhist Order, UK National Organisations
Postal Address: Birmingham Buddhist Centre, 11 Park Road, Moseley, Birmingham B13 8AB
Telephone Contact: 0121 449 5279
Email: info@birminghambuddhistcentre.org.uk
Website(s)
:www.birminghambuddhistcentre.org.uk

This group meets weekly on Wednesday evenings. There is a session of meditation (with full instruction for those who want), followed by talk and discussion on a particular aspect of Buddhism or meditation. Newcomers are welcome to join us on any week. For more details, or a map of the location, please contact the Birmingham Buddhist Centre.

WOLVERHAMPTON

WOLVERHAMPTON BUDDHA VIHARA
Tradition: Theravada
School: Ambedkarite
Meetings: Ambedkar Nagar, Upper Zoar Street, Pennfields, Wolverhampton, WV3 0JH
Postal Address: Buddha Vihara, Ambedkar Nagar, Upper Zoar Street, Pennfields, Wolverhampton, WV3 0JH
Telephone Contact: 01902 715094
Fax: 01902 715094
Email: ambedkarst@yahoo.co.uk or kamlachumber@hotmail.co.uk

A Theravadin Vihara. Please contact for details of current programme.

WEST SUSSEX

SANG-NGAK-CHO-DZONG
Tradition: Tibetan
School: Nyingma
Meetings: Please contact Clive Way for details.
Affiliated to: Sang-Ngak-Cho-Dzong, UK National Organisations
Charity No.: 1019886
Telephone Contact: 01730 816842
Email: cliveway@yahoo.com
Website(s): www.aroter.org

See UK National Organisations.

CHICHESTER

BODHICHARYA BUDDHIST GROUP
Tradition: Tibetan
Meetings: Hamblin Hall, Bosham House, Near Chichester, W.Sussex
Affiliated to: Bodhicharya UK, UK National Organisations
Postal Address: Ian Stuart, 46b Lyminster Road, Littlehampton, W.Sussex, BN17 7LB
Telephone Contact: 01903 733958
Email: enquiries@buddhalight.org
Website(s): www.bodhicharya.org

The group was founded in May 1998 and is under the direction of Ringu Tulku Rinpoche. There is a programme of regular weekly meetings in Emsworth, and it is hoped to be able to arrange twice-yearly teachings with Rinpoche and also teachings with other visiting teachers and lamas of all the Tibetan Buddhist orders; these special events will be held at different venues in the Chichester area.

CHICHESTER SERENE REFLECTION MEDITATION GROUP
Tradition: Zen
School: Soto
Meetings: Friends Meeting House, Priory Road, Chichester
Affiliated to: The Order Of Buddhists Contemplatives, UK National Organisations
Telephone Contact: 01243 604 180 (Roy Foley)

The group meets on the first Saturday of each month from 10am - 1pm. It receives visits from the Prior of Reading Buddhist Priory. Meditation instruction is available. Everyone welcome, please phone for details.

KAGYU SAMYE DZONG CHICHESTER
Meetings: Southern Comfort, West Bracklesham Drive Bracklesham Bay, Chichester, West Sussex PO20 8PF
Affiliated to: Kagyu Samye Ling Monastery And Tibetan Centre, UK National Organisations
Postal Address: Kagyu Samye Dzong, Southern Comfort, Bracklesham Bay, Chichester, West Sussex, PO20 8PF
Telephone Contact: 01243 671309
Fax: 01243 672872
Email: chichester@samye.org
Kagyu Samye Dzong Chichester is a branch of

Entry continued on the following page.

Kagyu Samye Ling Tibetan Buddhist Centre and Monastery in Scotland. Meditation sessions are held on Sundays 5.00 to 6.30pm. Instruction is given to beginners. The centre is under the direct guidance of Dr. Akong Tulku Rinpoche and Ven. Lama Yeshe Losal, Abbot and Retreat Master of Kagyu Samye Ling. All are welcome. Please telephone for details.

CHITHURST

CITTAVIVEKA, CHITHURST BUDDHIST MONASTERY
Tradition: Theravada
Meetings: Chithurst, Petersfield, Hampshire, GU31 5EU
Affiliated to: Amaravati Buddhist Monastery, UK National Organisations
Postal Address: Cittaviveka, Chithurst Buddhist Monastery, Petersfield, Hampshire, GU31 5EU
Telephone Contact: 01730 814986
Fax: 01730 817334
Website(s): www.cittaviveka.org

Cittaviveka is one of the British monasteries following the teaching and training of Venerable Ajahn Chah. It was established by Ajahn Sumedho, his first Western disciple, in 1979. The present abbot, Ajahn Sucitto, has been a disciple of Ajahn Sumedho since 1978. The monastery was founded as a place for long-term commitment in Vinaya training rather than as a meditation centre.

The monastic community generally comprises bhikkhus, siladhara (nuns) and male and female novices (anagarika). Lay people may come and stay as guests following the daily routines, which include an early morning meditation, work in the house, gardens or the appended forest, and evening meditation. They must also keep the Eight Precepts. There is no charge and guests may stay for one to three months if they are found to be suitable. Applicants should write to the Guest Monk or Guest Nun.

Visitors are also welcome to drop in. There are formal teachings given every Saturday after the evening meditation (begins 7.30 pm) to which all are welcome. Sunday is visitor's day (meal offering 10.30am, guided meditation etc at 5.00 pm).

STEYNING

STEYNING MEDITATION GROUP
Tradition: Theravada
Affiliated to: Cittaviveka, Chithurst Buddhist Monastery, Chithurst, West Sussex, England
Postal Address: Jayanti (Annie Cousins), 37 Hills Road, Steyning, West Sussex BN4 3QG
Telephone Contact: 01903 812130 (Jayanti)
Email: anniecousins@lantean.freeserve.co.uk

This is a Theravada group that meets and offers courses in the local area. Telephone for current details.

WEST YORKSHIRE

CALDERDALE

CALDERDALE ZEN GROUP
Tradition: Zen
School: Soto/Rinzai
Affiliated to: Zen Practice Centre Trust, UK National Organisations
Telephone Contact: 01422 824260 (Ian)
Email: jupiterandapollo@yahoo.co.uk.
Website(s): www.zenbuddhism.co.uk

Meets weekly in the Halifax/Hebden Bridge area.

HUDDERSFIELD

HUDDERSFIELD SAMATHA GROUP
Tradition: Theravada
Meetings: The Quaker Meeting House, Church

Street, Paddock, Huddersfield.
Affiliated to: Samatha Trust, UK National
Organisations
Telephone Contact: 01484 540747 (Chris
Rogers)
Email: info@samatha.org
Website(s):
www.samatha.org/manchester/nwgroups.html

Meets Tuesdays 8pm.

HUDDERSFIELD SERENE REFLECTION MEDITATION GROUP
Tradition: Zen
School: Soto
Affiliated to: The Order Of Buddhists
Contemplatives, UK National Organisations
Postal Address: Jim Gore-Langton, 19
Grasmere Road, Calmlands, Meltham, Holmfirth.
HD9 4HF   Tony Johnson, Bothy Cottage, 39 Cliff
Road, Holmfirth, Huddersfield HD7 1UY
Telephone Contact: 01484 340150 (Jim
Gore-Langton)
Or 01484 681300 (Tony Johnson)
Email: jim_gore-langton@ntlworld.com

The group meets on Thursday evenings at 7.30pm.
Meditation instruction is available and newcomers
are welcome. Occasional visits by a monk from
Throssel Hole Buddhist Abbey.

LEEDS

COMMUNITY OF INTERBEING - LEEDS SANGHA
Tradition: Zen
School: Thich Nhat Hanh
Affiliated to: The Community Of Interbeing,
UK, UK National Organisations
Telephone Contact: 01132 628373 (Nat)
Email: nat@asgardpublishing.org.uk
Website(s): www.interbeing.org.uk

Contact for information about local and regional
activities for meditation and Days of Mindfulness.

See UK National Orgaisations for details of The
Community of Interbeing.

DECHEN IN LEEDS
Tradition: Tibetan
School: Kagyu-Sakya
Meetings: Friends Meeting House, 188
Woodhouse Lane, Leeds LS2 9DX
Affiliated to: Dechen Community, UK National
Organisations
Charity No.: 1064198
Postal Address: Kagyu Dechen Dzong
Buddhist Centre, 2b Chudleigh Road, Harrogate
HG1 5NP
Telephone Contact: 01423 536915
Email: harrogate@dechen.org
Website(s): www.dechen.org
Introductory Classes are on the 1st and3rd
Tuesday of the month

7.30pm. The sessions consist of a short talk
followed by guided meditation, and cover the
understanding and motivation that underpin the
Buddhist path, giving newcomers a gentle and
relaxed opportunity to meet the sangha and
contemplate the teachings of Lord Buddha.

DHAMMAPALA THERAVADA GROUP
Tradition: Theravada
Meetings: Lutheran Church, Armley Road,
Headingley, Leeds
Affiliated to: Aruna Ratanagiri, England,
Northumberland, Belsay
Postal Address: Anne Grimshaw, 123
Cooper Lane, Shelf, Bradford, Yorkshire HX3 7RG
Telephone Contact: 01274 691447 (Anne
Grimshaw)
Or 0113 279 1375 (Daniella Loeb)
Or 0113 261 4084 (Bob)
Email: info@dhammapala.org.uk
Website(s):
www.leeds.buddhist.group.dsl.pipex.com

Please contact for details of current programme.

JAMYANG BUDDHIST CENTRE LEEDS
Tradition: Tibetan
School: Gelugpa
Meetings: Suite 39, Whingate Budiness Park, Leeds LS12 3AT
Affiliated to: Foundation For The Preservation Of The Mahayana Tradition, UK National Organisations
Charity No.: 1109242
Postal Address: Suite 39, Whingate Budiness Park, Leeds LS12 3AT
Telephone Contact: 07866 760460
Fax: 01132 754871
Email: smile@jamyangleeds.co.uk
Website(s): www.jamyangleeds.co.uk

Jamyang Buddhist Centre Leeds was established in 1996 and is affiliated to FPMT, which has 131 centres worldwide. We focus on the study and practice of Buddhism in the Tibetan Gelugpa tradition. Meditation classes are held on Monday evenings and Buddhist study classes on Wednesday and Thursday evenings, plus many weekends. We hold weekend meditation retreats throughout the year. As well as our regular teacher Ven. Mary Reavey, we have a programme of visiting teachers including Geshe Tashi Tsering, Ven. Steve Carlier, Mike Murray, and Andy Wistreich. See the website for the current programme.

(We are run entirely by volunteers and donations)

LEEDS BUDDHIST CENTRE (FWBO)
Tradition: FWBO
Affiliated to: Friends Of The Western Buddhist Order, UK National Organisations
Charity No.: 515679
Postal Address: Leeds Buddhist Centre, 9 Heddon Place, Meanwood, Leeds LS6 4EL or PO Box 448, Leeds LS7 9BB
Telephone Contact: 0113 278 3395
Email: enquiries@leedsbuddhistcentre.org
Website(s): www.leedsbuddhistcentre.org

Our beginners meditation courses and our regular

meditation practice nights are held in room 110 at the Swarthmore Centre, 2-7 Woodhouse Sq, Leeds, LS3 1AD

LEEDS BUDDHIST GROUP
Tradition: All
Telephone Contact: 01132 564330
Email: kbsec2000-leedsbuddhistgroup@yahoo.co.uk
Website(s): www.communigate.co.uk/brad/leedsbuddhistgroup

LEEDS ZEN DOJO
Tradition: Zen
School: Soto
Meetings: Office 5, Whingate House, Whingate Business Park, Leeds LS12 3BP
Affiliated to: International Zen Association UK, UK National Organisations
Charity No.: 1069941
Telephone Contact: 07939 800653 (Carol Young)
Website(s): www.izauk.org

Zazen Timetable: Monday: 6.15 pm, Thursday: 6.30 pm

Introduction: Thursday 5.45 pm

BRADFORD ON AVON

HOUSE OF INNER TRANQUILLITY
Tradition: Theravada
School: Vipassana
Meetings: 9 Masons Lane, Bradford-on-Avon, Wilts, BA15 1QN
Charity No.: 326938
Postal Address: House of Inner Tranquillity, 9 Masons Lane, Bradford-on-Avon, Wilts. BA15 1QN
Telephone Contact: 01225 866821
Fax: 01225 865262
Email: info@aukana.org.uk
Website(s): www.aukana.org.uk

The House of Inner Tranquillity, co-founded in

1980 by Alan James, is a meditation centre where the Buddha's teaching is presented in a modern Western context. The centre offers comprehensive instruction in meditation and the Buddhist path to enlightenment as laid down in the Pali Canon. While the central practice taught is vipassana (insight) meditation, much emphasis is placed on developing a committed and systematic approach to all aspects of the Buddha's eightfold path. We particularly stress the importance of ethical conduct (sila), mindfulness in daily life and metta (loving-kindness).

The House of Inner Tranquillity runs a full programme of events, including residential retreats, lectures and Pali Canon classes. In the late 1980's a new monastic order was established. Monks and nuns are fully supported by the Aukana Trust, the registered charity which administers the House of Inner Tranquillity and the two monasteries. The monastic discipline is in all important respects based on the Vinaya rules of the Theravadan school. New minor rules reflect modern cultural conditions. Monks and nuns follow the same rules. The Aukana Trust has published several books. All proceeds from the sales go to support the Meditation Centre and monasteries.

WILTSHIRE

CALNE

INTERNATIONAL MEDITATION CENTRE
Tradition: Theravada
School: Vipassana
Charity No.: 280134
Postal Address: Manager, International Meditation Centre, Splatts House, Heddington, Wiltshire, SN11 0PE
Telephone Contact: 01380 850 238
Fax: 01380 850 833
Email: imcuk@internationalmeditationcentre.com

Website(s):
www.internationalmeditationcentre.com

Splatts House is a residential meditation centre founded in 1979 by the Sayagyi U Ba Khin Memorial Trust. The Trust owns and runs the centre. The centre holds ten day courses monthly in Theravada Buddhist meditation in the tradition of Sayagyi U Ba Khin of Myanmar. The courses are under the guidance of Mother Sayamagyi and consist of the training of Anapana and Vipassana meditation. In Anapana meditation the student concentrates the attention on the breath in order to achieve one-pointedness of mind. This produces a calm and steady mind. In Vipassana meditation the meditator focuses the concentrated mind inside him/herself and experiences the realities of mind and body.

CHIPPENHAM

LAM RIM (WILTS & S.GLOUC)
Tradition: Tibetan
School: Gelugpa
Meetings: All Classes Held at Corsham
Affiliated to: Lam Rim Buddhist Centre, Wales, Monmouthshire, Penrhos
Charity No.: 1056564
Telephone Contact: 01249 715152 (Richard)
Or 01249 701941
Email: information@lamrimwg.org.uk
Website(s): www.lamrim.org.uk

The Venerable Geshe Damcho Yonten has been visiting Lam Rim (Wilts & Glos), to give teachings on the Lam Rim - the graduated path to enlightenment. The teachings followed are those of the Gelug-pa school, one of the four main lineages of Tibetan Buddhism.

Lam Rim (Wilts & Glos) Buddhists meet three times a week for meditation, discussion, puja and study, as well as the regular teachings given by Venerable Geshe Thinley. Visiting teachers often

Entry continued on the following page.

give courses at the weekends; the group has been visited by eminent Tibetan Lamas and Monks from the Gelug-pa tradition, and hope to host similar visits in the near future.

MARLBOROUGH

COMMUNITY OF INTERBEING - WHITE CLOUDS SANGHA - W. BERKS, WILTS AND AVON
Tradition: Vietnamese
School: Thich Nhat Hanh
Affiliated to: The Community Of Interbeing, UK, UK National Organisations
Telephone Contact: 01672 861497 (Jeannine - Marlborough)
Or 01672 520876 (Theresa - Swindon)
Or 0117 951 2591 (Duncan - Bristol)
Email: whitecloudssangha@yahoo.co.uk
Website(s): www.interbeing.org.uk

White Clouds Sangha is the collective name for Marlborough, Bath and Bristol micro-sanghas following the teachings and mindfulness practice of Thich Nhat Hanh.

Contact for information about local and regional activities for meditation and Days of Mindfulness. See UK National Orgaisations for details of The Community of Interbeing.

SALISBURY

JAMYANG SALISBURY
Tradition: Tibetan
School: Gelugpa
Meetings: Alabare House, 15 Tollgate Road, Salisbury SP1 2JA
Affiliated to: Foundation For The Preservation Of The Mahayana Tradition, UK National Organisations
Telephone Contact: 01202 422342
Email: jamyang.salisbury@ntlworld.com
Website(s): www.jamyang.co.uk/salisbury

Jamyang Salisbury is a small group with members from around Wiltshire, Dorset and Hampshire as well as Salisbury itself. We meet monthly during the winter months and twice monthly during the summer months in Salisbury. Geshe Tashi Tsering of the Jamyang Centre in London, kindly comes to give us teachings, generally between May and November, and Robin Bath (also from Jamyang London) comes to teach all year round.

We also have meditation and discussion during these meetings.

Additionally, a small group also meets regularly in Poole, Dorset, for meditation and discussion and we hope soon to set up a similar study group in Salisbury itself. As our members are geographically far apart, we hope to offer an online study group in the near future.

We have a small library of donated books, which members are welcome to borrow.

SWINDON

SWINDON CH'AN GROUP
Tradition: Chinese
School: Ch'an
Meetings: Friends Meeting House, 79 Eastcott Hill, Swindon SN1 3JF
Affiliated to: Western Ch'an Fellowship, UK National Organisations
Postal Address: c/o Hugh Carroll, 36 Prospect Hill, Swindon SN1 3JS
Or Mick Webb, c/o Friends Meeting House, 79 Eastcott Hill, Swindon SN1 3JF
Telephone Contact: 07949 605519 (Hugh Carroll)
Email: hughie@swindonchan.org
Website(s): www.swindonchan.org

Meets Mondays at 7.30pm for meditation and discussion.

Meditation Instructor: Hugh Carroll.

For further details refer to the entry for Western Ch'an Fellowship (UK National Organisations)

WORCESTERSHIRE

WORCESTER

WORCESTER BUDDHISM AND MEDITATION GROUP (FWBO)
Tradition: FWBO
Meetings: Conference Centre, University College Worcester, off Henwick Road, WR2 6AJ
Affiliated to: Friends Of The Western Buddhist Order, UK National Organisations
Postal Address: Birmingham Buddhist Centre, 11 Park Road, Moseley, Birmingham B13 8AB
Telephone Contact: 0121 449 5279
Email: info@birminghambuddhistcentre.org.uk
Website(s):
www.birminghambuddhistcentre.org.uk

Learn the basics of meditation and Buddhism on these introductory courses that take place in Worcester. By the end of the course you will know all you need to have your own meditation practice at home. There will also be presentations and discussions about the relevance of Buddhism to today's world. There is no need to book - just turn up on the night. For more details, or a map of the location, please contact the Birmingham Buddhist Centre.

For venues of day retreats, please phone 0121-447-7427.

WALES

ANGLESEY

CEMAES BAY

ANGLESEY THERAVADIN BUDDHIST GROUP
Tradition: Theravada
Meetings: The Firs, Cemlyn, Cemaes Bay, Anglesey LL67 ODU
Affiliated to: Amaravati Buddhist Monastery, UK National Organisations
Postal Address: Frank Youngs, Anglesey Theravadin Buddhist Group, The Firs, Cemlyn, Cemaes Bay, Anglesey N Wales LL67 ODU
Or Tom Kennedy, Arfryn, Lon St Ffraid, Trearddur, Anglesey, Wales LL65 2UD
Telephone Contact: 01407 710622 (Frank & Melvina Youngs)
Or 01407 860050 (Tom & Sue Kennedy)
Email: the-firs@supanet.com

Follows the Thai Forest Tradition of the Theravada school as taught by Ajahn Chah.

Meetings take place on Thursday of each week, 8.00 for 8.30pm. They consist of meditation followed by taped Dhamma talks by monks and nuns of the Theravadin Tradition. Tea and coffee and informal discussion close the evening at approx 10.00pm.

All are welcome. Meditation instruction is available if required.

CARDIFF

CARDIFF CH'AN GROUP
Tradition: Chinese
School: Ch'an
Meetings: Canton, Cardiff
Affiliated to: Western Ch'an Fellowship, UK National Organisations
Telephone Contact: 02920 229376 (Rob Stratton)
Or 07885 494471
Email: cardiff@westernchanfellowship.org

Website(s):
www.westernchanfellowship.org/cardiff

Refer to entry under Western Ch'an Fellowship under UK National Organisations.

A Ch'an (Chinese Zen Buddhism) meditation group, affiliated to the Western Ch'an Fellowship, meets in the Canton area of Cardiff on the first and third Wednesday of the month. Interested newcomers are welcome to try us out.

COMMUNITY OF INTERBEING - SOUTH WALES SANGHA
Tradition: Vietnamese
School: Thich Nhat Hanh
Affiliated to: The Community Of Interbeing, UK, UK National Organisations
Telephone Contact: 02920 706236
Email: pmobeswick@hotmail.com
Website(s): www.interbeing.org.uk

Contact for information about local and regional activities for meditation and Days of Mindfulness (usually in Cardiff). See UK National Orgaisations for details of The Community of Interbeing.

SANG-NGAK-CHO-DZONG
Tradition: Tibetan
School: Nyingma
Meetings: Please contact Ngakma Nor'dzin Pamo & Nkakpa 'o-Dzin Tridal for details.
Affiliated to: Sang-Ngak-Cho-Dzong, UK National Organisations
Charity No.: 1019886
Telephone Contact: 07092 010756
Email: khalding@gmail.com
Website(s): www.aroter.org

See UK National Organisations.

CARDIFF BUDDHIST CENTRE

Tradition: FWBO
Meetings: 12 St Peter's Street, Roath, Cardiff CF2 3BA
Affiliated to: Friends Of The Western Buddhist Order, UK National Organisations
Postal Address: Cardiff Buddhist Centre, 12 St Peter's Street, Roath, Cardiff CF2 3BA
Telephone Contact: 029 2046 2492
Email: connect@cardiffbuddhistcentre.com
Website(s): www.cardiffbuddhistcentre.com

The Buddhist Centre is now open Tuesday, Wednesday and Thursday, 2pm til 5pm

Feel free to call round to just have a cup of tea and a chat with someone about meditation and Buddhism, to browse our library, bookshop and general shop (including fine quality incense and singing bowls), or to use the shrine room for meditation.

Access to the centre is currently at the yoga studio entrance 10 yards down from the main door.

DZOGCHEN CARDIFF

Tradition: Tibetan
School: Dzogchen
Affiliated to: Dzogchen Community UK, UK National Organisations
Email: lgsinc123@hotmail.com
Website(s): www.dzogchencommunity.org

See UK NATIONAL ORGANISATIONS

ROKPA CARDIFF

Tradition: Tibetan
School: Karma-Kagyu
Meetings: Chapter Arts Centre, Canton, Cardiff CF5 1QE
Affiliated to: Kagyu Samye Ling Monastery And Tibetan Centre, UK National Organisations
Charity No.: 1059293
Postal Address: 100 Moorland Road, Cardiff CF24 2LP

Telephone Contact: 029 2049 9185
Email: info@rokpacardiff.com
www.rokpacardiff.com

Please contact for details of current programme.

CARDIGAN

PRECIOUS WOOD CH'AN GROUP

Tradition: Chinese
School: Ch'an
Meetings: Precious Wood
Affiliated to: Western Ch'an Fellowship, UK National Organisations
Postal Address: The Flat, Pantygog, Cwmhiraeth, Velindre, Llandysul, Carmarthenshire SA44 5XJ
Telephone Contact: 01559 370875 (Eric Johns)
Email: preciouswood@westernchanfellowship.org
Website(s): www.westernchanfellowship.org/preciouswood

Refer to entry under Western Ch'an Fellowship under UK National Organisations.

Eric Johns (Hin Lik) is the Dharma heir to Bill Pickard of Mousehole, Cornwall (Soto Zen). He has also received higher ordination and training under the Venerable Master Sing Yat (Rinzai Zen), at Po Lam Chan Monastery, Hong Kong in the lineage of Grand Master Hsu Yun. He now lives as a lay practitioner.

CARMARTHENSHIRE

NEWCASTLE EMLYN

BUDDHIST INSIGHT MEDITATION CENTRE OF WEST WALES

Tradition: Theravada
School: Vipassana
Meetings: Malindy Centre, Nr Newcastle

Emlyn, Carmarthenshire (Take the B4333 Newcastle Emlyn to Carmarthen Road.)
Affiliated to: House Of Inner Tranquillity, Bradford On Avon, Wiltshire, England
Telephone Contact: 01559 371993 (John Preston)

Meetings Alternate Tuesdays at 7.30pm - 10.00pm. The group is led by John Preston who trained as a Buddhist monk for five years with the Aukana Trust.

CEREDIGION

ABERYSTWYTH

ABERYSTWYTH BUDDHIST GROUP
Tradition: All
Meetings: Brynderwen, Cwmpadarn, Llanbardarn Fawr, Aberystwyth SY23 3QG
Affiliated to: Western Ch'an Fellowship, UK National Organisations
Postal Address: Ken Jones, Troedrhiwsebon, Cwmrheidol, Aberystwyth, SY23 3NB Ian Finlay, Brynderwen, Cwmpadarn, Llanbardarn Fawr, Aberystwyth SY23 3QG
Telephone Contact: 01970 880603 (Ken Jones)
Or 01970 625762
Email: genzan3@yahoo.com

This is an open group, and followers of all traditions are welcome, as well as absolute beginners and enquirers. Retreats are held from time to time. Newcomers please phone first.

DENBIGHSHIRE

CORWEN

VAJRALOKA BUDDHIST MEDITATION CENTRE FOR MEN (FWBO)

Tradition: FWBO
Meetings: Tyn-y-Ddol Treddol, Nr Corwen, LL21 OEN
Affiliated to: Friends Of The Western Buddhist Order, UK National Organisations
Charity No.: 514363 Vajraloka Retreat Centre, Tyn-y-Ddol, Treddol, Nr Corwen, Denbighshire, LL21 OEN
Telephone Contact: 01490 460406
Email: info@vajraloka.com
Website(s): www.vajraloka.org

Vajraloka is dedicated to the practice off meditation and holds more intensive retreats suitable for men with experience of the meditation practices taught within the FWBO.

LLANGOLLEN

LLANGOLLEN BUDDHIST GROUP (FWBO)
Tradition: FWBO
Affiliated to: Friends Of The Western Buddhist Order, UK National Organisations
Postal Address: Padmasara, Oakbine House, 1 Lys Rhedyn, Coedpoeth, Wrexham LL11 3NJ Llangollen Buddhist Group, c/o Vajraloka Retreat Centre, Tyn-y-Ddol, Treddol, Nr Corwen, Denbighshire, LL21 OEN
Telephone Contact: 01490 460 406
Email: info@vajraloka.com
Website(s): www.fwbo.org

GWYNEDD

COMMUNITY OF INTERBEING - DYFI VALLEY SANGHA
Tradition: Zen
School: Thich Nhat Hanh
Affiliated to: The Community Of Interbeing, UK, UK National Organisations
Telephone Contact: 01654 702690 (Hussam)
Website(s): www.interbeing.org.uk

Entry continued on the following page.

Contact for information about local and regional activities for meditation and Days of Mindfulness. See UK National Orgaisations for details of The Community of Interbeing.

CRICCIETH

AWAKENED HEART SANGHA
Tradition: Tibetan
School: Kagyu-Nyingma
Meetings: London and Ynys Graianog, Gwynedd
Charity No.: 1078783
Telephone Contact: 01766 523110
Email: info@ahs.org.uk www.ahs.org.uk

The Awakened Heart Sangha is a spiritual community in the Kagyu & Nyingma traditions of Tibetan Buddhism formed by students of Shenpen Hookham. A student of Kenpo Tsultrim Gyamtso Rinpoche, Shenpen has spent 9 years in retreat and has been teaching Buddhism for over 20 years.

The principal gateway into the Awakened Heart Sangha is Discovering the Heart of Buddhism, a systematic training in Buddhist study, contemplation and meditation. It is aimed both at those who have read about and practised Buddhism for some time, and at those who are completely new to it. Carefully structured coursebooks introduce the themes of the course and lead the student in contemplation, while personal contact with a teacher gives guidance and meditation advice. Participation is flexible and the course can be completed entirely from your own home.

Residential retreats and non-residential weekend courses provide important opportunities to go deeper into the practice, meet fellow students, and develop a sense of spiritual community. These events are a valuable supplement to Discovering the Heart of Buddhism (although optional).

The Awakened Heart Sangha seeks to provide the teachers, teaching and companions for a lifetime of practice, and so after Discovering the Heart of Buddhism there is an ongoing training tailored to the needs of the individual. Its heart is to plumb the depths of the teachings and one's experience, rather than acquiring endless knowledge or distraction: its steps are worked out in personal consultation with a teacher.

A current plan and long term goal is to provide opportunities for long-term retreat and intensive residential training to those who have the time and wish, thereby ensuring that the living flame of the practice tradition will pass down the generations.

PORTHMADOG

LONGCHEN FOUNDATION
Tradition: Tibetan
School: Kagyu-Nyingma
Meetings: Porthmadog
Affiliated to: Longchen Foundation, UK National Organisations
Telephone Contact: 01766 513131 (Pat MacDonald)
Email: garuda@deudraeth.net
Website(s): www.longchenfoundation.com

The Longchen Foundation was established by Chögyam Trungpa Rinpoche and Dilgo Khyentse Rinpoche, two of the great Tibetan teachers of the 20th century, to pass on the authentic Mahayana MahaAti (Dzogchen) teachings of the Nyingma lineage to the west. The spiritual director and principal teacher, Rigdzin Shikpo, one of Trungpa Rinpoche's earliest western students and a qualified lama of the Nyingma tradition, was entrusted by them to teach in direct response to the needs of Westerners and is among the most experienced and inspiring Buddhist teachers in Britain.
The Foundation is a community of Buddhist teachers, meditation instructors and students practising these teachings with the vision of

liberating the hearts of all beings. For details of weekend courses, retreats, publications, newsletters, please visit our website.

The Lion's Roar is a course that introduces the view and innermost teachings of the Longchen tradition and offers a deep and authentic grounding in the practice of meditation. It is suitable for total beginners and experienced meditators. The course is available in Britain and in Germany.

MONMOUTHSHIRE

PENRHOS

LAM RIM BUDDHIST CENTRE
Tradition: Tibetan
School: Gelugpa
Meetings: Pentwyn Manor, Penrhos, Raglan, Monmouthshire NP5 2LE
Charity No.: 326675
Postal Address: Lam Rim Buddhist Centre, Pentwyn Manor, Penrhos, Raglan, Monmouthshire NP5 2LE
Telephone Contact: 01600 780 383 (Margaret Travis)
Email: margaret@lamrim.org.uk
Website(s): www.lamrim.org.uk

The Centre follows the Tibetan Gelugpa Tradition under the guidance of Ven Geshe Damchö Yonten. Geshe-la teaches every Sunday at 3.30pm, on the 1st and 3rd Tuesdays in the month at 11.00am and on some weekend courses. Morning and evening puja are at 6.30am and 7.30pm respectively with afternoon sittings.

Pentwyn Manor is a mock-Tudor style family house standing in eight acres close to the Black Mountains. It is a residential centre with dormitory or single rooms available. Individual or group retreats are catered for. Past programmes have catered for Vipassana, Zen and Tibetan Buddhist retreats.

The Coach House, set apart from the main Centre, has been renovated to provide a high-quality environment with four self-contained, self-catering flats, fully insulated and centrally-heated, for individual practitioners who wish to complete a long-term retreat or study programme. Further information and details can be provided.

NEWPORT

NEWPORT

DHARMA CLOUD TRUST
Tradition: Zen
School: Soto
Affiliated to: The Order Of Buddhists Contemplatives, UK National Organisations
Charity No.: 1090129
Telephone Contact: 01633 250044 (Rev. Chushin)
Or 07984 632103
Email: revchushin@hotmail.com
Website(s): www.dharmacloud.org

Rev.Chushin is looking to establish a temple and retreat centre in South-East Wales.

Currently the group meets every Tuesday evening at 7.30pm. Please contact Rev Chushin for further details.

PEMBROKESHIRE

NARBERTH

DECHEN IN PEMBROKESHIRE
Tradition: Tibetan
School: Kagyu-Sakya
Meetings: Queen's Hall, High Street, Narberth, Pembrokeshire, South Wales
Affiliated to: Dechen Community, UK National Organisations
Charity No.: 282717

Entry continued on the following page.

Wales

Telephone Contact: 01437 541220
Email: pembrokeshire@dechen.org
Website(s): www.dechen.org

Introductory Classes are held on Mondays from 7.00pm to 9.00pm. Each session will include a short talk on an aspect of the Buddhist path, followed by guided meditation, questions and answers and refreshments.

NEVERN

THERAVADA BUDDHISM (SW WALES)
Tradition: Theravada
Meetings: Nevern, Haverfordwest, Newcastle Emlyn, and Llandysul. Please contact for details
Affiliated to: Amaravati Buddhist Monastery, UK National Organisations
Postal Address: Peter & Barbara Jackson, Rhoswrdan, Nevern, Newport, Pembrokeshire SA42 0NZ
Telephone Contact: 01239 820 790
Email: rhoswrdan@tesco.net

In association with the U.K. monasteries founded by the Venerable Sumedho, groups meet regularly for meditation, dhamma reflection and discussion, following the teachings of the Theravada Contemplative Forest Tradition. Full-moon Observances, educational visits and teaching visits by monastics are at Nevern.

Retreats are usually held twice a year.

At group meetings no charge is made other than a Dana Bowl to cover expenses.

Further details can be obtained by writing (enclose s.a.e. for a reply) or phoning. It is necessary to phone before visiting or attending a group.

NEWPORT

NEWPORT SAMATHA GROUP
Tradition: Theravada

Meetings: The Sessions House, Newport Pembrokeshire
Affiliated to: Samatha Trust, UK National Organisations
Postal Address: Marjorie Jack, Samatha Group, 3 Tower Hill, Brynhenllan, Dinas Cross, Pembrokeshire SA42 0SE
Or Alex Barr, Fronrhydd, Letterston, Haverfordwest SA62 5TL
Telephone Contact: 01348 811583 (Marjorie)
Or 01348 840309 (Alex)
Email: alexmcclure@btinternet.com
Website(s): www.samatha.org/pembrokshire

Please contact for details of current meeting times. All welcome, but it is a good idea to get further information about the class before attending.

POWYS

BRECON

TIRATANALOKA WOMEN'S ORDINATION RETREAT CENTRE
Tradition: FWBO
Meetings: Aberclydach House, Aber, Tallybont-on-Usk, Brecon, Powys LD3 7YS
Affiliated to: Friends Of The Western Buddhist Order, UK National Organisations
Charity No.: 1014180
Postal Address: Tiratanaloka, Aberclydach House, Aber, Tallybont-on-Usk, Brecon, Powys LD3 7YS
Telephone Contact: 01874 676482
Or 0845 3458539
Email: office@tiratanaloka.org.uk
Website(s): www.tiratanaloka.org

Tiratanaloka opened in late 1994 and is the base for retreats for women who have asked for ordination into the Western Buddhist Order.

136

HAY-ON-WYE

KUNSEL LING
Tradition: Tibetan
School: Dzogchen
Affiliated to: Dzogchen Community UK, UK
National Organisations
Postal Address: Nick Segust, 31 Whitland
Crescent, Fairwater, Cardiff CF5 3NL
Email: kunsellingbookings@yahoo.co.uk
Website(s):
www.dzogchencommunity.org/kunselling

Retreat Centre for the Dzogchen Community UK

See UK NATIONAL ORGANISATIONS

Kunselling is available as a retreat center to all
members of the Dzogchen Community.

KNIGHTON

SAMATHA CENTRE
Tradition: Theravada
Meetings: The Samatha Centre, Greenstreete,
Llangunllo, Nr. Knighton, Powys
Affiliated to: Samatha Trust, UK National
Organisations
Postal Address: The Secretary, The Samatha
Association, The Samatha Centre, Greenstreete,
Llangunllo, Nr. Knighton, Powys LD7 1SP
Telephone Contact: 01223 740407
(Rachael Hall)
Email: info@samatha.org
Website(s): www.samatha.org

The National Centre for the Samatha Trust, whose
purpose is to foster the development of Samatha
meditation, a traditional technique of self-
cultivation leading to inner strength, tranquility
and knowledge. The meditation method has its
origins in ancient India, but developed over recent
centuries in Thailand and was brought to Britain in
1963.

Residential meditation retreats/courses, open to
beginners and newcomers, are held periodically.
For information on weekend meditation courses,
please telephone. For all other enquiries, please
write or email.

LLANFYLLIN

LLANFYLLIN SAMATHA GROUP
Tradition: Theravada
Affiliated to: Samatha Trust, UK National
Organisations
Postal Address: Sue Steele, Bryn Hyfryd, off
Church St., Llandderfel, Gwynedd LL23 7HP
Telephone Contact: 01678 530446
Email: llanfyllin_enquiries@samatha.org
Website(s): www.samatha.org

A meditation class for beginners and the more
experienced.

Contact Sue Steele for details.

LLANGUNLLO

GREENSTREETE SAMATHA GROUP
Tradition: Theravada
Meetings: The Samatha Centre, Greenstreete,
Llangunllo (nr Knighton), Powys LD7 1PS
Affiliated to: Samatha Trust, UK National
Organisations
Postal Address: Heywood Hill, Harpton
Gardens, Walton, Prestigne, Powys, LD8 2RG
Telephone Contact: 01544 267849 (Sarah
Bamford)
Or 01544 350698 (Jenny Hill)
Email: d.s.bamford@btinternet.com
Website(s): www.samatha .org

Meditation classes for beginners are held monthly
on Sundays at 3.00pm.

Entry continued on the following page.

MACHYNLLETH

MACHYNLLETH MEDITATION GROUP
Tradition: All
Meetings: 9 Heol Pentrerhedyn, Machynlleth
(Near the central clock tower).
Telephone Contact: 01650 511350
Or 01654 702690
Email: tycerrig@lineone.net

Meets on Monday evenings at 8pm. Buddhists of
whatever doctrinal persuasion and non-Buddhists
are welcome.

SCOTLAND

ABERDEEN CITY

ABERDEEN

ABERDEEN BUDDHIST GROUP (FWBO)
Tradition: FWBO
Affiliated to: Friends Of The Western Buddhist Order, UK National Organisations
Telephone Contact: 01224 276810 (Alan Carter)
Email: aberdeenbuddhistgroup@yahoo.co.uk
Website(s):
www.aberdeen.buddhistnetwork.com

Meetings are held at 7.30pm (unless otherwise stated) at the Quaker Meeting House on Crown Street (Next to Shirlaw's Motorcycle Shop). The doors are shut at 7.40pm for reasons of safety.

ABERDEEN SERENE REFLECTION MEDITATION GROUP
Tradition: Zen
School: Soto
Meetings: Quaker Meeting House, Crown Street, Aberdeen
Affiliated to: The Order Of Buddhists Contemplatives, UK National Organisations
Telephone Contact: 01330 824339 (Bob McGraw)
Or 01467 681 525 (Joyce and Gordon Edward)

Group meetings take place every Monday at 6.30pm and regular day or half-day retreats are arranged, led by a priest from Throssel Hole Buddhist Abbey. Instruction in Serene Reflection Meditation is available through the group (which includes both men and women) and newcomers are welcome.

ROKPA ABERDEEN
Tradition: Tibetan
School: Karma-Kagyu
Affiliated to: Kagyu Samye Ling Monastery And Tibetan Centre, UK National Organisations
Postal Address: 6 Hosefield Road, Midstocket, Aberdeen AB15 5NB
Telephone Contact: 07986 956365
Email: info.rokpaaberdeen@gmail.com
Website(s): www.aberdeen.rokpa.org
Please see website for programme details.

ABERDEENSHIRE

COMMUNITY OF INTERBEING - ABERDEENSHIRE, BANCHORY SANGHA
Tradition: Zen
School: Thich Nhat Hanh
Affiliated to: The Community Of Interbeing, UK, UK National Organisations
Telephone Contact: 01330 825274 (Fiona or Mark)
Website(s): www.interbeing.org.uk

Contact for information about local and regional activities for meditation and Days of Mindfulness. See UK National Orgaisations for details of The Community of Interbeing.

CITY OF DUNDEE

DUNDEE

DUNDEE SERENE REFLECTION MEDITATION GROUP
Tradition: Zen
School: Soto
Meetings: The Chaplaincy Centre, The University of Dundee.
Affiliated to: The Order Of Buddhists Contemplatives, UK National Organisations
Telephone Contact: 01333 451788 (Elliott Forsyth)
Or 01382 452748 (Liz Evans)
Email: elsusan@tesco.net

The group meets on the first and third Tuesday of

Entry continued on the following page.

every month at 7pm and the last Saturday of the month at 10am. The group receives regular visits from the Prior of the Portabello Buddhist Priory. Please phone for details.

ROKPA DUNDEE
Tradition: Tibetan
School: Karma-Kagyu
Meetings: 51 Reform St. Dundee, DD1 4NG
Affiliated to: Kagyu Samye Ling Monastery And Tibetan Centre, UK National Organisations
Postal Address: Rokpa Dundee, 51 Reform Street, Dundee DD1 4NG
Telephone Contact: 01382 872020 (24 hour answer service)
Or 01382 872010
Email: jiga@ecosse.net
Website(s): www.rokpa.org/dundee

Rokpa Dundee, a branch of the Rokpa Trust, is situated in Dundee's premier street in the heart of the city, providing a refuge and an oasis of calm in the busy city centre. It occupies the whole of the second floor of a listed building, and in addition possesses a separate building which is the Lama's house. The Centre is open to all and was founded on the need for spiritual development, based on meditation, Loving Kindness and Compassion rooted in the Tibetan Buddhist tradition.

The Centre was opened in July 2000 by the City's Lord Provost, with the founding President of the Rokpa Trust, Dr Akong Tulku Rinpoche and the Abbot of Samye Ling Monastery, the Venerable Lama Yeshe Losal. Since then, it has steadily grown to include a Tibetan Tearoom and Tibetan Gift Shop. The Centre is attracting more people as the number and variety of classes, complementary treatments, therapies and workshops on offer increases. Its aim is to provide education, health, humanitarian and spiritual support locally, throughout Tayside and Angus.

DUMFRIES AND GALLOWAY

ESKDALEMUIR

KAGYU SAMYE LING TIBETAN CENTRE - ROKPA TRUST
Tradition: Tibetan
School: Karma-Kagyu

See UK National Organisations.

GALLOWAY

GALLOWAY SERENE REFLECTION MEDITATION GROUP
Tradition: Zen
School: Soto
Affiliated to: The Order Of Buddhists Contemplatives, UK National Organisations
Telephone Contact: 01556 504909 (Julia Langley or Penny Lilley)

The group meets weekly in the Castle Douglas area. There are regular visits from a monk from Throssel Hole Buddhist Abbey. Phone for details.

EDINBURGH

EDINBURGH

COMMUNITY OF INTERBEING - EDINBURGH SANGHA
Tradition: Vietnamese Thich Nhat Hanh
Affiliated to: The Community Of Interbeing, UK, UK National Organisations
Telephone Contact: 0131 339 8401 (Jon)
Website(s): www.interbeing.org.uk

Contact for information about local and regional activities for meditation and Days of Mindfulness.

See UK National Orgaisations for details of The Community of Interbeing.

EDINBURGH BUDDHIST CENTRE
Tradition: FWBO
Meetings: 30 Melville Terrace, Edinburgh, EH9 1LP
Affiliated to: Friends Of The Western Buddhist Order, UK National Organisations
Charity No.: SC017133
Postal Address: 30 Melville Terrace, Edinburgh, EH9 1LP
Telephone Contact: 0131 662 6699
Email: ebudc@supanet.com
Website(s):
www.edinburghbuddhistcentre.org.uk

We are the Friends of the Western Buddhist Order (Edinburgh), a Scottish charity, and we follow the Buddha's teachings in ways appropriate to how we live our lives today. We teach meditation, kindly awareness and wisdom through a regular programme of courses and classes. If you'd like to know more please see our website or telephone.

EDINBURGH DIAMOND WAY BUDDHIST CENTRE
Tradition: Tibetan
School: Karma-Kagyu
Meetings: 4 Leven Terrace, Flat 2, Edinburgh EH3 9LT
Affiliated to: Diamond Way Buddhism UK, UK National Organisations
Charity No.: 1093406
Postal Address: Edinburgh Diamond Way Buddhist Centre, 4 Leven Terrace, Flat 2, Edinburgh EH3 9LT
Email: edinburgh@dwbuk.org
Website(s):
www.diamondway-buddhism.co.uk

All newcomers are most welcome to come along for a cup of tea and a friendly chat about meditation and Diamond Way Buddhism. We have some books, magazines and lectures on CD that you can take away and enjoy at your leisure.

EDINBURGH SAMYE DZONG
Tradition: Tibetan
School: Karma-Kagyu
Meetings: The Theosophical Society, 28 Great King Street, Edinburgh
Affiliated to: Kagyu Samye Ling Monastery And Tibetan Centre, UK National Organisations
Telephone Contact: 0131 466 1978
Email: paulsde@blueyonder.co.uk
Website(s): www.edinburgh.samye.org

Please see website for programme details.

EDINBURGH SHAMBHALA MEDITATION GROUP
Tradition: Tibetan
School: Kagyu-Nyingma
Affiliated to: London Shambhala Meditation Centre, England, London, SW 4
Charity No.: 1073977
Postal Address: Edinburgh Shambhala Meditation Group, 4/12 Belhaven Place, Edinburgh, EH10 5JN
Telephone Contact: 0131 466 8566
Email: rodburstall@yahoo.co.uk
Website(s): www.shambhala.org

Regular meetings offer meditation practice and instruction, study of Buddha Dharma and discussion, following the teaching of Trungpa Rinpoche, a Tibetan Meditation Master, and his successor Sakyong Mipham Rinpoche.

Shambhala Training weekends offer a non-religious approach to working with meditation practice and creating a sane society. For further details, see website

EDINBURGH THERAVADA BUDDHIST GROUP
Tradition: Theravada
Meetings: The Eric Liddle Centre, 15 Morningside Road, Edinburgh, EH10 4DP

Entry continued on the following page.

Affiliated to: Aruna Ratanagiri, England, Northumberland, Belsay
Postal Address: Jody Higgs, 12 Saxe Coburg Street, Edinburgh EH3 5BN
Telephone Contact: 0131 332 7987 (Jody Higgs)
Or 0131 226 5044 (Neil Howell)
Or 0131 556 7000 (Myint Su)
Email: edinburghmeditation@hotmail.com

This group is associated with the British Buddhist monasteries established by the Venerable Ajahn Sumedho whose order of Western monks and nuns has its origin in Thailand.

The group meets every Thursday at 7.30pm. The group regularly receives teachings from a monk from Aruna Ratanagiri (Harnham Buddhist Monastery) in Northumberland.

PORTOBELLO BUDDHIST PRIORY
Tradition: Zen
School: Soto
Meetings: 27 Brighton Place, Portobello, Edinburgh EH15 1LL
Affiliated to: The Order Of Buddhists Contemplatives, UK National Organisations
Charity No.: SCO 31788
Postal Address: Portobello Buddhist Priory, 27 Brighton Place, Portobello, Edinburgh EH15 1LL
Telephone Contact: 0131 669 9622
Fax: 0131 669 9622
Email: prior@pbpriory1.freeserve.co.uk
Website(s): www.portobellobuddhist.org.uk
Contact Portobello Buddhist Priory, or see website for details.

PURE LAND BUDDHIST FELLOWSHIP

See UK NATIONAL ORGANISATIONS

RIGPA EDINBURGH
Tradition: Tibetan

School: Nyingma
Meetings: 2a Eldindean Place, Bonnyrigg and Salisbury Centre, Salisbury Road, Edinburgh
Affiliated to: Rigpa Fellowship, UK National Organisations
Postal Address: Rigpa Edinburgh, 2a Eldindean Place, Bonnyrigg, Edinburgh, EH19 2EY
Telephone Contact: 0131 663 7564
Or 0131 529 0111 (John Frame)
Or 0131 552 8085 (Nina Polli)
Email: rigpa@rigpaedinburgh.com
Website(s): www.rigpa.org.uk

See UK National Organisations.

TARA ROKPA EDINBURGH & THE INSTITUTE FOR TIBETAN MEDICINE
Tradition: Tibetan
School: Karma-Kagyu
Meetings: 15 Rosebery Crescent, Haymarket, Edinburgh EH12 5JY
Affiliated to: Kagyu Samye Ling Monastery And Tibetan Centre, UK National Organisations
Charity No.: 1059293
Postal Address: Tara Rokpa Edinburgh, 15 Rosebery Crescent, Haymarket, Edinburgh EH12 5JY
Telephone Contact: 0131 313 0304
Email: tararokpa@tiscali.co.uk
Website(s): www.tararokpa.org

The Institute for Tibetan Medicine holds clinics throughout the UK. For further information or to book an appointment with the Tibetan Doctor contact the above address. For further information please see website.

FIFE

COMMUNITY OF INTERBEING - POPPY SEED SANGHA, FIFE
Tradition: Vietnamese
School: Thich Nhat Hanh
Affiliated to: The Community Of Interbeing,

UK, UK National Organisations
Telephone Contact: 01337 810465 (Cathy)
Email: cathybache@highdoocot.freeserve.co.uk
Website(s): www.interbeing.org.uk

Meetings weekly on Mondays. Contact for information about local and regional activities for meditation and Days of Mindfulness. See UK National Orgaisations for details of The Community of Interbeing.

GLASGOW

GLASGOW

COMMUNITY OF INTERBEING - GLASGOW SANGHA
Tradition: Vietnamese
School: Thich Nhat Hanh
Affiliated to: The Community Of Interbeing, UK, UK National Organisations
Telephone Contact: 01236 825168 (Colin Bruce)
Website(s): www.interbeing.org.uk

Contact for information about local and regional activities for meditation and Days of Mindfulness. See UK National Orgaisations for details of The Community of Interbeing.

GLASGOW BUDDHIST CENTRE (FWBO)
Tradition: FWBO
Meetings: 329 Sauchiehall Street, Glasgow, G2 3HW
Affiliated to: Friends Of The Western Buddhist Order, UK National Organisations
Charity No.: SC006883
Postal Address: Secretary, Glasgow Buddhist Centre, 329 Sauchiehall St, Glasgow, G2 3HW.
Telephone Contact: 0141 333 0524
Email: glasgowbud@aol.com
Website(s): www.glasgowbuddhistcentre.com

Meditation, study, yoga and T'ai Chi classes. Teaching Mindfulness of Breathing and Metta Bhavana. Open for enquiries etc 10.00am - 4.00pm each weekday. Please see the website, call, write or telephone for details of the current programme.

GLASGOW THERAVADA BUDDHIST GROUP
Tradition: Theravada
Meetings: Rokpa House, 7 Ashley St, Woodlands, Glasgow, G3 6DR
Affiliated to: Aruna Ratanagiri, Belsay, Northumberland, England
Postal Address: James Scott, 3 Corrie Grove, Muirend, Glasgow, G44 3PP
Telephone Contact: 0141 637 9731

The purpose of the group is to offer an opportunity to investigate and follow the Buddhist way of life. Meetings are held on a regular basis, usually Friday evenings from 7.30pm until 10.30pm. The usual form is the Refuges and Precepts followed by a short period of meditation, then a Dhamma talk. There is an opportunity for questions during the preparation and serving of refreshments. The majority of our meetings are led by a monk from Aruna Ratanagiri, Harnham Buddhist Monastery.

GLASGOW ZEN DOJO
Tradition: Zen
School: Soto
Meetings: Rokpa Glasgow 7 Ashley Street, Glasgow G3 6DR
Postal Address: Glasgow Zen Dojo, c/o John Fraser, 15 Falkland Street, Glasgow G12 9PY
Telephone Contact: 0141 339 3888 (John Fraser)
Or 0141 959 1928 (Rachel Ball)
Email: JWFra29876@aol.com
Website(s): www.glasgowzen.org

An independent group of practitioners practising within the Soto Zen tradition.

Tuesday 19:00 and Saturday 08:30

Entry continued on the following page.

The Glasgow Zen group was established in 1990 and practices within the Soto Zen tradition. We are an independent group of practitioners endeavouring to take a constructive part in the on going reception of Zen in the West. We aim to foster links with other Zen groups in the UK, and to participate positively in the wider Buddhist community in Britain.

We meet meet regularly for zazen, which you are welcome to attend. We also organise longer events and also attend sesshins (intensive practice periods) in other parts of the UK. The group maintains a library within Rokpa House which contains a wide variety of books on Zen and related subjects.

Please see also www.dogensangha.org.uk

ROKPA GLASGOW
Tradition: Tibetan
School: Karma-Kagyu
Meetings: ROKPA House, 7 Ashley Street, Woodlands, Glasgow G3 6DR
Affiliated to: Kagyu Samye Ling Monastery And Tibetan Centre, UK National Organisations
Postal Address: Rokpa Glasgow, Rokpa House, 7 Ashley Street, Woodlands, Glasgow G3 6DR
Telephone Contact: 0141 332 9950
Or 0141 429 0300
Or 07748 656 022
Or 0141 429 0990
Email: glasgow@rokpa.org
Website(s): www.rokpa.org/glasgow

Charity work and weekly Dharma practices. Regular teachings. Contact for further details.

HIGHLAND

INVERNESS

ROKPA HIGHLANDS
Tradition: Tibetan
School: Karma-Kagyu
Meetings: Highland Council HQ, Glenurquhart Road, Inverness.

Postal Address: Kagyu Samye Ling Monastery And Tibetan Centre, UK National Organisations
Telephone Contact: 0790 056 1296
Email: info@highlands.rokpa.org
Website(s): www.highlands.rokpa.org

Rokpa Highlands was founded by Venerable Karma Jiga in 2001 and consists of meditation and yoga classes at present . The meditation class is held fortnightly and the yoga classes weekly. All the funds raised from the workshops and classes are put into a fund to buy a property to establish a residential centre in the beautiful surroundings of the highlands of Scotland.
See website for details of programme.

WESTER ROSS

SHANTI GRIHA
Meetings: Scoraig Peninsula, Wester Ross,
Postal Address: Brian and Kathrin Cooper, Shanti Griha, Rhireavach, Scoraig, Dundonnell, Wester Ross, IV23 2RE
Telephone Contact: 01854 633 260
Email: shantigriha@hotmail.com
Website(s): www.shantigriha.com

A Buddhist-oriented retreat and course centre accessible only on foot or by boat. Electricity comes from a windmill and water from a spring. Offers regular courses in Astanga Yoga, Thai Massage, Meditation and Buddhism, Singing and Windpower. Individual guests are also welcome.

MORAY

FORRES

COMMUNITY OF INTERBEING - NORTHERN LIGHTS SANGHA, FINDHORN
Tradition: Vietnamese
School: Thich Nhat Hanh
Affiliated to: The Community Of Interbeing, UK, UK National Organisations

Telephone Contact: 01309 690006
(Susanne)
Email: susanneolbrich@yahoo.co.uk
Website(s): www.interbeing.org.uk

Contact for information about local and regional activities for meditation and Days of Mindfulness. See UK National Orgaisations for details of The Community of Interbeing.

NORTH LANARKSHIRE

COATBRIDGE

BODHICHARYA UK
Tradition: Tibetan

See UK National Organisations.

OFF ARRAN

HOLY ISLAND
Tradition: Tibetan
School: Karma-Kagyu
Affiliated to: Kagyu Samye Ling Monastery And Tibetan Centre, UK National Organisations
Postal Address: Centre for World Peace & Health, Holy Island, Lamlash Bay, Isle of Arran, KA27 8GB
Telephone Contact: 01770 601100
Fax: 01770 601101
Email: reception@holyisland.org
Website(s): www.holyisland.org

This beautiful rugged island, off the coast of Arran in the Firth of Clyde, has a long sacred history with an ancient healing spring, the hermit-cave of a 6th century monk, St Molaise, and evidence of a 13th century monastery. Now, under the stewardship of the Samye Ling Buddhist Community, the island has become a focus for work on three great concerns of our time.

The environment: 35,000 native hardwood trees have been planted. Careful management of the environment is also helping to conserve the island's unique species of plants, and the wild Eriskay Ponies, Soay Sheep and Goats are benefitting from improved grazing. The Project is now part of the Alliance for Religion and Conservation, a world wide movement helping to channel the power of spiritual commitment to meet the challenges of ecological crisis.
Peace: The Holy Island Centre for World Peace and Health is available for hire for courses and workshops. It is also possible for individuals to stay at the Centre. Spirituality: A full programme of retreats runs during summer months.

See website for details of programme.

PERTH

PERTH

PERTH BUDDHIST GROUP (FWBO)
Tradition: FWBO
Meetings: St Paul's Centre (Perth Society for the Blind), 14 New Road, Perth PH1 5QA.
Affiliated to: Friends Of The Western Buddhist Order, UK National Organisations
Telephone Contact: 01764 663398
07889 117803
Email: email ric.crook@btinternet.com
Website(s):
http://groups.yahoo.com/group/perthsangha

Meetings every Wednesday evening at 7.15pm

Contact: Richard Crook

Occasional monthly Sunday retreats are hosted by Sangha members in the Perth area.

Regular monthly Saturday retreats are held at Dhanakosa Retreat Centre, near Balquhidder, arriving 9:30am for 10 am start.

Entry continued on the following page.

PERTH AND KINROSS

ABERFELDY

ABERFELDY SERENE REFLECTION MEDITATION GROUP
Tradition: Zen
School: Soto
Affiliated to: The Order Of Buddhists Contemplatives, UK National Organisations
Telephone Contact: 01887 820339 (Robin Baker)

The group meets on Tuesday evenings at 8pm and receives regular visits from the Prior of Portobello Buddhist Priory. Phone for details.

PERTH

PERTH THERAVADA GROUP
Tradition: Theravada
Affiliated to: Aruna Ratanagiri, England, Northumberland, Belsay
Telephone Contact: 07765 667499 (Neil Abbot)
Email: neilabbot@hotmail.com

SCOTTISH BORDERS

COMMUNITY OF INTERBEING - BORDERS AND LOTHIAN SANGHA
Tradition: Vietnamese
School: Thich Nhat Hanh
Affiliated to: The Community Of Interbeing, UK, UK National Organisations
Telephone Contact: 01896 756400 (Sandra)
Website(s): www.interbeing.org.uk

Contact for information about local and regional activities for meditation and Days of Mindfulness. See UK National Orgaisations for details of The Community of Interbeing.

SHETLAND ISLANDS

LERWICK

SHETLAND BUDDHIST GROUP (FWBO)
Tradition: FWBO
Meetings: Freefield Centre, North Road, Lerwick.
Affiliated to: Friends Of The Western Buddhist Order, UK National Organisations

Email: andrea.holmes@shb.shetland.scot.nhs.uk
Website(s):
www.fwbo.org/contacts/addresses-uk.html

Meeting fortnightly every second Monday.

Occasional weekend courses are held.

Contact Andrea Holmes for information.

SOUTH AYRSHIRE

AYR

AYR BUDDHIST GROUP (FWBO)
Tradition: FWBO
Affiliated to: Friends Of The Western Buddhist Order, UK National Organisations
Postal Address: Ayr Buddhist Group. 329 Sauchiehall Street, Glasgow, G2 3HW
Telephone Contact: 0141 333 0524
Email: glasgowbud@aol.com
Website(s):
www.fwbo.org/contacts/addresses-uk.html

STIRLING

BALQHUIDDER

DHANAKOSA RETREAT CENTRE (FWBO)
Tradition: FWBO

Meetings: Ledcreich House, Balquhidder, Lochearnhead Perthshire FK19 8PQ
Affiliated to: Friends Of The Western Buddhist Order, UK National Organisations
Postal Address: Dhanakosa Retreat Centre, Ledcreich House, Balquhidder, Lochearnhead Perthshire FK19 8PQ
Telephone Contact: 01877 384213 (10am to 5pm)
Fax: 01877 384213
Email: dhanakosa@compuserve.com
Website(s): www.dhanakosa.com

Dhanakosa is a Buddhist Retreat Centre in Scotland, UK, an ideal place for learning meditation and complimentary activities like yoga, tai chi, hillwalking, and shiatsu.

Dhanakosa sits by the shores of Loch Voil in the Balquhidder valley, and is surrounded by the magnificent mountains and forests of the southern Scottish Highlands. 15 miles from Callander and only one and a half hours drive from Glasgow or Edinburgh, Dhanakosa is easily accessible by public transport and provides a quiet and beautiful setting for retreats.

For further details on Dhanakosa or the various retreats on offer please see our website.

STIRLING

STIRLING BUDDHIST GROUP (FWBO)
Tradition: FWBO
Meetings: 13 Pitt Terrace, Stirling FK8 2EZ
Affiliated to: Friends Of The Western Buddhist Order, UK National Organisations
Postal Address: Glasgow Buddhist Centre, 329 Sauchiehall Street, Glasgow, G2 3HW
Telephone Contact: 01324 626587 (Jim Gardner)
Or 01324 861742 (Nick McBain)
Email: dhanakosa@compuserve.com or glasgowbud@aol.com

Website(s):
www.stirling-buddhist-centre.org.uk

Meditation and Buddhism in Central Scotland affiliated to the FWBO.

CHANNEL ISLANDS

GUERNSEY

GUERNSEY BUDDHIST GROUP
Tradition: Nichiren
Postal Address: The Guernsey Buddhist Group, SGI-UK Guernsey District, c/o Richard and Hazel Moorman, Maison Villocq Le Villocq Castel, Guernsey, GY5 7SF
Telephone Contact: 01481 255445
Fax: 01481 256512
Email: moorman@guernsey.net
Website(s): www.guernsey.net/~moorman/

The Guernsey Buddhist group holds regular meetings for Buddhist practice (chanting, meditation) and study (Dharma talks). Courses on the Basics of Buddhism are organised as the need arises. Practice is within the Nichiren tradition, but Buddhists of all schools and non-Buddhist are welcome at all meetings.

ST PETER PORT

GUERNSEY BUDDHIST ZEN CENTRE
Tradition: Zen
Postal Address: Guernsey Buddhist Zen Centre, Suite 1, Tower Hill House, St. Peter Port, Guernsey GY1 1BP
Telephone Contact: 01481 724016
Or 07781 426788
Email: Helen.Ackrill@thefortgroup.com

The Guernsey Zen Centre provides a venue for courses on Buddhist practice, group meetings, Buddhist meditation classes and group sittings. The centre operates under the spiritual direction of Venerable Myokyo-ni.

IRELAND

RIGPA IRELAND
Tradition: Tibetan
School: Nyingma
Affiliated to: Rigpa Fellowship, UK National Organisations
Charity No.: CHY9368
Postal Address: Rigpa Ireland, c/o Dzogchen Beara, Garranes, Allihies, West Cork, Ireland
Telephone Contact: +353 (0)27 73032
Fax: +353 (0)27 73177
Email: info@rigpa.ie
Website(s): www.rigpa.ie

Contact for Rigpa activities in Ireland.

SAMATHA GROUPS IN IRELAND
Tradition: Theravada
Affiliated to: Samatha Trust, UK National Organisations
Telephone Contact: 07896 213340 (Iain)
Email: ifoster@ntlworld.com
Website(s): www.samatha.org

Contact for Samatha Meditation classes in Ireland (Northern Ireland and the Republic).

CO ANTRIM

BALLYMENA

BLACK MOUNTAIN ZEN CENTRE
Tradition: Zen
School: Soto
Meetings: Ballymena Zen Group at (St.Johns Ambulance) St. Johns Hall, 11A Corlea Gardens, Ballymena, BT43 7AR
Affiliated to: Black Mountain Zen Centre, Ireland, Co Antrim, Belfast
Postal Address: 1st Floor, 64 Donegall Street, Cathedral Quarter, Belfast, BT1 2GT.
Telephone Contact: 028 90244010
Or 07745 468995
Or 0790 5367611
Email: ballymenazen@yahoo.ie

Website(s): www.blackmountainzencentre.org

Black Mountain Zen Centre has local affiliated groups in Belfast, Larne, Coleraine, Ballymena, and Newcastle, and is willing to give help and advice to anyone wishing to set up a similar group in their own area. Please see the 'Local Groups' page on our website for details.

Meets at 7:00 PM each Sunday.

BELFAST

BLACK MOUNTAIN ZEN CENTRE
Tradition: Zen
School: Soto
Meetings: 1st Floor, 64 Donegall Street, Belfast, BT1 2GT. (opposite St. Anne's Cathedral)
Telephone Contact: 028 90244010
Or 07745 468995
Or 0790 5367611
Email: contact@blackmountainzencentre.org
Website(s): www.blackmountainzencentre.org

Originally known as Belfast Meditation Centre, we came together in the year 2000, and launched Black Mountain Zen Centre in 2004.

The practice of Black Mountain Zen Centre is Soto Zen in the lineage of Shunryu Suzuki Roshi, our founder in the West, and we are affiliated to San Francisco Zen Center.

We emphasize the practice of ZaZen (sitting Zen) as the essence of Shakyamuni Buddha's practice, together with the practice of Precepts (ethics) and the cultivation of Compassion and Wisdom (Prajna).

Black Mountain Zen Centre has local affiliated groups in Belfast, Larne, Coleraine, Ballymena, and Newcastle, and is willing to give help and advice to anyone wishing to set up a similar group in their own area. Please see the 'Local Groups' page on our website for details.

Entry continued on the following page.

Belfast:

07.00 am to 08.15 am Zazen Meditation Mon to Fri

10:30 am to 11:45 am Zazen Meditation & Service each Sun

07:00 pm to 08:15 pm Zazen Meditation & Service each Tues

07:00 pm to 08:15 pm Zazen Meditation & Service each Fri

Zazenkai - Full Day Meditation. Meets on the third Sunday of every month from 09:00 am to 05:00 pm.

JAMPA LING BELFAST
Tradition: Tibetan
School: Gelugpa
Postal Address: Frank Liddy, 26 Kansas Avenue, Belfast BT15 5AW
Telephone Contact: 028 9074 5685 (Liz)
Email: jampaling@ntl.com
Website(s): www.jampaling.org

Jampa Ling Belfast is an off-shoot of Jampa Ling, Co. Cavan, Republic of Ireland. The name Jampa Ling means 'place of infinite loving-kindness'. It was started in 1998 by Buddhist students under the guidance and direction of Ven. Lama Panchen Otrul Rinpoche. There are regular meditation sessions and teachings. The centre has links with Drepung Monastic University in southern India.

CO CAVAN

BAWNBOY

JAMPA LING TIBETAN BUDDHIST CENTRE
Tradition: Tibetan
School: Gelugpa
Meetings: Owendoon House, Bawnboy, Co.

Cavan, Republic of Ireland
Charity No.: CHY 10452
Postal Address: Jampa Ling Tibetan Buddhist Centre, Owendoon House, Bawnboy, Co. Cavan, Republic of Ireland
Telephone Contact: +353 (0)4995 23448
Fax: +353 (0)4995 23067
Email: jampaling@eircom.net
Website(s): www.jampaling.org

Jampa Ling Centre is under the patronage of HH the Dalai Lama. It is situated in the peaceful and beautiful countryside of West Cavan. Jampa Ling means 'a place of loving kindness' and the Centre's main aim is to promote peace and happiness for all living beings. Its 13 acres of grounds include orchard, pasture and mature woodland bordering onto a lake. It offers seclusion, tranquillity and views of the Cuileagh mountains. The Centre is residential and offers periodic teachings, meditation and retreat courses. Given the growth in the number of visitors, we are at present fund raising to provide additional accommodation and a retreat house.

There are strong connections with the Gungru Khangsten of Drepung Gomang Monastic University. Help is given by sponsoring individual monks and fund raising for a new hostel which is being built.

The Centre follows the Gelugpa tradition of Buddhism. It was started in 1990 under the spiritual direction of Ven Lama Panchen Otrul Rinpoche. He started his training in Tibet at a very early age and studied under many renowned and highly qualified teachers.

CO CLARE

SIX MILE BRIDGE

SUNYATA RETREAT CENTRE
Tradition: Theravada

Meetings: Snata, Sixmilebridge, Co Clare, Ireland
Affiliated to: Amaravati Buddhist Monastery, UK National Organisations
Postal Address: Stanley and Clare de Freitas, Sunyata Retreat Centre, Snata, Sixmilebridge, Co Clare Ireland Peter Carey, Trinity College, Oxford OX1 3BH
Telephone Contact: +353 (0) 61 367073 (Retreat Centre)
Email: info@sunyatacentre.com
Website(s): www.sunyatacentre.com

Sunyata is a Buddhist inspired Retreat Centre offering a variety of Meditation, Yoga, Chi-Kung and Self-Development workshops on its programme. It is set on a beautiful 10-acre property amidst the rolling hills of E. Clare (West Ireland)- a spacious haven outside the bustle of modern life, perfectly situated for relaxation and contemplation.

This unique workshop venue is also available for hire to outside groups to run their workshops. There is deluxe self-catering accommodation available at times for personal retreats [outside of the scheduled programme].

Our main connection is with the Thai forest tradition of Theravada Buddhism (the word 'Sunyata' is from the ancient Pali language, meaning 'the spaciousness behind all form'). We welcome people of all traditions and beliefs, (or none).

CO CORK

ADRIGOLE, BEARA

PASSADDHI MEDITATION CENTRE
Tradition: Theravada
School: Vipassana
Meetings: Various
Postal Address: Passaddhi Vipassana

Meditation Retreat Centre, Marjo Oosterhoff, Leitrim Beg, Adrigole, Beara, Co Cork Ireland
Telephone Contact: +353 (0)27 60223 (Marjo Oosterhoff)
Fax: +353 (0)27 60223
Email: info@passaddhi.com
Website(s): www.passaddhi.com or www.vipassana.ie

Passaddhi Meditation Centre offers retreats in the Buddhist practices of vipassana (insight-meditation) and metta (loving-kindness meditation), in the tradition of Ven. Mahasi Sayadaw of Burma. Marjo Oosterhoff is resident teacher and manager at Passaddhi. She teaches also at other venues. At Passaddhi a chalet is available for personal retreats. For details of retreat, please visit our websites.

ALLIHIES

DZOGCHEN BEARA
Tradition: Tibetan
School: Nyingma
Meetings: Garranes, Allihies, West Cork, Ireland
Affiliated to: Rigpa Fellowship, UK National Organisations
Charity No.: CHY9368
Postal Address: Dzogchen Beara, Garranes, Allihies, West Cork, Ireland
Telephone Contact: +353 (0)27 73032
Fax: +353 (0)27 73177
Email: info@rigpa.ie
Website(s): www.rigpa.ie

Dzogchen Beara is a Tibetan Buddhist Retreat under the spiritual direction of Sogyal Rinpoche, author of the Tibetan Book of Living and Dying, and is affiliated to Rigpa. The centre is situated on the wild and beautiful Beara Peninsula in south-west Cork, Ireland, with breathtaking views out over the Atlantic ocean.

Dzogchen Beara provides facilities for Rigpa

Entry continued on the following page.

students to undertake long-term secluded retreats. The centre also offers a wide range of activities and facilities are open to everyone: weekend and longer retreats led by Sogyal Rinpoche and other eminent Tibetan masters; student-led weekends offering an introduction to the practices of meditation, loving kindness and compassion; daily meditation classes; seminars on spiritual care for the dying for medical professionals; and cottage and hostel accommodation.

The extraordinary qualities of Dzogchen Beara, its setting and natural beauty, together with its atmosphere of spiritual practice, make it an ideal environment for quiet reflection, healing and renewal. We welcome everyone, from those who wish to study and explore the timeless truths of Tibetan Buddhism, to those who simply like to rest and relax in a beautiful and unspoilt environment.

CORK CITY

CORK ZEN DOJO
Tradition: Zen
School: Soto
Meetings: 19 North Main Street, Cork, Ireland
Postal Address: 19 North Main Street, Cork, Ireland
Telephone Contact: 21-4662917
Email: irish_zen@hotmail.com
Website(s): http://www.iolfree.ie/~irish_zen
Contact: Fergus Galvin

KAGYU SAMYE DZONG CORK
Tradition: Tibetan
School: Karma-Kagyu
Meetings: 'High Meadows', 6 Upper Panorama Terrace, Sunday's Well, Cork
Affiliated to: Kagyu Samye Ling Monastery And Tibetan Centre, UK National Organisations
Postal Address: Kagyu Samye Dzong Cork, 'High Meadows', 6 Upper Panorama Terrace, Sunday's Well, Cork Ireland
Telephone Contact: (21) 394117
Email: info@buddhism.ie

Website(s): www.buddhism.ie

The centre, located a short distance from Cork city centre, includes shrine room, reception and accomodation for visiting teachers. A weekly programme of meditation and studies is maintained. Lamas, monks, nuns and lay teachers visit frequently and give a variety of courses.

RIGPA CORK
Tradition: Tibetan
School: Nyingma
Affiliated to: Rigpa Fellowship, UK National Organisations
Postal Address: Rigpa Cork, 6 Sydney Place, Wellington Road, Cork, Ireland
Telephone Contact: +353 (0)21 450 7033
Email: cork@rigpa.ie
Website(s): www.rigpa.ie

VIPASSANA MEDITATION GROUP
Tradition: Theravada
School: Vipassana
Meetings: The Alpha Centre, 26 Parnell Place, Cork City, Ireland
Telephone Contact: +353 (0)211 831519
(Dan Kelly)

CO DUBLIN

DUBLIN

COPPER PIPE ZEN GROUP OF DUBLIN
Tradition: Korean
School: Kwan Um School
Meetings: 32 Collins Avenue, Killester, Dublin 5
Affiliated to: Zen London, England, London, N 4

Contact: Brendan Breen

Tradition: Korean Chogye Order

Lineage: Seung Sahn

DUBLIN BUDDHIST CENTRE (FWBO)
Tradition: FWBO
Meetings: 42 Lower Leeson Street, Dublin 2
Affiliated to: Friends Of The Western
Buddhist Order, UK National Organisations
Charity No.: CHY_11311
Postal Address: Dublin Buddhist Centre, 42
Lower Leeson Street, Dublin 2, Ireland
Telephone Contact: +353 (0)1 661 5934
Fax: +353 (0)1 661 5934
Email: info@dublinbuddhistcentre.org
Website(s): www.dublinmeditationcentre.org

We are a general Dharma centre, teaching
meditation, Buddhism and yoga; we run five-week
long courses in meditation and yoga, one evening
a week we have a Dharma Class with meditation,
talk, discussion and ritual. We organise regular
weekend and week long retreats.

If you wish to speak to someone in the Centre
please phone (01) 661 5934, Monday - Friday,
12.30pm - 2pm and 3pm - 6pm, or you can also
contact us via email.

DUBLIN SHAMBHALA STUDY GROUP
Tradition: Tibetan
School: Kagyu-Nyingma
Meetings: 19 Herbert Street, Dublin 2
Affiliated to: London Shambhala Meditation
Centre, England, London, SW 4, England
Charity No.: 1073977
Postal Address: 19 Herbert Street, Dublin 2
Telephone Contact: +353 (0)1 212 3849
Or +353 (0)1 642 5885
Email: info@shambhala.ie
Website(s): www.shambhala.ie or
www.dublin.shambhala.ie

See London Shambhala Centre, England, London,
SW4 for further details.

DUBLIN ZEN DOJO
Tradition: Zen
School: Soto

Meetings: 1 Upper Gardiner Street, Dublin 1
(near Mountjoy Square)
Telephone Contact: 085 779 6319 - Mary
(01) 873 0944
Email: irish_zen@hotmail.com
Website(s): www.iolfree.ie/~irish_zen

The Irish Zen Group has been active since 1991
and has three practice centres (dojos), in Galway,
Dublin and Cork.

We focus on the practice of zazen (sitting
meditation), and we are open to everyone
interested in taking up the practice of meditation.

We practice according to the Japanese Soto Zen
tradition, as transmitted by Taisen Deshimaru,
who brought Zen to Europe

in 1967. Deshimaru was a disciple of Kodo
Sawaki.

Alain Liebmann is the leader of our group. He is a
Zen monk with 35 years experience of meditation.
He studied with Taisen Deshimaru.

Our group is affiliated to AZI (Association Zen
Internationale) an worldwide Zen organization
based in Paris, France.

INSIGHT MEDITATION GROUP
Tradition: Theravada
School: Vipassana
Postal Address: 67 Venetian Hall, Howth
Road, Dublin 5, Ireland.
Telephone Contact: 003531 8314650
Or 003531 2828199
Email: noirinsheahan@eircom.net
Website(s): www.insightmeditationdublin.com

We are a meditation group having Vipassana as the
main meditation practice. Close links with Theravadin
Buddhist groups and monasteries are maintained. We
organise retreats and invite monks and nuns from
abroad to lead retreats on a regular basis.

IRISH VIPASSANA ASSOCIATION
Tradition: Theravada
School: Vipassana
Meetings: 91 Ballsbridge Woods, Dublin 4
Telephone Contact: 01 6677844
(voicemail)
Email: info@ie.dhamma.org

Vipassana Meditation as taught by SN Goenka in the tradition of Sayagyi U Ba Khin

KAGYU SAMYE DZONG
Tradition: Tibetan
School: Karma-Kagyu
Meetings: Kilmainham Well House, 56 Inchicore Road, Kilmainham, Dublin 8
Affiliated to: Kagyu Samye Ling Monastery And Tibetan Centre, UK National Organisations
Charity No.: CHY 13981
Postal Address: The Secretary, Kagyu Samye Dzong, Kilmainham Well House, 56 Inchicore Road, Kilmainham, Dublin 8, Republic of Ireland
Telephone Contact: +353 (0)1 453 7427
Fax: +353 (0)1 453 9312
Email: info@buddhism.ie
Website(s): www.buddhism.ie

Founded in 1977, this is the longest established Buddhist centre in Ireland. The Centre includes a large shrine room, decorated and furnished in traditional Tibetan style, reception (including bookstall), office and visiting teachers' accommodation. The garden features a holy well and the centre is located in a historic area of Dublin with several museums and extensive parks nearby.

There is a weekly programme of meditation and study and occasional (non-residential) retreats. The basic teaching is that which is common to all the major Buddhist traditions plus specialised teachings particular to the Kagyu tradition of Tibetan Buddhism. Lamas, nuns, monks and lay teachers visit frequently and give a variety of courses.
Open to visits from school groups etc by arrangement.

RIGPA DUBLIN
Tradition: Tibetan
School: Nyingma
Meetings: 3rd floor, 12 Wicklow Street, Dublin 2
Affiliated to: Rigpa Fellowship, UK National Organisations
Postal Address: Rigpa, 12 Wicklow Street, Dublin 2, Republic of Ireland
Telephone Contact: +353 (0)1 670 3358
Fax: +353 (0)1 670 3358
Email: dublin@rigpa.ie
Website(s): www.rigpa.org

See Rigpa Fellowship, UK National Organisations for an explanation of the aims of Rigpa.

The centre follows the Nyingma School of Tibetan Buddhism. Please telephone, email or check the Dublin page at www.rigpa.org for the current programme.

CO GALWAY

GALWAY

GALWAY ZEN DOJO
Tradition: Zen
School: Soto
The Bridge Mills (2nd floor) Galway
Telephone Contact: Alain (091) 585 499 or Tom (091) 563 435
Email: alainliebmann@eircom.net
Website(s): www.iolfree.ie/~irish_zen

Founder: Taisen Deshimaru

Teacher: Alain Liebmann

Affiliation: A.Z.I

Contact: Taï Nan Alain Liebmann

RIGPA GALWAY
Tradition: Tibetan
School: Nyingma
Affiliated to: Rigpa Fellowship, UK National Organisations
Telephone Contact: +353 (0)91 585583
Fax: +353 (0)85 7205855
Email: galway@rigpa.ie
Website(s): www.rigpa.ie

CO KERRY

KILLARNEY

RIGPA KERRY
Tradition: Tibetan
School: Nyingma
Affiliated to: Rigpa Fellowship, UK National Organisations
Postal Address: Rigpa Kerry, 7 Church Street, Milltown, Killarney, Co. Kerry
Telephone Contact: +353 (0)87 687 2204
Email: kerry@rigpa.ie
Website(s): www.rigpa.ie

CO LIMERICK

LIMERICK

RIGPA LIMERICK
Tradition: Tibetan
School: Nyingma
Affiliated to: Rigpa Fellowship, UK National Organisations
Postal Address: Rigpa Limerick, 78 O'Connell Street, Limerick, Ireland
Telephone Contact: +353 (0)61 409 863
Email: limerick@rigpa.ie
Website(s): www.rigpa.ie

CO WESTMEATH

ATHLONE

RIGPA ATHLONE
Tradition: Tibetan
School: Nyingma
Affiliated to: Rigpa Fellowship, UK National Organisations
Postal Address: Rigpa Athlone, 1 Bastion Street, Athlone
Telephone Contact: +353 (0)90 6476401 Or +353 (0)87 7496498
Fax: +353 (0)90 6493648
Email: athlone@rigpa.ie
Website(s): www.rigpa.ie

CO WICKLOW

RIGPA WICKLOW
Tradition: Tibetan
School: Nyingma
Affiliated to: Rigpa Fellowship, UK National Organisations
Postal Address: Rigpa Wicklow, Ballydonagh Cottage, Delgany, Co Wicklow, Ireland
Telephone Contact: +353 (0)1 287 7128
Website(s): www.rigpa.ie

ULSTER

COLERAINE

BLACK MOUNTAIN ZEN CENTRE
Tradition: Zen
School: Soto
Meetings: Single Grain Of Sand Zen Group, Kilcranny House, 21 Cranagh Road, Coleraine.
Affiliated to: Black Mountain Zen Centre, Ireland, Co Antrim, Belfast
Postal Address: 1st Floor, 64 Donegall Street, Cathedral Quarter, Belfast, BT1 2GT.

Entry continued on the following page.

Telephone Contact: 028 90244010
Or 07745 468995
Or 0790 5367611
Email: singlegrainofsand@yahoo.co.uk
Website(s): www.blackmountainzencentre.org

Black Mountain Zen Centre has local affiliated
groups in Belfast, Larne, Coleraine, Ballymena,
and Newcastle, and is willing to give help and
advice to anyone wishing to set up a similar group
in their own area. Please see the 'Local Groups'
page on our website for details.

Meets from 07:30 PM to 09:30 PM each
Wednesday.

RETREAT CENTRES

This section gives reference to entries in the main body of the Directory which have their own accommodation for residential retreats and will consider applications from non-members. Full details should be sought in the main entries.

Those new to Buddhism practice should be aware that a Buddhist Retreat is usually somewhat different from what might be expected in some other spiritual traditions. Generally speaking, it is a period of special effort, usually created around meditation practice, although rituals, sermons and manual labour may also be involved. There is usually a detailed timetable allowing little free time or choice of activity. The retreatant should also be clear what kind of accommodation is on offer (dormitory style accommodation with segregation of the sexes in not unusual) and whether observance of other disciplines such as silence, not eating after midday, or abstaining from sexual activity, will be expected.

Disclaimer: The Buddhist Society is dependant upon the information supplied by the contributing centres and cannot accept responsibility for any disappointments or difficulties, whether caused by the intending retreatant failing to check the details listed above, or by the centre failing to comply with the information given. **Caveat meditator!**

ABERYSTWYTH BUDDHIST GROUP   *All Traditions*
WALES, CEREDIGION, ABERYSTWYTH 133

AMARAVATI BUDDHIST RETREAT CENTRE   *Theravada*
ENGLAND, HERTFORDSHIRE, HEMEL HEMPSTEAD..62

AMIDA TRUST   *Pure Land, Amida-Shu*
UK NATIONAL ORGANISATIONS 9

ARUNA RATANAGIRI, HARNHAM BUDDHIST MONASTERY   *Theravada*
ENGLAND, NORTHUMBERLAND, BELSAY 102

AWAKENED HEART SANGHA   *Tibetan, Kagyu-Nyingma*
WALES, GWYNEDD, CRICCIETH..134

BARN RURAL RETREAT CENTRE   *All Traditions*
ENGLAND, DEVON, TOTNES 46

BIRMINGHAM BUDDHIST VIHARA   *Theravada*
ENGLAND, WEST MIDLANDS, BIRMINGHAM 118

BLACK MOUNTAIN ZEN CENTRE   *Zen, Soto*
IRELAND, CO ANTRIM, BELFAST..151

BLACK MOUNTAIN ZEN CENTRE   *Zen, Soto*
ENGLAND, TYNE AND WEAR,NEWCASTLE UPON TYNE 115

BLACK MOUNTAIN ZEN CENTRE   *Zen, Soto*
IRELAND, ANTRIM, BALLYMENA..151

BLACK MOUNTAIN ZEN CENTRE   *Zen, Soto*
IRELAND, ULSTER, COLERAINE 157

BRISTOL BUDDHIST CENTRE (FWBO)   *FWBO*
ENGLAND, AVON, BRISTOL 28

BRISTOL SHAMBHALA MEDITATION GROUP   *Tibetan, Kagyu-Nyingma*
ENGLAND, AVON, BRISTOL 28

BRITISH BUDDHIST ASSOCIATION   *All Traditions*
ENGLAND, LONDON, W 9 89

BUDDHAPADIPA TEMPLE   *Theravada*
ENGLAND, LONDON, SW 19 83

BUDDHAVIHARA TEMPLE   *Theravada*
ENGLAND, WEST MIDLANDS, BIRMINGHAM 119

BUDDHIST HOUSE *Pure Land,*   *Amida-Shu*
ENGLAND, LEICESTERSHIRE, NARBOROUGH 71

BUDDHIST SOCIETY OF MANCHESTER   *Theravada*
ENGLAND, GREATER MANCHESTER, SALE 58

COMMUNITY OF INTERBEING, U.K.   *Vietnamese, Thich Nhat Hanh*
UK NATIONAL ORGANISATIONS 12

CROYDON BUDDHIST CENTRE   *FWBO*
ENGLAND, LONDON: SURREY, CROYDON 93

DHANAKOSA RETREAT CENTRE (FWBO)   *FWBO*
SCOTLAND, STIRLING, BALQHUIDDER 146

DHARMAPALA COLLEGE FWBO STUDY CENTRE   *FWBO*
RELATED ORGANISATIONS 168

DOGEN SANGHA BUDDHIST GROUP   *Zen, Soto*
ENGLAND, AVON, BRISTOL 29

DRAGON BELL TEMPLE   *Zen, Soto*
ENGLAND, DEVON, EXETER 43

DZOGCHEN BEARA   *Tibetan, Nyingma*
IRELAND, CO CORK, ALLIHIES 153

DZOGCHEN COMMUNITY UK   *Tibetan, Dzogchen*
UK NATIONAL ORGANISATIONS 13

Retreat Centres

FOREST HERMITAGE (WAT PAH SANTIDHAMMA) *Theravada*
ENGLAND, WARWICKSHIRE, SHERBOURNE 117

FRIENDS OF THE WESTERN BUDDHIST ORDER *FWBO*
UK NATIONAL ORGANISATIONS 15

GAIA HOUSE *Theravada, Vipassana*
ENGLAND, DEVON, NEWTON ABBOT...45

GLASGOW ZEN DOJO *Zen, Soto*
SCOTLAND, GLASGOW, GLASGOW 143

GOLDEN BUDDHA CENTRE *All Traditions*
UK NATIONAL ORGANISATIONS 15

HARLOW BUDDHIST SOCIETY *Theravada*
ENGLAND, ESSEX, HARLOW 52

HOLY ISLAND *Tibetan, Karma-Kagyu*
SCOTLAND, NORTH LANARKSHIRE, OFF ARRAN..145

HOUSE OF INNER TRANQUILLITY *Theravada, Vipassana*
ENGLAND, WILTSHIRE, BRADFORD ON AVON..126

INSIGHT MEDITATION GROUP *Theravada, Vipassana*
IRELAND, CO DUBLIN, DUBLIN 155

INTERNATIONAL MEDITATION CENTRE *Theravada, Vipassana*
ENGLAND, WILTSHIRE, CALNE 127

INTERNATIONAL NETWORK OF ENGAGED BUDDHISTS *All Traditions*
RELATED ORGANISATIONS 171

JAMPA LING TIBETAN BUDDHIST CENTRE *Tibetan, Gelugpa*
IRELAND, CO CAVAN, BAWNBOY..152

JAMYANG BUDDHIST CENTRE *Tibetan, Gelugpa*
ENGLAND, LONDON, SE 11 80

JAMYANG BUDDHIST CENTRE LEEDS *Tibetan, Gelugpa*
ENGLAND, WEST YORKSHIRE, LEEDS 126

KUNSEL LING *Tibetan, Dzogchen*
WALES, POWYS, HAY-ON-WYE 137

LAM RIM BUDDHIST CENTRE *Tibetan, Gelugpa*
WALES, MONMOUTHSHIRE, PENRHOS..135

Retreat Centres

LONDON BUDDHIST CENTRE (FWBO)   *FWBO*
ENGLAND, LONDON, E 2 73

LONDON ZAZEN GROUP   *Zen,Soto*
ENGLAND, LONDON, W 2 86

LONGCHEN FOUNDATION   *Tibetan, Kagyu-Nyingma*
UK NATIONAL ORGANISATIONS 16

MAITRIKARA   *Tibetan, Nyingma*
ENGLAND, EAST SUSSEX, BRIGHTON 50

MARPA HOUSE - Chos Khor Ling   *Tibetan, Karma-Kagyu*
ENGLAND, ESSEX, ASHDON 52

NETWORK OF ENGAGED BUDDHISTS (UK)   *All Traditions*
UK NATIONAL ORGANISATIONS 18

NEW KADAMPA TRADITION   *Tibetan,New Kadampa Tradition*
UK NATIONAL ORGANISATIONS 19

NEWCASTLE BUDDHIST CENTRE (FWBO)   *FWBO*
ENGLAND, TYNE AND WEAR, NEWCASTLE UPON TYNE 115

OXFORD BUDDHIST VIHARA   *Theravada*
ENGLAND, OXFORDSHIRE, OXFORD 105

PADMALOKA MEN'S RETREAT CENTRE (FWBO)   *FWBO*
ENGLAND, NORFOLK, SURLINGHAM 99

PASSADDHI MEDITATION CENTRE   *Theravada, Vipassana*
IRELAND, CO CORK, ADRIGOLE, BEARA 153

PRECIOUS WOOD CH'AN GROUP   *Chinese,Ch'an*
WALES, CARDIGAN 132

READING BUDDHIST PRIORY   *Zen, Soto*
ENGLAND, BERKSHIRE, READING 32

RIGPA FELLOWSHIP   *Tibetan, Nyingma*
UK NATIONAL ORGANISATIONS 22

RIVENDELL RETREAT CENTRE   *FWBO*
ENGLAND, EAST SUSSEX, HIGH HURSTWOOD 51

ROCHDALE ZEN RETREAT   *Zen, Soto*
ENGLAND, GREATER MANCHESTER, BOLTON 55

Retreat Centres

SAMATHA CENTRE   *Theravada*
WALES, POWYS, KNIGHTON 137

SAMATHA TRUST   *Theravada*
UK NATIONAL ORGANISATIONS 22

SANG-NGAK-CHO-DZONG   *Tibetan, Nyingma*
UK NATIONAL ORGANISATIONS 24

SARANIYA DHAMMA MEDITATION CENTRE   *Theravada, Vipassana*
ENGLAND, GREATER MANCHESTER, SALFORD 58

SATIPANYA BUDDHIST TRUST   *Theravada*
RELATED ORGANISATIONS 175

SHANTI GRIHA   *All Traditions*
SCOTLAND, HIGHLAND, WESTER ROSS 144

SHARPHAM CENTRE FOR CONTEMPORARY BUDDHIST ENQUIRY   *All Traditions*
ENGLAND, DEVON, ASHPRINGTON 43

SHEN PHEN THUBTEN CHOELING (Centre for socially and ecologically engaged Buddhism)   *Tibetan, Gelugpa*
ENGLAND, HEREFORDSHIRE, HEREFORD 61

SUNYATA RETREAT CENTRE   *Theravada*
IRELAND, CO CLARE, SIX MILE BRIDGE 152

TARALOKA RETREAT CENTRE FOR WOMEN   *FWBO*
ENGLAND, SHROPSHIRE, WHITCHURCH 108

THEOSOPHICAL SOCIETY   *All Traditions*
RESOURCES, BOOKSHOPS, LONDON 188

THROSSEL HOLE BUDDHIST ABBEY   *Zen, Soto*
ENGLAND, NORTHUMBERLAND, HEXHAM 103

TIRATANALOKA WOMEN'S ORDINATION RETREAT CENTRE   *FWBO*
WALES, POWYS, BRECON 136

VAJRALOKA BUDDHIST MEDITATION CENTRE FOR MEN (FWBO)   *FWBO*
WALES, DENBIGHSHIRE, CORWEN 133

VAJRASANA RETREAT CENTRE (FWBO)   *FWBO*
ENGLAND, SUFFOLK, BURY ST EDMUNDS 112

VIPASSANA TRUST   *Theravada, Vipassana*
ENGLAND, HEREFORDSHIRE, HEREFORD 61

Retreat Centres

WESTERN CH'AN FELLOWSHIP *Chinese, Ch'an*
UK NATIONAL ORGANISATIONS 25

WINTERHEAD RETREAT HOUSE *Zen*
ENGLAND, SOMERSET, SHIPHAM..109

YORK CH'AN BUDDHIST GROUP *Chinese, Ch'an*
ENGLAND, NORTH YORKSHIRE, YORK..101

ZEN PRACTICE CENTRE TRUST (Affiliated to the Kanzeon Sangha) *Zen, Soto/Rinzai*
UK NATIONAL ORGANISATIONS 26

RELATED ORGANISATIONS

ANGULIMALA: BUDDHIST PRISON CHAPLAINCY ORGANISATION
Affiliated to: Forest Hermitage, England, Warwickshire, Sherbourne
Charity No.:294939
Postal Address: Angulimala, c/o Santidhamma Forest Hermitage, Lower Fulbrook, Warwick CV35 8AS

Email: angulimala@foresthermitage.org.uk
Website(s): www.angulimala.org.uk

The objects of Angulimala are to make available facilities for the teaching and practice of Buddhism in Her Majesty's Prisons and other places of lawful detention or custody; to recruit and advise a team of Buddhist visiting chaplains to be available as soon as there is a call for their services; to act in an advisory capacity, and to liaise with the Home Office chaplaincy officials, with individual chaplains within Her Majestys Prisons, and with any other relevant bodies or officials; and to provide an aftercare and advisory service for prisoners after release.

Angulimala also tries to provide pen-friends for prisoners, reading material and tapes and appropriate Buddhist artefacts like rosary beads and Buddha-Rupas.

Membership is open to anyone sympathetically disposed to the organisation's aims, whether or not they may wish to play an active part. The current membership subscription is £10.00 per annum. Training workshops for Buddhist prison chaplains are held quarterly at the Forest Hermitage. Buddhist visiting chaplains are expected to be paid-up members and to attend at least one workshop every year.

Angulimala, which does not favour any form of Buddhism over another, has the backing of most major Buddhist organisations in the UK and is recognised by the Home Office as the official representative of Buddhism in all matters concerning the prison service.

ARMED FORCES CHAPLAINCY
Tradition: All
Postal Address: Dr. Sunil M Kariyakarawana, Chaplain's Branch, HQ London District, Wellington Barracks, Birdcage Walk, London SW1E 6HQ
Telephone Contact: 020 7414 3411
Or 07785 727134
Or 94 631 3411 (Mil)

Email: sunilkari@hotmail.com

BRIGHTON TIBET LINK
Affiliated to: Maitrikara, England, East Sussex, Brighton
Telephone Contact: 01273 328998 (Lucy Porter)
Email: info@brightontibetlink.org.uk
Website(s): www.brightontibetlink.org.uk

Brighton Tibet Link aims to help people find out more about Tibet, thus enabling them to 'keep Tibet on the map' and support the Tibetans' campaign for independence and freedom. We have a fully active Campaigns group which is constantly in touch with the Free Tibet Campaign (UK).

We are not only political. We try to uphold both the cultural and spiritual traditions of Tibet through Maitrikara, our Tibetan Buddhist Group (see under Brighton in the main body of the Directory) and through the variety of events we run throughout the year. We also have local work-related projects to support Tibetan refugees in exile. These include the driving school 'Driving for Tibet' and Trager massage. We have a goods and book stall, and also an exhibition which we are very happy to loan out.

BUDDHAFIELD (FWBO)
Tradition: FWBO
Meetings: Various
Affiliated to: Friends Of The Western Buddhist Order, UK National Organisations

Entry continued on the following page.

Charity No.: 1108826
Postal Address: Trevince House, Hittisleigh, Exeter EX6 6LP
Telephone Contact: 01647 24539
Or 07747 446040
Email: info@buddhafield.com
Website(s): www.buddhafield.com

BuddhaField is a collective of Friends of the Western Buddhist Order (FWBO) Buddhists from all over the UK and beyond. We teach meditation and Buddhism at festivals,fairs and similar events. We also hold our own retreat camps, run the Buddhafield Cafe and organise our own festival!

The concept of a Buddhafield or Buddhafields originates in the Mahayana Buddhist sutras. In these sutras Buddhafields are worlds of great beauty created by the compassionate action of a Buddha. Such a Buddhafield is an environment in which all the conditions are conducive to spiritual practice and enlightenment

BUDDHIST CO-OPERATIVE
Telephone Contact: 020 8693 9951
Email: buddhistcoop@hotmail.co.uk

Affiliated to a parent organisation in Asia, this aims to promote the growth of Buddhist Economics, Right Livelihood, Useful Unemployment, etc. A forum for Right Living.

BUDDHIST EDUCATION FOUNDATION (UK)
Charity No.: 1073008
Postal Address: Buddhist Education Foundation (UK), 7 Squirrels, Langdon, Basildon, Essex, SS16 6HT
Buddhist Education Foundation (UK), BCM 9459, London, WC1N 3XX
Telephone Contact: 01268 540522 (Mr Shing Kee Lee)
Email: info@buddhisteducation.co.uk (English text) or cei
Website(s): www.buddhisteducation.co.uk

A charitable organisation limited by guarantee and devoted to the promotion of Buddhist education

BUDDHIST HOSPICE TRUST
Charity No.: 298859
Postal Address: The Buddhist Hospice Trust, 31 Weir Gardens, Rayleigh, Essex SS6 7TQ
Telephone Contact: 01268 775521 (Peter Goble)
Or 07951 869265
Fax: 01268 775521 (Peter Goble)
Email: pgoble@buddhisthospice.org.uk
Website(s): www.buddhisthospice.org.uk

Formed in 1986 as the Buddhist Hospice Project, the Trust is supported entirely by donations and covenants.

The aims of the Trust are to provide emotional and spiritual support for dying people and those close to them when requested to do so, as well as working with the hospice movement as and when possible. An important aspect of the work of the Trust is to be a source of education and information for Buddhists, health carers and the general public on request.

A register is kept of volunteers throughout the country who are prepared to visit dying people and those close to them who request such a contact. These volunteers are known as the Ananda Network.

In addition the Trust holds seminars, study days and organises weekend events to promote education and exchanges of wide ranging views. It is non-sectarian and welcomes the involvement of non-Buddhists who are sympathetic to Buddhism. There is a twice yearly magazine, and information leaflet / booklet form.

The Buddhist Hospice Trust welcomes Buddhists of all traditions or none, whether they want to take an active part or simply to receive information.

BURMA CAMPAIGN UK

Postal Address: The Burma Campaign UK,
28 Charles Square, London, N1 6HT
Telephone Contact: 020 7324 4710
Fax: 020 7324 4717
Email: info@burmacampaign.org.uk
Website(s): www.burmacampaign.org.uk

A political organisation campaigning for
democracy and human rights in Burma (now
officially known as Myanmar).

CAMBRIDGE BUDDHIST INSTITUTE

Email: cbi@edlis.org
Website(s): www.edlis.org/cbi

The Cambridge Buddhist Institute serves as a focus
for those interested in Buddhist studies in
Cambridge, both in the University of Cambridge and
in the region.
If you are coming to Cambridge to work on Buddhist
material, or you are already here, feel free to e-mail
the Cambridge Buddhist Institute and make yourself
known. The institute is interested in including
anyone working on anything connected with
Buddhism, from music to art history, from meditation
to bibliography, from museums to politics, from
manuscripts to anthropology, from medicine to
history, from monasticism to sociology, from
Mongolia to Singapore...

The institute publishes the Cambridge Buddhist
Institute Series with the publisher Hardinge
Simpole.

CENTRE FOR MEDITATION AND PSYCHOTHERAPY

Postal Address: The Centre for Meditation
and Psychotherapy, 20 Goodhall Street, London
NW10 6TU
Telephone Contact: 020 8961 7802

Although the essence of meditation is simply
being, it is difficult to see where and how your
heart has been pulled out of itself and become
confused with a story your mind insists on. Group
and individual sessions are available which help
you to recognise the stories your mind is telling
you and to fall back into being

CHARITY BANK

Charity No.: 1091648
Postal Address: The Charity Bank Ltd,
PO Box 398, 194 High Street, Tonbridge,
Kent TN9 9BD.
Telephone Contact: 01732 77405
Email: enquiries@charitybank.org
Website(s): www.charitybank.org

Charity Bank is leading the way as a specialist
lender to not-for-profit organisations. The charity
provides loans of up to £750,000 and their
lending terms are amongst the most favourable
available. As a charity they put your interests
ahead of commercial profit. Charity Bank also
provides deposit accounts for surplus funds.

COMMUNITY OF INTERBEING - DEEP LISTENING SANGHA

Tradition: Zen
School: Thich Nhat Hanh
The Community Of Interbeing, UK, UK National
Organisations
Telephone Contact: 01278 458617
Maxine.Phillips@btinternet.com
Website(s): www.interbeing.org.uk

Practices by teleconference including guided
meditations, readings, and sharing.

CULT INFORMATION CENTRE

Charity No.: 1012914
Postal Address: Cult Information Centre,
BCM Cults, London WC1N 3XX
Telephone Contact: 0870 777 3800
Or 01689 833800
Website(s): www.cultinformation.org,uk

An independent charity which collects and

Entry continued on the following page.

disseminates information about cults and their recruitment methods. It offers advice and information to ex-cult members, families and the general public. It also gives educational talks and lectures.

The charity has developed an international network of cult aware contacts, who can offer further help and information to clients.

DHARMA SCHOOL
Charity No.: 1015691
Postal Address: The Dharma School, White House, Ladies Mile Road, Patcham, Brighton BN1 8TB
Telephone Contact: 01273 502055
Fax: 01273 556580
Email: office@dharmaschool.f9.co.uk
Website(s): www.dharmaschool.co.uk

The Dharma School Trust was established in 1992 to develop the provision of high quality education grounded on Buddhist teaching for children up to the age of sixteen. The present school is limited to a maximum of sixty primary level pupils in its present location and is fundraising to enable it to expand.

The school is open to children of all cultural and religious backgrounds, and is Buddhist in the values it imparts rather than in the formal study of scriptures and doctrine. Head teacher: Kevin Fossey.

DHARMAPALA COLLEGE FWBO STUDY CENTRE
Tradition: FWBO
Meetings: Madhyamaloka, 30 Chantry Road, Moseley, Birmingham, B13 8DH
Affiliated to: Friends Of The Western Buddhist Order, UK National Organisations
Postal Address: Dharmapala College, Madhyamaloka, 30 Chantry Road, Moseley, Birmingham, B13 8DH
Telephone Contact: 0121 449 3700
Website(s): www.dharmapalacollege.org

The Dharmapala College plays an active part in the emerging Buddhist culture in the West. Initiated by members of the Western Buddhist Order, it invites the participation of everyone inspired by the ideals of collaborative enquiry into reality and open-handed sharing of understanding and experience.

As a community of enquiry we aim to merge in-depth spiritual practice with both rigorous scholarly questioning and appreciative exploration of the cultural and artistic heritage of the world cultures.

The College is currently based at Madhyamaloka in Birmingham, UK, but we also offer an increasing range of events at local Buddhist centres across the UK as well as on the European Continent.

DRUKPA TRUST
Tradition: Tibetan Kagyu/Drikung
Charity No.: 1014948
Postal Address: Drukpa London. 114 Harvist Road, London, NW6 6HJ
Telephone Contact: 020 8964 2337 (Diana Cook - Teaching and Practice)
Email: london@drukpa.org.uk
Website(s): www.drukpa.org.uk

The Drukpa Trust was set up as a registered U.K. charity in 1992 to advance education in the universal philosophy and non-sectarian practice of Tibetan Buddhism, under the guidance of His Holiness 12th Gyalwang Drukpa.

Four Main Areas of Activity:

1. A landmark education project, involving construction of an award-winning school, Druk White Lotus School (DWLS), for up to 750 children in Ladakh, Northern India, together with related teacher training and enterprise activities. The school is intended to provide local children with a practical modern education, based in their

unique cultural and spiritual traditions.

2. Inviting H.H. Gyalwang Drukpa and other leading Buddhist teachers to the U.K. to give public talks, retreats and teachings in spiritual practice.

3. A sponsorship scheme to help educate and provide basic needs for children, monks and nuns in Ladakh, Northern India and Nepal.

4. Practice groups which meet on a regular basis. These groups provide the opportunity for students and friends to practice together, find mutual support and deepen their understanding of Tibetan Buddhist philosophy.

ENGLISH BUDDHIST MONASTERY TRUST
Tradition: All
Charity No.: 1088804
Postal Address: English Buddhist Monastery Trust, 40 St Dunstan's Road, Worthing, West Sussex BN13 1AB
Telephone Contact: 01903 218963 Kate Corlett (EBMT Trustee)
Email: info@ebmtrust.org
Website(s): www.ebmtrust.org

The English Buddha Monastery Trust seeks to establish a non-sectarian Buddhist monastery in England. Until such time the charity has, with the kind help of a sponsor, set up the Bodhi Garden Dharma Centre (see Brighton, England) to help in a small way with allowing the Dharma to take root and flourish in the West. If you require further information, or would like to make a donation, please contact the address below.

ENGLISH SANGHA TRUST
Amaravati Buddhist Monastery, UK National Organisations
Charity No.: 231310
Postal Address: English Sangha Trust, c/o Amaravati Buddhist Monastery, Great Gaddesden, Hemel Hempstead, Hertfordshire, HP1 3BZ
Telephone Contact: 01442 842455 01442 843721

Email: est@amaravati.org
www.buddhamind.info

The Trust was established in 1956 to promote the teachings of the Buddha in the UK by providing and maintaining residences for monastics and others under religious training. Today it is responsible for the upkeep of Amaravati and Cittaviveka Buddhist monasteries and acts as steward of donations offered to the Sangha.

EUROPEAN BUDDHIST UNION
Postal Address: Maria Angela Fala, Via Euripide 137, 00125 Rome, Italy
Claudine Shinoda, 41 Boulevard Meusnier de Querlon, 44000 Nantes, France
Email: mariaangela.fala@fastwebnet.it or claudine_shinoda@hotmail.com
Website(s): www.e-b-u.org

The European Buddhist Union (EBU) is an umbrella organization of Buddhist communities and organizations in Europe. As a union it is broad, impartial and open to Buddhists of all schools and traditions. Its principal aims are:

To promote the fellowship of and encourage co-operation between the Buddhists in Europe.

To promote Buddhists in Europe to meet and to get acquainted.

To promote the development of friendly relations between Buddhist organizations and consequently to promote co-operation on matters that are of interest to all.

As such EBU supports and promotes a natural growth of Buddhism in Europe.

European Buddhists and Buddhist organizations who are interested in the European dynamics, i.e. meeting, getting acquainted, developing friendly relations and working together on matters that are of interest to all, should consider applying for

Entry continued on the following page.

membership of EBU. For information about membership of the Union, please contact Maria Angela Falà (details below).

INFORM: (Information Network Focus on Religious Movements)
Charity No.: 801729
Postal Address: Inform, Houghton Street, London WC2A 2AE
Telephone Contact: 020 7955 7654
Fax: 020 7955 7679
Email: inform@lse.ac.uk
Website(s): www.inform.ac

An independent charity which collects and disseminates information about New Religious Movements.

INTER FAITH NETWORK FOR THE UNITED KINGDOM
Charity No.: 1068934
Postal Address: The Inter Faith Network for the UK, 8A Lower Grosvenor Place, London SW1W 0EN
Telephone Contact: 020 7931 7766
Fax: 020 7931 7722
Email: ifnet@interfaith.org.uk
Website(s): www.interfaith.org.uk

The Network links 100 member organisations with an interest in promoting mutual understanding and good relations between Britain's different faith communities. Its members include representative bodies from these communities; national and local interfaith organisations; and educational and academic bodies. In addition to arranging meetings and seminars, it provides a central point of information and advice on interfaith matters. It also produces a number of publications. Its membership includes The Buddhist Society and the Network of Buddhist Organisations (UK).

INTERNATIONAL BUDDHIST RELIEF ORGANISATION
Charity No.: 1049429
Postal Address: International Buddhist Relief Organisation, 216 New John Street West, Hockley, Birmingham B19 3UA
Telephone Contact: 0121 523 6660
Fax: 0121 523 6660
Email: ibrouk1@hotmail.com
Website(s): www.ibro.co.uk

The International Buddhist Relief Organisation was established in 1993 by a group of Buddhists headed by the Ven W. Kassapa who is current patron and president. This organisation was established particularly to help Buddhist and non-Buddhist communities suffering all kinds of hardships all over the world according to the Buddhist teachings. Many different nationalities are involved in this project and eventually branches will be established in major cities all over the world to help cope with continuing problems. The membership is open to anybody regardless of his or her gender, caste, colour, religion or geographical background if they are interested on doing or helping with humanitarian activities.

Scholarships are awarded every year by a select committee to children selected from poor countries. We also send second-hand goods to third world countries.

At present there are branches in Sri Lanka, Singapore, Malaysia, Belarussia, Tanzania, Zambia, Italy, Switzerland, India, Germany, USA, Brazil and France who are conducting humanitarian services to local communities.

INTERNATIONAL DUNHUANG PROJECT
Postal Address: The International Dunhuang Project, The British Library, 96 Euston Road, London NW1 2DB
Telephone Contact: 020 7412 7319
Fax: 020 7412 7641

Email: idp@bl.uk
Website(s): idp.bl.uk

IDP is a ground-breaking international collaboration based at the British Library to make information and images of more than 100,000 manuscripts, paintings, textiles and artefacts from Dunhuang and other Silk Road sites freely available on the Internet.

The high quality colour images and historically accurate information are searchable on the IDP DATABASE. Items are shown in context, with bibliographies, maps, photographs, site plans and other information relating to their provenance, history and present condition. This gives the scholar, the student and the layman a unique insight into Silk Road life during the first millennium AD.

INTERNATIONAL NETWORK OF ENGAGED BUDDHISTS
Tradition: All
Postal Address: International Network of Engaged Buddhists, 666 Charuen-Nakorn Rd., Klungsan, Bangkok 10600, Thailand
UK Contact: Ken Jones, Troedrhiwsebon, Cwmrheidol, Aberystwyth, SY23 3NB
Telephone Contact: +662 433 7169
Fax: +662 860 2194
Email: ineboffice@yahoo.com
Website(s): www.inebnetwork.org

Provides an international network and forum for socially concerned Buddhist groups in order to faciliate co-operation and joint action. Present areas of concern are alternative education and spiritual training, peace work, human rights, women's issues, ecology, family concerns, rural development, alternative economics, communications and concerns of monks and nuns.

The Network holds annual conferences and reports its activities in the international magazine, Seeds of Peace. The UK affiliate is the Network of Engaged Buddhists.

KAILASH CENTRE
Tradition: Tibetan
Postal Address: Kailash Centre of Oriental Medicine, 7 Newcourt Street, London, NW8 7AA
Telephone Contact: 020 7722 3939
Fax: 020 7586 1642
Email: info@kailash.fsnet.co.uk
Website(s): www.orientalhealing.co.uk

London's leading clinic specialising in Oriental Medicine, offers a tranquil environment for treatments by experienced physicians and practitioners.

It provides a platform for practice, research and education of Oriental medical and philosophical traditions.

Oriental Medicine is based on the Principle of Vitality, the force governing all changes in the human body, which is called Qi in China, Ki in Japan, Prana in India and rLung in Tibet.

Treatments at Kailash aim to restore the patient's natural balance of this vital force.

KARUNA TRUST AND AID FOR INDIA
Charity No.: 280551 (Aid for India)
Charity No.: 177401 (Karuna Trust)
Postal Address: Karuna Trust 72 Holloway Rd London N7 8JG
Telephone Contact: 020 7700 3434
Fax: 020 7700 3535
Email: info@karuna.org
Website(s): www.karuna.org

The Karuna Trust is a charity established and run by members of the Western Buddhist Order to raise funds for social work projects, principally among Indian Buddhists from poor communities. Since it was founded Karuna has raised several million pounds, mainly in the form of covenanted donations. It now funds a network of educational, health and livelihood projects in India and has also raised money for Dharma work there. Karuna also

Entry continued on the following page.

supports the Indo-Tibetan Cultural Institute in Kalimpong which provides an education in traditional arts and skills for Tibetan refugee children.

LEEDS BUDDHIST COUNCIL

Postal Address: The Secretary, Leeds Buddhist Council, 12 Granby View, Leeds, LS6 3AT
Telephone Contact: 0113 275 2353
Email: leedsbuddhistcouncil@hotmail.com

Founded in 1998, Leeds Buddhist Council is an inter-tradition organisation representing the Buddhist Community in Leeds. Its aims are to build cooperation and better understanding between the members, other faiths, Government and Local Government.

It comprises representatives of:-
Dhammapala (Leeds) a lay group of Harnham Vihara - FWBO (Leeds) - Jamyang (Leeds) - Dechen Community (Yorkshire) - Soka Gakkai International (Leeds) - New Kadampa Tradition (Pocklington - York) - Leeds Zen Group - International Zen Association UK (Leeds) - Buddhist Hospice Trust

Representatives on Leeds Buddhist Council currently work on the following:-

Leeds Faith Communities Liaison Forum on which are represented the Christian, Jewish, Muslim, Buddhist, Hindu and Ba'hai faiths; through this LBC links up to Local Government and Government initiatives.

Visiting Buddhist patients in Hospital or Hospices, Conducting Buddhist Funerals, Teaching NHS Staff stress relief, Visiting and teaching meditation in H M Prisons, Representing Buddhists on SACRE (Standing Advisory Commitee on Religious Education)

We are presently working towards the feasibility of Regional Government representation, and then we hope to expand our membership and area base further

LONDON INTER FAITH CENTRE

Meetings: 125 Salisbury Road, London NW6 6RG
Postal Address: London Inter Faith Centre, 125 Salisbury Road, London NW6 6RG
Telephone Contact: 020 7604 3053
Fax: 020 7604 3052
Email: info@londoninterfaith.org.uk
Website(s): www.londoninterfaith.org.uk
London Inter Faith Centre is a place of meeting, study and dialogue among the world's religions. It is funded and run by the Christian community, with many faith involvement. The London Inter Faith Centre seeks to build bridges between the faith communities, teach the host culture about other religions, and liaise with other agencies in related work.

The London Inter Faith centre offers a variety of activities from meditation to a two-year certificate course in interfaith relations, from multi-faith musical events to lectures.

LOTHLORIEN

Affiliated to: Kagyu Samye Ling Monastery And Tibetan Centre, UK National Organisations
Charity No.: 105293
Postal Address: Lothlorien, Corsock, Castle Douglas, Dumfriesshire DG7 3DR
Telephone Contact: 01644 440602
Email: lothlorien1@btopenworld.com
Website(s): www.lothlorien.tc

Lothlorien is a therapeutic community for people with mental health problems, situated in a quiet rural setting in South West Scotland. Lothlorien was originally started by the Haughton family in 1974, and has been run since 1989 by the Rokpa Trust, an international charity founded by Dr. Akong Tulku Rinpoche of Kagyu Samye Ling Tibetan Centre in Dumfriesshire. Buddhist values of compassion and tolerance are the basis of our approach, but we are not a religious community and are open to everyone.

Related Organisations

The community consists of 8 residents with mental health problems and 4 voluntary co-workers, living in the main 14 bedroomed log house and a further 5 people living in the long term house, Roan Lodge, which opened in April 2003. The community has 17 acres of land, including vegetable gardens, woodland and pasture land. The main house has wheelchair access and a disabled toilet on the ground floor.

MIDLANDS BUDDHIST COMMUNITY ASSOCIATION
Postal Address: Midlands Buddhist Community Association, 23 Weycroft Road, Perry Common, Birmingham B23 5AD
Telephone Contact: 0121 382 7108
Fax: 0121 384 8333
Email: mibauk86@hotmail.com
Website(s): www.purebuddhism.com

The main aims and objectives of the Association are:

To provide facilities for mentally and physically handicapped children and their parents.

To help relieve the suffering of people regardless of their status and to advance and relieve people in need.

To advance the training, education and employment opportunities of the local community e.g. young people, the unemployed, single parents and women returning to work.

To provide indoor and outdoor activities for young people.

To provide welfare advice, practical assistance or any kind of social work support to families in need.

To seek, develop and promote good community relations.

To help to develop child care activities such as nurseries and to help to look after the elderly and disabled people in the community.

MYANMAR ASSOCIATION (UK)
Postal Address: Myanmar Association (UK), 19A Charles Street, London W1X 8ER
Telephone Contact: 020 7499 8841 ext. 222 or 236
Email: minzawaung@hotmail.com
Website(s): www.myanmarmauk.co.uk

NETWORK OF BUDDHIST ORGANISATIONS (UK)
Postal Address: Network of Buddhist Organisations, 6 Tyne Rd, Bishopston, Bristol BS7 8EE
Telephone Contact: 0845 345 8978
Email: secretary@nbo.org.uk
Website(s): www.nbo.org.uk

The Network aims to promote fellowship and dialogue between member Buddhist organisation and to facilitate co-operation in matters of common interest. It also works in harmony with Buddhist and likeminded organisations around the world. General meetings are held in different parts of the country. Business meetings are open to representatives of organisations and associate members.

OFFICE OF TIBET
Postal Address: Tsering Tashi, Representative of His Holiness the Dalai Lama for Northern Europe, Baltic Countries and Poland, Office of Tibet, Tibet House, 1 Culworth Street, London NW8 7AF
Telephone Contact: 020 7722 5378
Fax: 020 7722 0362
Email: info@tibet.com
Website(s): www.tibet.com

The Office of Tibet is the official agency in London of His Holiness the Dalai Lama. As well as looking after the interests of the Tibetan people, the Office

Entry continued on the following page.

works towards creating a better understanding in Europe of Tibet and Tibetans. It supervises arrangements for His Holiness the Dalai Lama's visits to Northern Europe and strives to spread his message of peace and harmony in the world.

The Office serves as a source of authentic information on the culture of Tibet, on its religion, history and way of life and on current affairs regarding Tibet and the Tibetans in exile. With a view to improving the conditions of the people in Tibet, the office monitors the situation there and makes available the latest information.

Since it co-ordinates the work being done by organisations and individuals in Europe and the West, the Office of Tibet provides a forum for information and contacts of all kinds. It also attempts to help the various agencies of the Tibetan administration in India.

PHIROZ MEHTA TRUST
Charity No.: 328061
Postal Address: Phiroz Mehta Trust, 47 Lillian Road, London SW13 9JF
Telephone Contact: 020 8748 3218 01689 825 724
Fax: 020 8302 0163
Email: info@phirozmehtatrust.org.uk
Website(s): www.phirozmehtatrust.org.uk

The Phiroz Mehta Trust exists to promote the study and practice of the world's great religions and the art of religious living, which is truly human living, i.e. the art of living the ordinary everyday life virtuously, with a view of the wellbeing and fulfilment of oneself and all others. Its purpose is to provide the facilities whereby each and every person can develop his or her own understanding and explore the pathways to truth in co-operation with others. Towards fulfilling this purpose, the books and collection of recorded talks and lectures by Phiroz Mehta, together with his library of books on philosophy and religion, now housed by the Trust, are available for use by all who are interested.

Phiroz Mehta (1902-1994), who had made a profound study of the major religions of the world, always insisted that he was not to be regarded as a leader of any movement, but as a fellow-student. He regarded every person as being unique, discovering truth through his or her own way of life. He was the author of six books on religion: Early Indian Religious Thought, The Heart of Religion, Zarathustra, the Transcendental Vision, Buddhahood, Holistic Consciousness and The Oakroom Talks on Buddhism.

QUAKER COMMITTEE FOR CHRISTIAN AND INTERFAITH RELATIONS (CIR)
Postal Address: The Clerk CIR, c/o Recording Clerk's Office, Friends' House, Euston Road, London NW1 2BJ
Telephone Contact: 020 7663 1060 (Marigold Bentley)
Fax: 020 7663 1001
Email: marigoldb@quaker.org.uk
Website(s): www.quaker.org.uk

The Committee is responsible for keeping the Yearly Meeting of the Religious Society of Friends in Britain informed of the various movements towards co-operation within the Christian Church and opportunities for interfaith dialogue, and for responding on behalf of the Yearly Meeting so that Friends' views on issues of faith and order are represented to other churches and communities of faith. Members of the Committee represent the Yearly Meeting on the Churches' Commission for Inter Faith Relations and the Interfaith Network for the UK.

ROKPA TRUST
Tradition: Tibetan
School: Karma-Kagyu
Affiliated to: Kagyu Samye Ling Monastery And Tibetan Centre, UK National Organisations
Charity No.: 105293

Rokpa is a Tibetan word meaning help, helping or

serving. Rokpa Trust is the UK part of a worldwide group of non-political, non-sectarian organisations working to help those in need and to improve the quality of life and has three main areas of activity:

Spiritual - See www.samyeling.org

Therapy and medicine - see www.tararokpa.org

Charitable and humanitarian - see www.rokpa.org

These organisations have activities ranging from soup kitchens in Europe to the teaching of traditional folk medicine in Tibet; helping street kids in Nepal to pioneering a 5-year psychotherapy training programme in Europe; and from planting trees in deforested Himalayas to creating a centre for interfaith understanding on Holy Island in Scotland.

SAKYADHITA INTERNATIONAL - UK CHAPTER
Tradition: All
Email: sakyadhita.uk@europe.com
Website(s): www.sakyadhita-europe.de or www.sakyadhita.org

Sakyadhita, 'Daughters of the Buddha', is an International Association of Buddhist Women, founded at the conclusion of the first International Conference on Buddhist Women, held in Bodhgaya, India, in 1987. Sakyadhita seeks to unite Buddhist women of various countries and traditions - nuns and laywomen alike - and to offer support for education and training for Buddhist women, in order to advance their spiritual and secular welfare, for the benefit of humanity as a whole. It is non-profit making.

International conferences are held every two years and members receive a newsletter twice a year. For more information of Sakyadhita International and the various projects it supports, please visit the website www.sakyadhita.org

If you want to receive more information on the UK

Chapter of Sakyadhita, and its activities, please visit the website www.sakyadhita-europe.de and/or send an email to sakyadhita.uk@europe.com.

The next Sakyadhita International Conference is planned to take place in Mongolia in 2008.

SATIPANYA BUDDHIST TRUST
Tradition: Theravada
Charity No.: 1116668
Postal Address: Satipanya Buddhist Trust, Whitegrit, Minsterly, Shropshire SY5 0JN
Telephone Contact: +44 (0) 1588 650752
Email: manager@satipanya.org.uk
Website(s): www.satipanya.org.uk

The Satipanya Buddhist Trust is grounded in the Buddhist Tradition of Theravada as practised in South-East Asia. Satipanya is located in Powys, Wales, in UK, south of Shrewsbury and near the Shropshire border. We run retreats devoted to contemplative living and vipassana insight meditation in the tradition of the Mahasi Sayadaw of Burma.

Satipanya wishes to cultivate a meditative and contemplative atmosphere devoted to the two duties the Buddha would have us fulfil: to practise Vipassana and to study the Dhamma.

The Mahasi Sayadaw came to UK during the '70's. Although there are city centres in UK where this tradition is being taught, there is no retreat as such devoted to this practice.

Bhante Bodhidhamma, an English monk is the Spiritual Director of the Satipanya Buddhist Trust has been practising in the Mahasi Tradition since 1979 and has been teaching since 85. Such has been the interest among lay people in this practice, especially in the UK and Ireland, that support came to establish Satipanya.

Satipanya is a small, intimate place of retreat that

Entry continued on the following page.

allows the kind of individual guidance that the Mahasi Sayadaw encouraged.

Our main purpose, therefore, is to teach the Mahasi Tradition of Vipassana Insight Meditation. It will be expected that anyone coming to the retreat will have this as their principle practice.

SHRIMALA TRUST
Tradition: Tibetan
Kagyu-Nyingma

Affiliated to: Awakened Heart Sangha, Wales, Gwynedd, Criccieth
Charity No.: 1078783
Postal Address: Shrimala Trust, 5A High Street, Criccieth, Gwynedd LL52 0RN
Telephone Contact: 01766 523110
Email: info@ahs.org.uk
Website(s): www.ahs.org.uk

The Shrimala Trust is a charitable company that exists to support the activity of the Awakened Heart Sangha

STILLPOINT
Tradition: All
Postal Address: David Meanwell, 31 Caversham Avenue, Sutton, Surrey, SM3 9AQ
Telephone Contact: 0208 644 9715 (David Meanwell - Administrator)
Or 07748 485516 (Joelle Marlow - Coordinator)
Email: info@stillpointmeditation.org.uk
Website(s): www.stillpointmeditation.org.uk

Resources and virtual Sangha support for Buddhists especially beginning meditators practising with illness. Contacts for all Buddhist traditions, non affiliated. Noticeboard for events & communities. Postal lending library. E-newsletter at
http://groups.yahoo.com/group/breathing_space

'Monday Metta' virtual meditation and mutual

support. Guidelines for organisations wishing to be more inclusive of practitioners who are disabled, or living with chronic illness. Wesite fully disabled accessible.

TARA COLLEGE OF TIBETAN MEDICINE
See ROKPA TRUST in Related Organisations

TASHI KHYIL TRUST
Tradition: Tibetan
School: Gelugpa
Charity No.: X0948/90
Postal Address: Sally Taylor, 14 Drumnaconnell Road, Saintfield, Co Down BT24 7NB
Telephone Contact: 028 9751 0232 (Sally Taylor)
Email: tashikhyil@saltr.clara.co.uk
Website(s): www.tashi-khyil.org

Under the patronage of His Holiness the Dalai Lama and the direction of Panchen Ötrul Rinpoche. Tashi Khyil is a fundraising Trust for Tibetan refugees and the future re-establishment of monasteries in Tibet; Tashi Khyil is also assisting with the rebirth of Buddhism in Mongolia and is working to redress some of the current social problems there.

Tashi Khyil is closely linked with Jampa Ling Tibetan Buddhist Centre, Bawnboy, Co Cavan (see Ireland).

TASHI LHUNPO MONASTERY UK TRUST
Tradition: Tibetan
School: Gelugpa
Charity No.: 1100175
Postal Address: Tashi Lhunpo Monastery UK Trust, The Round House, Netton, Salisbury SP4 6AW
Telephone Contact: 01722 782265
Fax: 01722 782703
Email: info@tashi-lhunpo.org.uk
Website(s): www.tashi-lhunpo.org.ukTashi

Lhunpo Monastery UK Trust was founded in September 2003. The Patron of the Trust is His Holiness the Dalai Lama.

Tashi Lhunpo Monastery is one of the most important of the Gelugpa monasteries, and the seat of the Panchen Lama. Re-established in India in 1972, the monks follow the same pattern of teaching as they would have done within their monasteries, as well as from Bhutan, Sikkim, Himachal and Nepal.

The UK Trust aims to develop awareness and facilitate access to the unique culture of Tibet, and especially of Tashi Lhunpo Monastery, by organising artistic tours, educational workshops and cultural exchanges. Proceeds from the tours of cham dancing, sand mandala exhibitions and workshops go directly to the monastery. There is a developing programme of work within schools, during which children are offered a taste of Tibet's monastic culture and have an opportunity to meet the monks and try their hand at traditional Tibetan arts. The Trust supports Tashi Lhunpo Monastery in exile in Bylakuppe Tibetan Settlement in South India by raising money for construction projects and for day-to-day living expenses, education and medical care of the monks. The Trust also runs a sponsorship programme.

Information on the monastery, the Trust and forthcoming cultural tours, as well as an order form to purchase items from the monastery, is available on the website at www.tashi-lhunpo.org.uk.

TIBET FOUNDATION
Charity No.: 292400
Postal Address: The Tibet Foundation, 1 St James's Market London SW1Y 4SB
Telephone Contact: 020 7930 6001
Fax: 020 7930 6002
Email: office@tibet-foundation.org
Website(s): www.tibet-foundation.orgTibet Foundation is a registered charity, founded in

1985, which works towards creating greater awareness of all aspects of Tibetan culture and the needs of the Tibetan people. The patron of the foundation is His Holiness the Dalai Lama.

Aims:

To create a greater awareness of His Holiness the Dalai Lama's message of peace and harmony. To further the understanding of Tibetan Buddhism and Tibet culture, and to work towards their continuity and preservation.

To improve education and health care and to alleviate poverty among people of Tibetan origin in different parts of the world.

In pursuit of these aims the Foundation organises study courses, language classes, translation services, publications, exhibitions and cultural events open to the public, and maintains a Tibetan Culture centre in central London.

Visiting Tibetan doctors give the public the opportunity to benefit from this ancient medical practice by offering consultations and workshops to those interested in the practice.

Through its Tibet Shop in central London (Tel: 020 7930 6005) offers a large selection of Buddhist literature, audio and visual tapes of Tibetan religious and secular music and Tibetan handicrafts.

TIBET HOUSE TRUST
Charity No.: 1037230
Postal Address: Tibet House Trust, Tibet House, 1 Culworth Street, London NW8 7AF
Telephone Contact: 020 7722 5378
Fax: 020 7722 0362
Email: secretary@tibet-house-trust.co.uk
Website(s): www.tibet-house-trust.co.uk

The Tibet House Trust is a UK registered official Tibetan charity, inaugurated by His Holiness the

Entry continued on the following page.

Dalai Lama on 17 September 1994, to preserve Tibetan culture and identity and to provide assistance in rehabilitating Tibetan refugees.

Its aims are: To help relieve poverty and rehabilitate Tibetans in need so as to ensure self-sufficiency in the refugee population; To provide assistance in the fields of health, education, training in different skills and management; To preserve and promote the Tibetan culture and way of life, traditional Tibetan medicine, language, literature, music and art; To promote His Holiness the Dalai Lama's message of peace, universal responsibility, compassion, ethics and the environment and; To provide educational materials and support events about Tibet and Tibetan culture, art, history and religion.

The Trust ensures that every donation received goes directly to the intended recipient. Through the trust, organisations and individuals have supported many projects, with an emphasis on education, economic and community development, religion and health - as a means of ensuring the preservation of Tibetan identity, culture and religion.

For further details, contact the Secretary.

TIBET SOCIETY AND TIBET RELIEF FUND UK
Charity No.: 1061834
Postal Address: Tibet Society and Tibet Relief Fund UK, Unit 9, 139 Fonthill Road, London N4 3HF
Telephone Contact: 020 7272 1414
Fax: 020 7272 1410
Email: info@tibetsociety.com
Website(s): www.tibetsociety.com

The Tibet Society and the Tibet Relief Fund of the UK is the oldest voluntary group supporting Tibet in the world.

The Objects of the Society are:

1) By non-party political action to promote the cause of Tibetan independence and to bring before the world the sufferings of the oppressed people of Tibet.

2) To assist those Tibetans who fled over the Himalayas to India and elsewhere.

3) To promote understanding of Tibetan history, culture and religion, both on account of the great intrinsic value which such studies have for the West and that we may more effectively befriend the exiled people of Tibet.

The charitable arm of the Tibet Society, the Tibet Relief Fund sponsors children's education as well as elderly Tibetan refugees and helps educational, social and cultural projects in refugee settlements in India. The annual Membership subscription is £15.00

UK ASSOCIATION FOR BUDDHIST STUDIES
Postal Address: UK Association for Buddhist Studies, c/o Prof Ian Harris, Dept. of Religion & Philosophy, University College of St. Martin, Lancaster, LA1 3JDUK Association for Buddhist Studies, c/o Prof. Richard Gombrich, 11 Barton Lane, Oxford, OX3 9J
Telephone Contact: 01524 384528 (Prof. Harris)
Email: i.harris@ucsm.ac.uk
Website(s): www.sunderland.ac.uk/%7EosOdwe/bsa.shtml

The Association aims to act as a focus for Buddhist Studies in the UK. Currently, the scholarly study of Buddhism in the UK is carried out by lone individuals or fairly small groups of people at any one location. Moreover, scholars may be located in a range of departments: Anthropology, Asian Studies, Comparative Religion, Law, Oriental Studies, Philosophy, Psychology, Religious Studies, Theology, etc. Membership of the Association is therefore open to academics, post-graduates and unaffiliated Buddhist scholars or interested Buddhist practitioners.

The association aims to hold an annual conference and to help inform people of the ongoing work of others and of any relevant conferences, visiting scholars, seminar series, etc. To this end it maintains a web-site and publishes an electronic newsletter, an annual handbook and its journal, Buddhist Studies Review.

Enquiries about membership should be addressed to: Dr Elizabeth Harris, UKABS Treasurer, 33 Buck Lane, Kingsbury, London NW9 0AP, ejharris@gn.apc.org

Submissions to Buddhist Studies Review, the journal of UKABS, should be sent to Prof. Peter Harvey, peter.harvey@sunderland.ac.uk (School of Arts, Design, Media and Culture, University of Sunderland, Preistman Building, Green Terrace, Sunderland, SR1 3PZ

WEST MIDLANDS BUDDHIST COUNCIL
Postal Address: West Midlands Buddhist Council, c/o Keith Jones, 71 Fountain Road, Edgbaston, Birmingham B17 8NP
Telephone Contact: 0121 429 5098 Or 07870 146716

The aims and objectives of the WMBC are to promote Buddhist dialogue among all professed Buddhists in the West Midlands.

WORLD CONGRESS OF FAITHS (The Interfaith Fellowship)
Charity No.: 244096
Postal Address: World Congress of Faiths, c/o London Inter Faith Centre, 125 Salusbury Rd, London NW6 6RG
Telephone Contact: 020 8959 3129 01403 257 801
Fax: 020 8959 3129
Email: enquiries@worldfaith.org
Website(s): www.worldfaiths.org

The World Congress of Faiths offers an opportunity

for people of many countries and creeds to come together. Members seek to understand each other's religions. Together they try to promote ethical values to enhance human welfare and peace. To this end it publishes a Journal and other publications.

The World Congress of Faiths is concerned for Religious Education and Spiritual Growth: whilst encouraging fellowship between faiths and seeking to combat prejudice and intolerance, it does not exalt one faith, nor does it syncretise. Its patron is His Holiness the Dalai Lama. The Joint Presidents are Revd. Marcus Braybrooke and Revd. Prof. Keith Ward.

The World Congress of Faiths has a programme of lectures, seminars and retreats open to non-members and members alike and publishes its Journal Interreligious Insight and One Family Newsletter four times a year.

WORLD FELLOWSHIP OF BUDDHISTS
Postal Address: World Fellowship of Buddhists, 616 Benjasiri Park, Sol Medhinivet off Soi Sukhumvit 24, Sukhumvit Road, Bangkok 10110 Thailand
Telephone Contact: +66 (0)2 6611284-87
Fax: +66 (0)2 661-0555
Email: wfb_hq@asianet.co.th
Website(s): www.wfb-hq.org

The World Fellowship of Buddhists (WFB) was founded on May 25 B.E.2493 (1950) in Colombo, Sri Lanka, where representatives from 27 countries in Asia, Europe and North America (including Hawaii) met for this purpose. Nearly every school of Buddhism in the Mahayana, Theravada, and Vajrayana traditions was represented by members of the Sangha as well as laity. This was probably the first time in the history of Buddhism that such a gathering was held. No Buddhist sect, school or organization was unwilling to attend the meeting. Thus founded, the WFB represents the common interests of

Entry continued on the following page.

Buddhists throughout the world numbering
hundreds of millions.

The Aims and Objectives of the World Fellowship
of Buddhists are

1. To promote among the members strict
observance and practice of the teachings of the
Buddha;

2. To secure unity, solidarity, and brotherhood
amongst Buddhists;

3. To propagate the sublime doctrine of the
Buddha;

4. To organize and carry on activities in the field of
social, educational, cultural and other
humanitarian services;

5. To work for happiness, harmony and peace on
earth and to collaborate with other organizations
working for the same ends.

RESOURCES

AUDIO VISUAL

BECKMANN VISUAL PUBLISHING
Postal Address: Beckmann Visual Publishing, Milntown Lodge, Lezayre Road, Ramsey, Isle of Man IM8 2TG
Telephone Contact: 01624 816585
Email: videos@beckmanndirect.com
Website(s): www.beckmanngroup.co.uk
Beckmann Visual Publishing was established in 1983 to specialise in the publishing of documentary and factual programmes.

The company has focused on the publication of programmes which meet the needs of enthusiasts for detailed and expert visual information on the subjects which fascinate and interest them.

The result is our unique catalogue which features unrepeatable historic footage, top events and performances, in-depth analysis and the widest range of experts and expertise available to view on screen. We now have more than 300 titles and continue to add quality how-to, sports, health, yoga, history, heritage, travel and wildlife titles to our ever growing list of subjects.

BUDDHIST SOCIETY
Affiliated to: Buddhist Society, UK National Organisations
Charity No.: 1113705
Postal Address: Audio Department, The Buddhist Society, 58 Eccleston Square, London SW1V 1PH
Telephone Contact: 020 7834 5858
Fax: 020 7976 5238
Email: info@thebuddhistsociety.org
Website(s): www.thebuddhistsociety.org

The Society's Audio department offers CD's and tapes of public talks, lectures and courses on Buddhism and other topics related to Buddhism that have been given at The Buddhist Society and at our Summer School, recently and over the past years. We now have two Audio Catalogues; one containing talks recorded prior to 2006 which is available from the Society at the cost of £1.00 and the other containing talks from 2006 which is available by sending a stamped addressed envelope. Both catalogues are available to view on our website.

We continually add new recordings to the catalogue in order to make the teachings available, so it is by no means a conclusive list. We try to record all talks given at The Buddhist Society and make them available for purchase. We regularly update our catalogue but if you know of a talk that is not listed in the catalogue please do enquire.

Most of the older talks were originally recorded on tapes and some have been transferred to CD so that they are available on both types of media however some are only available on tape or CD, please see the catalogue for details. Some of the oldest talks have been taken from the archives and the recordings and their quality is by no means perfect.

Tape Library for The Blind

The tapes in this catalogue are available on loan entirely free of charge to the registered blind. For free posting, the tapes are sent in a special wallet marked 'Articles for the Blind'. Please write for the talking catalogue which includes full instructions for posting and ordering.

CHRISTMAS HUMPHREYS MEMORIAL LIBRARY
Affiliated to: Amaravati Buddhist Monastery, UK National Organisations
Postal Address: The Librarian, Amaravati Buddhist Monastery, Great Gaddesden, Hemel Hempstead, Hertfordshire HP1 3BZ
Telephone Contact: 01442 842455
Fax: 01442 843721

We have a tape lending library within the book library. We have several hundred tapes for loan - recordings of talks by Sangha members as well as by other spiritual teachers. The tapes can also be listened to in the Library.

Resources

CLEAR VISION TRUST
Affiliated to: Friends Of The Western Buddhist Order, UK National Organisations
Charity No.: 1019669
Postal Address: The Clear Vision Trust, 16-20 Turner Street, Manchester M4 1DZ
Telephone Contact: 0161 839 9579
Fax: 0870 139 1699 (education only) or 0870 134 7354 (for non-education)
Email: clearvision@clear-vision.org
Website(s): www.clear-vision.orgClear Vision was founded by Mokshapriya in the early 1990s to record the teachings of Sangharakshita, the founder of the Friends of the Western Buddhist Order. Produces videos about Buddhism and the FWBO and educational materials on Buddhism for schools. It became a registered charity in 1993, devoted to promoting Buddhism through the audio-visual media.

We hold the FWBO archive of images and video, and we have plans for more educational products, especially using interactive media.

The Clear Vision offices are situated in the Manchester Buddhist Centre

COMMUNITY OF INTERBEING
Tradition: Vietnamese
School: Thich Nhat Hanh
Affiliated to: The Community Of Interbeing, UK, UK National Organisations
Postal Address: Jacqui Schweitzer, Col Book Service, Dunrozel, Farnham Lane, Haslemere, Surrey GU27 1 HD
Telephone Contact: 0870 850 2615
Email: bookshop@interbeing.org.uk
Website(s): www.interbeing.org.uk/bookshop

The Community offers a service for the purchase of books, tapes and videos of Thich Nhat Hanh's teachings. If you would like a list of available titles, or wish to place an order, please contact the address below, enclosing a stamped, self-addressed envelope.

CROYDON BUDDHIST CENTRE BOOKSHOP
Affiliated to: Friends Of The Western Buddhist Order, UK National Organisations
Charity No.: 270460
Postal Address: Croydon Buddhist Centre, 96-98 High Street, Croydon, Surrey CR0 1ND
Telephone Contact: 020 8688 8624
Fax: 020 8649 9375
Email: info@croydonbuddhistcentre.com
Website(s): www.croydonbuddhistcentre.com
The centre includes a bookshop.

DHAMMA THREADS
Theravada

Affiliated to: Amaravati Buddhist Monastery, UK National Organisations
Postal Address: River Trading (UK) Ltd, The Old Forge, Longhorsley, Morpeth, Northumberland NE65 8UZ
Telephone Contact: 01670 788834 (Nick Pearce or Penny Cooley)
Website(s): www.dhammathreads.org

In the summer of 2005 a small group of people interested in the distribution of digitalised Dhamma gathered at Amaravati Buddhist Monastery. For many years Amaravati Cassettes had ably produced audio (analogue) tapes but with the increased use of CDs, MP3s, internet etc. a need arose to manage the new emerging medium. This group called itself Dhamma Threads.

DHARMACHAKRA TAPES
Affiliated to: Friends Of The Western Buddhist Order, UK National Organisations
Charity No.: 294143
Dharmacakra, 9 Coldmans Business Park, Norman Way, Cambridge CB1 3LH
Telephone Contact: 01223 868625
Fax: 01223 868627
Email: info@dharmachakra.com
Website(s): www.dharmachakra.com

Dharmachakra is the sound archive of the Western Buddhist Order, dedicated to distributing cd's and tapes on Buddhism and meditation. We hold over 200 lectures and readings by Urgyen Sangharakshita, the founder of the Order, but also a growing archive of over 550 talks by other members of the W.B.O. on a wide range of topics concerning Buddhism in the modern world. We also provide a range of excellent introductions to meditation, yoga and massage, as well as talking books on Buddhism and recordings of Buddhist sutras, devotional ceremonies and chanting. All our titles are available to order online via our website, by post or by telephone. Please send for a free colour cd catalogue of our main archive list. A regularly updated version of our full list of talks is available at dharmachakra.com.

GANESHA PRESS
Affiliated to: Dechen Community, UK National Organisations
Telephone Contact: 020 7706 2425
Email: paul.haddon@dechen.org
Website(s): www.dechen.org/shop

The publishing arm of the Dechen Community, Ganesha Press publishes books, booklets and audio tapes on Buddhist thought and practice. For details contact your nearest Dechen centre

GARUDA TRADING - TIBETAN DHARMA SUPPLIES
Affiliated to: Garuda Trading - Tibetan Dharma Supplies, Resources, Other Buddhist Requisites
Postal Address: Garuda Trading, Hedra, Grenville Road, Lostwithiel, Cornwall PL22 0EP
Telephone Contact: 01208 873785
Fax: 01208 873785
Email: garuda@talk21.com
Website(s): www.tibetanbuddhism.co.uk

Supply individual practitioners and Buddhist centres worldwide with Tibetan Buddhist Dharma supplies. We stock a wonderful range of quality

Thangkas, Rupas, Malas, Prayer Flags, Dharma Books, Ritual Aids, Meditation Cushions, Tibetan and Bhutanese Incense and much more. We can also undertake specialist orders on our regular buying trips to Nepal. Wholesale enquiries are most welcome.

INSIGHT TALKS
Insight Talks, Gaia House, West Ogwell, Newton Abbot, Devon TQ12 6EN
Telephone Contact: 01626 333613
Email: gaiahouse@gn.apc.org
Website(s): www.gaiahouse.co.uk

Readings of Dharma talks given at Gaia House by teachers including Christina Feldman, Christopher Titmuss, Stephen Batchelor, Fred von Allmen, Martine Batchelor, Kittisaro, Thanissara, Yanai Postelnik , Sharda Rogell, Reb Anderson and Joseph Goldstein.

Please send for a free catalogue.

LIVING DHARMA TAPES
Postal Address: Living Dharma Tapes, Poulstone Court, Kings Caple, Herefordshire HR1 4UA
Telephone Contact: 01432 840860
Fax: 01432 840860
Email: info@livingdharma.co.uk
Website(s): www.livingdharma.co.uk

Specialises in audio tapes by Ram Dass, Stephen Levine and Emmanuel. Small selection of books by these authors - send for a free catalogue.

MERIDIAN TRUST
Charity No.: 326903
Postal Address: Meridian Trust, 5 Torrens Street, London EC1V 1NQ
Telephone Contact: 020 7278 2576
Fax: 020 7837 2800
meridiantrust@compuserve.com

Entry continued on the following page.

Website(s): www.meridian-trust.org

The Meridian Trust is one of the foremost Buddhist film and video archives specialising in Tibetan Buddhism and culture but including all the major Buddhist traditions. Edited programmes, including teachings, documentaries, feature films and unedited archival footage are available in video format. Meridian continues to both make and distribute new video programmes as well as holding old archival footage.

Free catalogues are available on request.

THROSSEL HOLE BUDDHIST BOOKSHOP
Affiliated to: The Order Of Buddhists Contemplatives, UK National Organisations
Postal Address: Throssel Hole Buddhist Bookshop, Carrshield, Hexham, Northumberland NE47 8AL
Telephone Contact: 01434 345204 (9.30am - 11.30am and 2.30pm - 4.30pm.)
Fax: 01434 345216
Email: sales@buddhistsupplies.co.uk
Website(s): www.buddhistsupplies.co.uk

Mail order supplies of incense, books and recorded Dharma talks on CD and DVD.

TIBET SHOP
Affiliated to: Tibet Foundation, Related Organisations
Charity No.: 292400
Tibet Shop, 1a St James's Market, London SW1Y 4SB
Telephone Contact: 020 7930 6005
Email: shop@tibet-foundation.org or riga@tibetshop.co.uk
Website(s): www.tibetshop.org.uk or www.tibet-foundation.org

Tibet Shop presents a wide range of traditional Tibetan arts and crafts and books on Tibetan Buddhism and culture. We buy direct from

Tibetans living in exile in India and Nepal, helping them to keep their traditions alive.
The Shop sells a variety of Tibetan handicrafts, clothing, jewellery, carpets, ritual and decorative items, musical instruments and thangka paintings.It also sells greeting cards, posters, incense, CDs and cassettes of Tibetan music and chant, videos and books on Tibetan Buddhism and the Dalai Lama. We offer discounts to wholesalers.

Tibet Shop is solely owned by Tibet Foundation and all profits go to the charitable purposes of the Foundation.

BOOKS BY POST

COMMUNITY OF INTERBEING
Tradition: Vietnamese
School: Thich Nhat Hanh
Affiliated to: The Community Of Interbeing, UK, UK National Organisations
Postal Address: Jacqui Schweitzer, Col Book Service, Dunrozel, Farnham Lane, Haslemere, Surrey GU27 1 HD
Telephone Contact: 0870 850 2615
Email: bookshop@interbeing.org.uk
Website(s): www.interbeing.org.uk/bookshop

The Community offers a service for the purchase of books, tapes and videos of Thich Nhat Hanh's teachings. If you would like a list of available titles, or wish to place an order, please contact the address below, enclosing a stamped, self-addressed envelope.

GARUDA TRADING - TIBETAN DHARMA SUPPLIES
Affiliated to: Garuda Trading - Tibetan Dharma Supplies, Resources, Other Buddhist Requisites
Postal Address: Garuda Trading, Hedra, Grenville Road, Lostwithiel, Cornwall PL22 0EP
Telephone Contact: 01208 873785
Fax: 01208 873785

Resources

Email: garuda@talk21.com
Website(s): www.TibetanBuddhism.co.uk
Supplying individual practitioners and Buddhist centres worldwide with Tibetan Buddhist Dharma supplies. We stock a wonderful range of quality Thangkas, Rupas, Malas, Prayer Flags, Dharma Books, Ritual Aids, Meditation Cushions, Tibetan and Bhutanese Incense and much more. We can also undertake specialist orders on our regular buying trips to Nepal. Wholesale enquiries are most welcome.

GREENSLEEVES

Postal Address: Greensleeves Books, PO Box 156 Chipping Norton, Oxon OX7 3XT England
Telephone Contact: 01993 832423
Fax: 01608 676140
Email: info@greensleevesbooks.co.uk or greensleeves@v21mail.co.uk
Website(s): www.greensleevesbooks.co.uk

We carry a wide range of Eastern and Western Esoteric Philosophy, modern psychology and alternative therapy books. Both new and second hand. We purchase books.

INTERNET BOOKSELLERS

There are many general booksellers offering books, CDs etc via the Internet and Buddhist books can certainly be obtained from them. Many of these Internet booksellers are offshoots of traditional bookshops while others operate only through the Internet. There are too many of these services to list them all here, and it would be invidious to list only a selection. In any case, as with all aspects of the Internet, the situation is developing so rapidly that any information is likely to be out-of-date very soon. You are advised to make use of the many Internet search engines etc.

KINGSWOOD BOOKS

Postal Address: 17 Wick Road, Milborne Port, Sherborne, Dorset DT9 5BT

Telephone Contact: 01963 250280
Fax: 01963 250280
Email: Kingwoodbooks@btinternet.co.uk
Website(s): www.kingswoodbooks.btinternet.co.uk

Antiquarian and second hand books. Searches undertaken. We are catalogue booksellers operating from private premises. Visits by appointment only.

We also trade on the internet with Abebooks.co.uk and from our own website.

For a complete list of our books on the net please look at: www.abebooks.com/home/kingswooduk and www.ukbookworld.com/members/kingswood. Please also visit our own website: www.kingswoodbooks.btinternet.co.uk.

Proprietors: A J Dollery and A C Rockall.

MOTILAL (UK) BOOKS OF INDIA

Tradition: All
Postal Address: Motilal Books, 367 High Street, London Colney, St. Albans, Herts AL2 1EA
Telephone Contact: 01727 761677 (Richard Neil)
Or 07973 377824 (Ray McLennan)
Fax: 01727 761357
Email: info@mlbduk.com

European distributors for Motilal Banasidass Ltd, one of the largest and most reputable publishers in India, also specialist suppliers of Indian titles from all major Indian publishers,in English. Large selection of Buddhist titles from Sanskrit and Pali, written by scholars from all schools.

Largest European supplier to the booktrade, including academic libraries, retail chains and internet booksellers.

Entry continued on the following page.

PURELAND BUDDHISM
Tradition: Pure Land
Email: paschalmcsweeney@hotmail.com
Website(s): www.purelandbuddhism.com
Cork City, Ireland

Contact: Paschal McSweeney

The purpose of this website is to distribute books on Buddhism, in particular Pure Land Buddhism.

These books are available free of charge - being supplied by the Amitabha Buddhist Society of New York.

WINDHORSE PUBLICATIONS
Affiliated to: Friends Of The Western Buddhist Order, UK National Organisations
Charity No.: 272329
Postal Address: Windhorse Publications, 11 Park Road, Moseley, Birmingham B13 8AB
Telephone Contact: 0845 4589514
Or 0121 449 9191 (Sales and Distribution)
Fax: 0845 449 9191
Email: info@windhorsepublications.com
Website(s): www.windhorsepublications.com
See Resources Publishers.

WISDOM BOOKS
Wisdom Books, Resources, Bookshops, London
Postal Address: 25 Stanley Road, Ilford, Essex IG1 1RW
Telephone Contact: 020 8553 5020
Fax: 020 8553 5122
Email: sales@wisdom-books.com
Website(s): www.wisdom-books.com

The leading specialists in books on Buddhism, Tibet and related subjects, with over 6000 titles on their lists. All available books from all the major Buddhist traditions are covered. Exclusive European distributor for most of the major Buddhist publishers, also distributors for the Buddhist Publication Society, Kandy, Sri Lanka. Also provided is a long-established

and continually expanding mail order service to customers in the UK, Europe and Overseas. These can now be ordered online at www.wisdom-books.com

ZAM
Postal Address: ZAM SARL, Route de Millan, 34700 Lodeve, France
Telephone Contact: +33 (0)4 67 88 91 00
Fax: +33 (0) 4 67 88 46 31
Email: enquiries@zamstore.com
Website(s): www.zamstore.com

Zam is located in the Rigpa London centre and has been set up as the trading arm of Rigpa's activities in order to raise funds for various areas of the work of the Rigpa Fellowship and to support the Dzogchen Monastery in India. Zam aims to make available such items as Buddhist books, Tibetan calendars, thangkas, statues, ritual and practice objects, incense, meditation cushions, audio and video tapes, cards and posters etc whilst helping Tibetans in the Himalayan region who make and supply some of these goods.

BOOKSHOPS

CAMBRIDGE

W HEFFER & SONS
Postal Address: W Heffer & Sons, 20 Trinity Street, Cambridge CB2 1TY
Telephone Contact: 01223 568568
Fax: 01223 568591
Email: heffers@heffers.co.uk
Website(s): www.heffers.co.uk
Large oriental department. Now a division of Blackwell Retail Ltd.

CROYDON

CROYDON BUDDHIST CENTRE BOOKSHOP
Affiliated to: Friends Of The Western Buddhist Order, UK National Organisations

Resources

Charity No.: 270460
Postal Address: Croydon Buddhist Centre, 96-98 High Street, Croydon, Surrey CRO 1ND
Telephone Contact: 020 8688 8624
Fax: 020 8649 9375
Email: info@croydonbuddhistcentre.com
Website(s): www.croydonbuddhistcentre.com
This FWBO centre includes a bookshop.

LONDON

ARTHUR PROBSTHAIN

Postal Address: Arthur Probsthain, 41 Great Russell Street, London WC1B 3PE
SOAS Bookshop, University of London, Thornhaugh Street, Russell Square, London WC1H 0XG
Telephone Contact: 020 7636 1096
Or 020 7898 4470
Fax: 020 7636 1096
Email: arthurprobsthain@hotmail.com
freespace.virginnet.co.uk/arthur.probsthain

Useful and varied selection of new and secondhand Buddhist & Oriental books. Searches undertaken. There is a branch bookshop at the School of Oriental and African Studies. Secondhand stock is listed at www.tinyurl.com/2ruw7 (AbeBooks secondhand website).

BUDDHIST SOCIETY

Affiliated to: Buddhist Society, UK National Organisations
Charity No.:1113705
Postal Address: The Buddhist Society, 58 Eccleston Square, London SW1V 1PH

Telephone Contact: 020 7834 5858
Fax: 020 7976 5238
Email: info@thebuddhistsociety.org
Website(s): www.thebuddhistsociety.org

The Society's Book Stall is located in the Library.

Like the Library itself, its scope is constrained by the available space, but it covers the major Buddhist traditions and includes a range of books from those suitable for the beginner to more advanced works. The Society's own publications are always available. We also sell a limited range of other items including Buddhist picture cards and incense. However, there is no space for bulky items such as meditation mats, cushions and posters.

A Reading List is available containing a selection of basic publications which we try to have in stock, but intending purchasers should bear in mind that titles tend to go out of print without warning.

The Bookstall and Library are open to personal callers 2.00-6.00pm Monday to Friday, and 2.00pm-5.00pm Saturday. A mail order service is available.

FINE BOOKS ORIENTAL LTD

Postal Address: Fine Books Oriental, 38 Museum Street, London WC1A 1LP
Telephone Contact: 020 7242 5288
020 7242 5344
Email: oriental@finebooks.demon.uk
Website(s): www.finebooks.demon.co.uk

Fine Books Oriental are the UK's foremost authority on rare and antiquarian Oriental publications. We have over 10,000 rare books for sale as well as outstanding collections of other publications, postcards and photographs from all parts of the Orient. Situated in the very heart of London, directly opposite the famous British Museum, we are ideally placed to find and to offer exceptional items.

Please do take the time to browse our online inventory of books. If you don't find exactly what you are looking for then do get in touch with us to register the books you are seeking or to request a personalised catalogue.

LONDON BUDDHIST VIHARA BOOKSTALL
Tradition: Theravada
Affiliated to: London Buddhist Vihara,
England, London, W 4
Postal Address: The London Buddhist
Vihara, Dharmapala Building, The Avenue,
Chiswick, London W4 1UD

Telephone Contact: 020 8995 9493 (Ven.
Bogoda Seelawimala)

Fax: 020 8994 8130
Email: london.vihara@virgin.net
Website(s): www.londonbuddhistvihara.org

Stocks particularly books on Theravada Buddhism,
especially those published by the Buddhist
Publication Society, Kandy, Sri Lanka including a
selection of the Wheel booklets.

THEOSOPHICAL SOCIETY
Tradition: Theosophical Society, 50 Gloucester
Place, London W1U 8EA
Postal Address: Tekels Park Guest House,
Camberly, Surrey, GU15 2LF
Telephone Contact: 020 7563 9817
Or 020 7563 9815
Or 020 7563 9818
Fax: 020 7935 9543
Email: office@theosoc.org.uk
Website(s): www.theosoc.org.uk

There is no religion higher than Truth, is the motto
of The Theosophical Society, an organization
which has done much to popularize in the West
such concepts as reincarnation and karma.
Theosophy is a Greek word meaning 'Divine
wisdom'.

The modern Theosophical Society was established
in 1875 in New York City. In his inaugural address
President Henry S. Olcott, remarked If I correctly
interpret our public work, it is to aid in freeing the
public mind of religious superstition. We are

simply investigators of earnest purpose and
unbiased mind who study all things, prove all
things and hold fast to all that which is good.
Olcott was amongst three principal founders. The
others were Helena P. Blavatsky, and William Q.
Judge. Blavatsky claimed that she was the agent
of a body of Adepts or Masters of Wisdom, who
are dedicated to the welfare of humanity, and that
her work was under their direction.

Adyar, Chennai (Madras), India has been the
international seat of The Theosophical Society
since 1882. The Society is represented in 60
countries; there are 36 branches in England.

The Headquarters of The Theosophical Society in
England has a lending library of 13,000 volumes
and one of the finest bookshops on Theosophy.
Lectures, seminars and courses are held regularly
on different aspects of the Ageless Wisdom.

TIBET SHOP
Affiliated to: Tibet Foundation, Related
Organisations
292400
Postal Address: Tibet Shop, 1a St James's
Market London SW1Y 4SB
Telephone Contact: 020 7930 6005
Email: shop@tibet-foundation.org or
riga@tibetshop.co.uk
Website(s): www.tibetshop.org.uk or
www.tibet-foundation.org

Tibet Shop presents a wide range of traditional
Tibetan arts and crafts and books on Tibetan
Buddhism and culture. We buy direct from
Tibetans living in exile in India and Nepal, helping
them to keep their traditions alive.

The Shop sells a variety of Tibetan handicrafts,
clothing, jewellery, carpets, ritual and decorative
items, musical instruments and thangka paintings.
It also sells greeting cards, posters, incense, CDs
and cassettes of Tibetan music and chant, videos
and books on Tibetan Buddhism and the Dalai

Resources

Lama. We offer discounts to wholesalers.

Tibet Shop is solely owned by Tibet Foundation (reg. charity 292400) and all profits go to the charitable puposes of the Foundation.

WATERSTONES (Formerly Dillons)
Postal Address: Waterstones, 82 Gower Street, London WC1E 6EQ
Telephone Contact: 020 7636 1577
Fax: 020 7580 7680
Email: secondhand@gowerst.waterstones.co.uk
Website(s): waterstones.co.uk
New and secondhand stock on Buddhism.

WATKINS BOOKS
Postal Address: Watkins Books, 19-21 Cecil Court, London WC2N 4EZ
Telephone Contact: 020 7836 2182
Fax: 020 7836 6700
Email: service@watkinsbooks.com
Website(s): www.watkinsbooks.com
Excellent choice of new Buddhist books and some secondhand.

WISDOM BOOKS
Postal Address: 25 Stanley Road, Ilford, Essex IG1 1RW
Telephone Contact: 020 8553 5020
Fax: 020 8553 5122
Email: sales@wisdom-books.com
Website(s): www.wisdom-books.com

The leading specialists in books on Buddhism, Tibet and related subjects, with over 6000 titles on their lists. All available books from all the major Buddhist traditions are covered. Exclusive European distributor for most of the major Buddhist publishers, also distributors for the Buddhist Publication Society, Kandy, Sri Lanka. Also provided is a long-established and continually expanding mail order service to customers in the UK, Europe and Overseas.

These can now be ordered directly online via the new Wisdom books website - www.wisdom-books.com

NORTHUMBERLAND

THROSSEL HOLE BUDDHIST BOOKSHOP
Affiliated to: The Order Of Buddhists Contemplatives, UK National Organisations
Postal Address: Throssel Hole Buddhist Bookshop, Carrshield, Hexham, Northumberland NE47 8AL
Telephone Contact: 01434 345204 (9.30am - 11.30am and 2.30pm - 4.30pm)
Fax: 01434 345216
Email: sales@buddhistsupplies.co.uk
Website(s): www.buddhistsupplies.co.uk

Mail order supplies of incense, books and recorded Dharma talks on CD and DVD.

OXFORD

BLACKWELLS
Postal Address: Blackwells, 48-51 Broad Street, Oxford OX1 3BQ
Telephone Contact: 01865 333667
Fax: 01865 794143
Email: oxford@blackwellsbookshops.co.uk
Website(s): www.bookshop.blackwell.co.uk

Large Religious department.

SUFFOLK

JOHN RANDALL BOOKS OF ASIA
Telephone Contact: 020 7636 2216
Fax: 020 7436 3955
Email: johnrandall@booksofasia.com
Website(s): www.booksofasia.com

We are a booksellers specialising in rare, antiquarian, out of print and scholarly books

Entry continued on the following page.

189

relating to Asia and in particular to the Buddhist, Hindu, Muslim and tribal cultures of Asia. We hold a large stock of books relating to Tibet, India, Burma, Thailand and other parts of Asia with a particular emphasis on books on the arts, history and cultures of the areas. If a rare book is being sought, a preliminary enquiry in writing is preferred as this gives us time to search through our extensive stock. We are always keen to purchase antiquarian and out of print books in this field. We do not generally keep in stock a wide range of Buddhist texts although we do buy old editions whenever possible. We do not keep popular paperbacks, nor Indian reprints.

SUPPLEMENT

See also the following centres in other sections of the Directory:

Amida Trust (Pure Land): UK National Organisations

Amrita Dzong (Tibetan): England, London, E 2

Birmingham Buddhist Vihara (Theravada): England, West Midlands, Birmingham

Bodhicharya Buddhist Group (Tibetan): England, West Sussex, Chichester

Buddha Vihara (Theravada): England, London: Middlesex, Southall

Buddhist House (Pure Land): England, Leicestershire, Narborough

Cham Tse Ling Buddhist Group (Tibetan): England, Lancashire, Preston

Community Of Interbeing (Vietnamese): UK National Organisations

Federation Of Ambedkarite Buddhist Organisations UK (Theravada): UK National Organisations

Jamyang Buddhist Centre (Tibetan): England, London, SE 11

Jamyang Buddhist Centre Leeds (Tibetan): England, West Yorkshire, Leeds

Lam Rim Bristol Buddhist Centre (Tibetan): England, Avon, Bristol

Lam Rim Buddhist Centre (Tibetan): Wales, Monmouthshire, Penrhos

Marpa House - Chos Khor Ling (Tibetan): England, Essex, Ashdon

Samye Ling Tibetan Centre Bookshop: Resources, Other Buddhist Requisites

Thrangu House Buddhist Centre (Tibetan): England, Oxfordshire, Oxford

Throssel Hole Buddhist Abbey (Zen): England, Northumberland, Hexham

LIBRARIES

BERKSHIRE

INSTITUTE OF ORIENTAL PHILOSOPHY UK
Affiliated to: SGI-UK, UK National Organisations
Postal Address: The Institute of Oriental Philosophy UK, Taplow Court, Taplow, Maidenhead, Berkshire SL6 OER
Telephone Contact: 01628 591213 (Jamie Cresswell)
Fax: 01628 591244
Email: jc@iopec.org
Website(s): www.iopuk.org

A research and study centre non-religiously affiliated to SGI-UK and concentrating on Asian religions and thought, though with an emphasis on Buddhism. It is based around a continually growing library, currently containing around 12,000 volumes of source and secondary literature, covering all traditions of Buddhism as well as other religions. In addition we subscribe to around 80 journals and periodicals and we have a continually growing database of newspaper cuttings related to Buddhism. The library may be consulted by anyone carrying out study or research and the entire catalogue is available on computer database.

Multi-disciplinary and cross traditional research is undertaken and lectures and seminars are held regularly, delivered by scholars of religious studies and related fields, as well as by Buddhist practitioners from a variety of traditions.

Please ring for further information and library opening times.

HERTFORDSHIRE

CHRISTMAS HUMPHREYS MEMORIAL LIBRARY
Affiliated to: Amaravati Buddhist Monastery, UK National Organisations
Postal Address: The Librarian, Amaravati Buddhist Monastery, Great Gaddesden, Hemel Hempstead, Hertfordshire HP1 3BZ
Telephone Contact: 01442 842455
Fax: 01442 843721
Email: library@amaravati.org
Website(s): www.amaravati.org

The library at Amaravati covers every aspect of Buddhism and many areas of the world's other spiritual paths. Please contact for details of opening hours and current facilities.

LONDON

BRITISH LIBRARY
Postal Address: The British Library, Asia, Pacific and Africa Collections, 96 Euston Road, London NW1 2DB

Telephone Contact: 020 7412 7873 (APAC Reference Enquiries)
Or 020 7412 7676 (Reader Admissions)
Fax: 020 7412 7641 (APAC)
Email:
apac-enquiries@bl.uk, reader-registration@bl.uk
Website(s): www.bl.uk

The British Library's various departments hold material relating to Buddhism in Western and Asian languages. Works published in the UK are received by copyright deposit; American, European and other foreign imprints acquired mainly by purchase. Not all the Library's holdings can be stored at St Pancras: some are kept at other locations in London and some at Boston Spa in West Yorkshire. Material not held at St Pancras should be available within 24 hours. Materials in Western languages can be seen in either of the two Humanities reading rooms or in the Asian and African Studies Reading Room on the 3rd floor.

Most material from the Buddhist world of India, Nepal, Sri Lanka, Southeast Asia, Central and East Asia is held in the Oriental and India Office Collections and can be consulted in the Oriental Reading Room. This department was formed in 1991 through the amalgamation of the British Library's Department of Oriental Manuscripts and Printed Books and the India Office Library and Records (formerly administered by the Foreign Office). Amongst its holdings are rare and early Buddhist manuscripts and printed texts, illustrated manuscripts with scenes from the life of the Buddha and the Jataka stories, printed editions of Buddhist texts and literature and up-to-date acquisitions of works on Buddhist topics.

BUDDHIST SOCIETY
Affiliated to: Buddhist Society, UK National Organisations
Charity No.: 1113705
Postal Address: The Buddhist Society, 58 Eccleston Square, London SW1V 1PH
Telephone Contact: 020 7834 5858

Entry continued on the following page.

(Opening hours only)
Fax: 020 7976 5238
Email: library@thebuddhistsociety.org
Website(s): www.thebuddhistsociety.org

The Society has possessed a Library since the earliest days; the first accessions records date from 1926. It is continually being reorganised and developed to make it of maximum benefit to all those interested in Buddhism.

The size of the Library is limited by the space presently available to about 3,000 volumes on the Ground Floor plus approximately 1,500 more elsewhere in the building. The core of the collection is material supporting the belief and practice of present-day Buddhists in the UK, although peripheral subjects such as Buddhism and Psychology, Buddhism and Philosophy etc are covered as well as the culture and history of traditionally Buddhist countries.

Most of the books are available for loan to members resident in the U.K. Non-members may consult books during the hours when the Society is open to the public.

Advance notice is required if you want reserve material which is not kept on the Ground Floor.

The Library catalogue is available for searching on line (click on the links provided from the Society's website).

The room next to the Library is now reserved for quiet reading during weekday opening hours.

The Library is open to personal callers 2.00-6.00pm Monday to Friday, and 2.00pm-5.00pm Saturday.

LONDON BUDDHIST VIHARA LIBRARY
Affiliated to: London Buddhist Vihara, England, London, W 4
Postal Address: The London Buddhist

Vihara, Dharmapala Building, The Avenue, Bedford Park, Chiswick, London W4 1UD
Telephone Contact: 020 8995 9493
Fax: 020 8994 8130
Email: london.vihara@virgin.net
Website(s): www.londonbuddhistvihara.org

There is a reference library of some 3,500 books. A library catalogue is available. New books are on sale.

SCHOOL OF ORIENTAL AND AFRICAN STUDIES LIBRARY
Postal Address: The Library, The School of Oriental and African Studies, Thornhaugh Street, Russell Square, London WC1H 0XG
Telephone Contact: 020 7898 4163
Fax: 020 7898 4159
Email: libenquiry@soas.ac.uk
Website(s): www.soas.ac.uk

The nucleus of the Library was formed at the time of the School's foundation by the collection of Oriental books owned by the London Institution. The University library and the libraries of University and Kings College transferred to the School their Oriental books (other than Hebrew and Syriac) in exchange for the Western books from the London Institution Library. Foremost among these collections were the printed books and manuscripts, containing many rare editions and unique items, presented to Kings College in 1835 by the Orientalist and numismatist William Marsden. The present Library accommodation, opened in 1973, is arranged on six floors and has space for about 1.5 million volumes and seats for 900 readers.

SUPPLEMENT

See also the following entries in other sections of the Directory, where library facilities are reported. Please note that the books may not be available to non-members or for reference.

A Shared Offering (All): England, East Riding Of Yorkshire, Withernsea

Aberfeldy Serene Reflection Meditation Group (Zen): Scotland, Perth And Kinross, Aberfeldy
Amida Trust (Pure Land): UK National Organisations

Birmingham Buddhist Vihara (Theravada): England, West Midlands, Birmingham

Bodhi Garden Dharma Centre (All): England, East Sussex, Brighton

Bodhicharya Buddhist Group (Tibetan): England, West Sussex, Chichester

Brighton Theravadan Group (Theravada): England, East Sussex, Brighton

Bristol Shambhala Meditation Group (Tibetan): England, Avon, Bristol

Buddha Vihara (Theravada): England, London, E 13

Buddha Vihara (Theravada): England, London: Middlesex, Southall

Buddhapadipa Temple (Theravada): England, London, SW 19

Buddhist House (Pure Land): England, Leicestershire, Narborough

Cham Tse Ling Buddhist Group (Tibetan): England, Lancashire, Preston

Diamond Way Buddhism UK (Tibetan): UK National Organisations

Dorjechang Buddhist Centre (Tibetan): England, London, SW 19

Dragon Bell Temple (Zen): England, Devon, Exeter

Edinburgh Samye Dzong (Tibetan): Scotland, Edinburgh, Edinburgh

Federation Of Ambedkarite Buddhist Organisations UK (Theravada): UK National Organisations

Fo Guang Shan (Manchester) (Chinese): England, Greater Manchester, Manchester

Forest Hermitage (Wat Pah Santidhamma) (Theravada): England, Warwickshire, Sherbourne

Glasgow Zen Dojo (Zen): Scotland, Glasgow, Glasgow

Golden Buddha Centre: UK National Organisations

Harlow Diamond Way Buddhist Centre (Tibetan): England, Essex, Harlow

Hartridge Buddhist Monastery (The Devon Vihara) (Theravada): England, Devon, Honiton

House of Inner Tranquillity (Theravada): England, Wiltshire, Bradford On Avon

Isle Of Wight Buddhist Group (All): England, Isle Of Wight, Newport

Jamyang Brighton (Tibetan): England, East Sussex, Brighton

Jamyang Buddhist Centre (Tibetan): England, London, SE 11

Jamyang Buddhist Centre Leeds (Tibetan): England, West Yorkshire, Leeds

Jamyang Salisbury (Tibetan): England, Wiltshire, Salisbury

Kagyu Samye Ling Monastery and Tibetan Centre - Rokpa Trust (Tibetan): UK National Organisations

Khandro Ling (Tibetan): England, Cheshire, Macclesfield

Lam Rim Bristol Buddhist Centre (Tibetan): England, Avon, Bristol

Resources

Lam Rim Buddhist Centre (Tibetan): Wales, Monmouthshire, Penrhos

Leicester Buddhist Vihara (East Midlands Buddhist Association) (Theravada): England, Leicestershire, Leicester

Leicester Serene Reflection Meditation Group (Zen): England, Leicestershire, Leicester

Liverpool Diamond Way Buddhist Centre (Tibetan): England, Merseyside, Liverpool

Liverpool Serene Reflection Meditation Group (Zen): England, Merseyside, Liverpool

London Diamond Way Buddhist Centre (Tibetan): England, London, WC 1

London Fo Guang Temple (Chinese): England, London, W 1

London Inter Faith Centre: Related Organisations

London Serene Reflection Meditation Group (Zen): England, London, N 1

Marpa House - Chos Khor Ling (Tibetan): England, Essex, Ashdon

Mid-Kent And Medway Buddhist Group (Theravada): England, Kent, Maidstone

Modern Buddha Way (All): England, Surrey, Guildford

Newcastle Diamond Way Buddhist Centre (Tibetan): England, Tyne And Wear, Newcastle Upon Tyne

Norwich Serene Reflection Meditation Group (Zen): England, Norfolk, Norwich

Palyul Centre UK (Tibetan): UK National Organisations

Phiroz Mehta Trust: Related Organisations

Reading Buddhist Priory (Zen): England, Berkshire, Reading

Reading Diamond Way Buddhist Centre (Tibetan): England, Berkshire, Reading

Rochdale Zen Retreat (Zen): England, Greater Manchester, Bolton

Samadhi Meditation Centre (Theravada): England, London, N9

Samatha Centre (Theravada): Wales, Powys, Knighton

Samatha Trust (Theravada): UK National Organisations

Stafford Buddhist Information (All): England, Staffordshire, Stafford

Stillpoint (All): Related Organisations

Telford Buddhist Priory (Zen): England, Shropshire, Telford

Thames Buddhist Vihara (Theravada): England, London: Surrey, Selsdon

Theosophical Society: Resources, Bookshops, London

Thrangu House Buddhist Centre (Tibetan): England, Oxfordshire, Oxford

Vajrakuta Buddhist Study Centre (FWBO): Wales, Denbighshire, Corwen

West Cornwall Zen Centre (Zen / Ch'an): England, Cornwall, Helston

Winterhead Retreat House (Zen): England, Somerset, Shipham

OTHER BUDDHIST REQUISITES

ACRE MOUNTAIN
Postal Address: Acre Mountain, 61 Moor Park Close, Rainham, Kent ME8 8QT.
Email: enquiries@acremountain.com
Website(s): www.acremountain.co.uk

We are the suppliers of best quality meditation cushion, stools, timers, accessories and meditation mats. Buy zafu and zabuton which will provide you support while doing meditation thus enabling you to maintain your posture.

BLUE BANYAN
Postal Address: Blue Banyan Ltd, Unit 25, Mold Business Park, Wrexham Road, Mold, Flintshire, CH7 1XP
Telephone Contact: 01352 759 111
Email: info@bluebanyan.co.uk
Website(s): www.bluebanyan.co.uk

High quality crafted products for sitting meditation. We make a range of meditation cushions, supports, adjusters and mats. All are available in a choice of five colours.

We also offer a beautifully designed meditation stool, crafted from American ash, as well as portable meditation cushion and mat sets and mats for massage, shiatsu and yoga. We also supply quality Tibetan and Japanese incense, and books and tapes related to Buddhism and meditation. Please contact us for a colour brochure.

BUDDHIST INSURANCE SCHEMES
Postal Address: Buddhist Insurance Schemes, Peter Sellers Insurance Brokers A Division of OAMPS (UK) Ltd, Buckland House, 38 Albert Road, Reigate, Surrey, RH2 9EH
Telephone Contact: 020 3251 1001 (Clive Adams)
Or 01737 230315 (Martin Robinson)
Fax: 020 3251 1002
Email: clive.s.adams@btinternet.com
Website(s): www.buddhistinsurance.co.uk

Insurance for Buddhist Centres, Places of Worship, Retreat Centres, Residential Communities and connected Businesses (Importers, Cafes, Bookshops, Publishers etc.).

Our schemes have been specifically designed for Buddhists and incorporate various benefits not usually found in standard policies.

Insurances arranged include buildings, contents, residents/retreatants possessions, employers liability, public liability, trustees indemnity and charity vehicles.

Preferential terms and a three year fixed rate help contain costs.

We currently advise around 140 Buddhist organisations in the UK and are always happy to answer any insurance related query from the Buddhist community. See our advertisement for further details.

OAMPS (UK) Ltd is Authorised and Regulated by the Financial Services Authority. Reg No. 302649

BUDDHIST PUBLISHING GROUP
Affiliated to: Buddhist Publishing Group, Resources, Publishers
Postal Address: Buddhist Publishing Group, PO Box 173, Totnes, Devon, TQ9 9AE
Telephone Contact: 01803 898176
Email: bpg@buddhistpublishing.com
Website(s): www.buddhistpublishing.com

Formed in 1983. BPG import Japanese incense, sell by mail order, publish and distribute free booklets and organise a Buddhist Summer School every year.

Incorporating
Buddhist Insurance Schemes

We offer a unique insurance scheme providing cover for buildings, contents, loss of income, loss of money and liability insurance for Buddhist centres, places of worship, retreat centres, residential communities and connected businesses (giftware, cafes, bookshops, publishers etc.). The policy incorporates various benefits not usually found in standard 'off the shelf' policies.

Benefits:

- *Specialist knowledge* – we currently advise around 140 Buddhist charities and businesses. This knowledge has been gained over a 20 year period of working with Buddhists
- *Assistance* - in determining your cover requirements. What to insure and also what not to insure!
- *Risk management advice* – particularly important where the charity undertakes un-usual projects such as building work or extends its general activities
- *Claims advice* – particularly important if a claim or part of a claim is rejected. We have negotiated settlement on claims initially rejected by insurers. The scheme has also paid sizeable claims not covered under 'standard' policies
- *Friendly and professional advice* - from a dedicated expert service team
- *Buying power* - enables us to negotiate very competitive rates. Savings of 20/30% are possible
- *Efficiency* - scheme documentation is produced by us, usually within 48 hours
- *Preferential terms* - and a three year fixed rate help contain costs
- *One stop* - we are also able to place your other insurance requirements such as trustee indemnity and charity vehicles. These are placed outside of the scheme with a panel of carefully selected insurers

We currently advise around **140** Buddhist organisations in the UK and are always happy to answer any insurance related query from the Buddhist community.

Contact information:

Clive Adams Dip CII Tel: 020 3251 1001 E-mail: clive.s.adams@btinternet.com

Martin Robinson Tel: 01737 230315 E-mail: martinr@oamps.co.uk

Buddhist Insurance Schemes, OAMPS (UK) Ltd, Buckland House, 38 Albert Road North, Reigate, Surrey, RH2 9EH.

Fax: 020 3251 1002

Internet: buddhistinsurance.co.uk

OAMPS (UK) Ltd is Authorised and Regulated by the Financial Services Authority. Reg No 302649.

Resources

GARUDA TRADING - TIBETAN DHARMA SUPPLIES
Postal Address: Garuda Trading, Hedra, Grenville Road, Lostwithiel, Cornwall PL22 0EP
Telephone Contact: 01208 873785
Fax: 01208 873785
Email: garuda@talk21.com
Website(s): www.tibetanbuddhism.co.uk

Supplying individual practitioners and Buddhist centres worldwide with Tibetan Buddhist Dharma supplies. We stock a wonderful range of quality Thangkas, Rupas, Malas, Prayer Flags, Dharma Books, Ritual Aids, Meditation Cushions, Tibetan and Bhutanese Incense and much more. We can also undertake specialist orders on our regular buying trips to Nepal. Wholesale enquiries are most welcome.

KARMA SHOP
Postal Address: 23 Portland Street, Leamington Spa, CV32 5EZ
Telephone Contact: 01926 886200
Website(s): www.karma-buddha.co.uk

We aim to provide unique Buddha handicrafts and accessories from around the world of the highest quality at very affordable prices.

Currently in stock we have a variety of Buddha Statues, Buddha Heads, Miniatures, Altars, Tibetan Jewellery (Necklaces & Power Bracelets) and other accessories and Interior Design products.

SAMYE LING TIBETAN CENTRE BOOKSHOP
Affiliated to: Kagyu Samye Ling Monastery And Tibetan Centre, UK National Organisations
Postal Address: The Bookshop, Samye Ling Tibetan Centre, Eskdalemuir, Langholm, Dumfriesshire DG13 0QL
Telephone Contact: 01387 373337
Fax: 01387 373223
Email: sales@samyelingshop.com

Website(s): www.samyelingshop.com Books and artefacts perpetuating the living skills and traditions of Tibetan Buddhism.

TEA CIRCLE
Postal Address: Tea Circle, 8657 Lancaster Drive, Rohnert Park, CA 94928 USA
Telephone Contact: +1 707 792 1619 Or +1 707 792 1946
Email: tcircle@sonic.net
Website(s): www.tea-circle.com

We are an online resource featuring a full line of supplies for practitioners of the Japanese tea ceremony. Our goal is to offer a wide variety of items from kaishi papers to tatami mats. The majority of items are from Japan, but we are also featuring wares made by Northern California artists. Please visit our web-site or, if you would like to receive a printed version of our catalog, please write or call us.

THROSSEL HOLE BUDDHIST BOOKSHOP
Affiliated to: The Order Of Buddhists Contemplatives, UK National Organisations
Postal Address: Throssel Hole Buddhist Bookshop, Carrshield, Hexham, Northumberland NE47 8AL
Telephone Contact: 01434 345204 (9.30am - 11.30am and 2.30pm - 4.30pm)
Fax: 01434 345216
Email: sales@buddhistsupplies.co.uk
Website(s): www.buddhistsupplies.co.uk

Mail order supplies of incense, books and recorded Dharma talks on CD and DVD.

TIBET SHOP
Affiliated to: Tibet Foundation, Related Organisations
Charity No.: 292400
Postal Address: Tibet Shop, 1a St James's Market, London SW1Y 4SB
Telephone Contact: 020 7930 6005

Email: shop@tibet-foundation.org or riga@tibetshop.co.uk
Website(s): www.tibetshop.org.uk or www.tibet-foundation.org

Tibet Shop presents a wide range of traditional Tibetan arts and crafts and books on Tibetan Buddhism and culture. We buy direct from Tibetans living in exile in India and Nepal, helping them to keep their traditions alive.

The Shop sells a variety of Tibetan handicrafts, clothing, jewellery, carpets, ritual and decorative items, musical instruments and thangka paintings. It also sells greeting cards, posters, incense, CDs and cassettes of Tibetan music and chant, videos and books on Tibetan Buddhism and the Dalai Lama. We offer discounts to wholesalers.

Tibet Shop is solely owned by Tibet Foundation and all profits go to the charitable purposes of the Foundation.

WINDHORSE IMPORTS
Postal Address: Windhorse Imports (Noble Truth Ltd), PO Box 2687, Swindon SN4 7ZQ
Telephone Contact: 01793 855839
Fax: 01793 855839
Email: sales@windhorse.co.uk
Website(s): www.windhorse.co.uk

Windhorse is a mail order and wholesale business importing meditation objects and related handicraft items from India and Nepal started by a Buddhist practitioner in 1986. It specializes in crystal Buddhas and sacred objects, Nepalese/Tibetan jewellery, Tibetan incense, Nepalese statues, brocade wall hangings, door curtains, Tibetan ritual objects, all kinds of prayer beads including gemstone and conch shell, & singing bowls. A free colour catalogue is available on request.

Windhorse is able to offer a unique personalized service to meet your requirements wherther you

are ordering for yourself, running a workshop or managing a shop. We can also obtain special orders, which have included the finest skull damarus, meteorite phurbas, antique singing bowls, the highest quality Nepalese statues, vajras and phurbas, and made-to-order tankhas that are great works of art.

Our wholesale rates are very competitive.

ZAZEN (Sacred Icons)
Jeremy Sellars, Zazen, 19 Fox Lane, Bromsgrove B61 7NJ
Telephone Contact: 01252 731333
Fax: 01252 727618
Email: sales@dharma-store.com
Website(s): www.dharma-store.com

We import mainly from India, Nepal and Japan and offer a wide range of Buddha rupas, Nepali, Tibetan and Japanese incense, 'dharmaware', prayer flags, malas and related items. We also market meditation cushions, mats and stools made in the UK. Free mail order brochure available on request. Trade customers welcome.

PUBLICATIONS

BUDDHADHARMA: THE PRACTITIONER'S QUARTERLY
Tradition: All
Postal Address: Buddhadharma: The Practitioner's Quarterly, 1660 Hollis Street, Suite 701, Halifax, Nova Scotia, Canada B3J 1V7
Telephone Contact: (+1) 902 422 8404
Fax: (+1) 902 423 2701
Email: mdeshong@shambhalasun.com
Website(s): www.thebuddhadharma.com

The in-depth, practice-oriented journal for Buddhists of all traditions.

Entry continued on the following page.

SHAMBHALA SUN MAGAZINE
Postal Address: Shambhala Sun Magazine, 1660 Hollis Street, Suite 701, Halifax, Nova Scotia, Canada B3J 1V7
Email: mdeshong@shambhalasun.com
Website(s): www.shambhalasun.com

Today's leading Buddhist publication, bringing a Buddhist view to all the issues in life.

TRICYCLE: THE BUDDHIST REVIEW
Postal Address: Tricycle: The Buddhist Review, 92 Vandam Street, New York, NY 10013
Email: info@tricycle.com
Website(s): www.tricycle.com

Tricycle: The Buddhist Review is published The Tricycle Foundation.

PUBLISHERS

ARO BOOKS INC
Affiliated to: Sang-Ngak-Cho-Dzong, UK National Organisations
Postal Address: Aro Books, PO Box No 12, Penarth, Wales CF64 1XN
Telephone Contact: 01291 431389
Email: doctogden@dial.pipex.com

Aro Books was founded in 1994, when the need was perceived for the establishment of a publishing house which would produce books on Buddhist inner Tantra, and, in particular, the teachings and histories of female Lamas, in fresh, creative, contemporary language; addressed to a non-specialist audience. It is dedicated to publishing the complete cycle of pure vision Termas of Khyungchen Aro Lingma. These teachings are surprising in their simplicity, vibrance of presentation and in their direct applicability to the heterodox complexity of our post-industrial society.

It publishes the teachings of Ngakpa Rinpoche, Khandro Dechen, Ngakpa Rigdzin Dorje and other Lamas associated with the Nyingma ngakphang

sangha and wishes to encourage a living tradition which addresses Western society without entering into popularization on the one hand or academia on the other.

Spiritual directors: Ngakpa Rinpoche and Khandro Dechen

Managing Director: Ngakma Yeshe

Editor in chief: Ngakma Shardrol

BUDDHISM NOW
Affiliated to: Buddhist Publishing Group, Resources, Publishers
Postal Address: Buddhist Publishing Group, PO Box 173, Totnes, Devon, TQ9 9AE
Telephone Contact: 01803 898176
Email: bn@buddhistpublishing.com
Website(s): www.buddhistpublishing.com

Buddhism Now magazine was first published in 1989. Independent of any one tradition, organisation or teacher, it deals with living a Buddhist way of life and offers practical help for ordinary people. Available on subscription.

BUDDHIST PUBLISHING GROUP
Postal Address: Buddhist Publishing Group, PO Box 173, Totnes, TQ9 9AE
Telephone Contact: 01803 898176
Email: bpg@buddhistpublishing.com
Website(s): www.buddhistpublishing.com

Formed in 1983. Publishers of a range of Buddhist books, CDs and MP3 downloads, and a magazine, Buddhism Now. BPG also import Japanese incense, sell by mail order and organise a Buddhist Summer School every year.

BUDDHIST RESEARCH
Tradition: All
Postal Address: Buddhist Research, 133 Wells Road, Bath BA2 3AN

Resources

Telephone Contact: +44(0)1225-471453
Email: buddhistresearchcentre@yahoo.co.uk

The Buddhist Research Centre is a non-sectarian research unit dedicated to the research in all aspects of Buddhism including contemporary practices in Asia and the West. The objective of The Buddhist Research Centre is to publish critical scholarly works on Buddhism and facilitate the critical examination and the study of Buddhist principles, practices, schools and traditions.

BUDDHIST SOCIETY PUBLICATIONS
Affiliated to: Buddhist Society, UK National Organisations
Charity No.: 1113705
Postal Address: The Buddhist Society, 58 Eccleston Square, London SW1V 1PH
Telephone Contact: 020 7834 5858
Fax: 020 7976 5238
Email: info@thebuddhistsociety.org
Website(s): www.thebuddhistsociety.org

The Society publishes 'The Buddhist Directory' a directory of Buddhist Centres, groups and other related organizations, in the UK and Ireland. Each entry gives details of the aims of the Centre, whether it is affiliated to a particular tradition, the nature of its activities and contact details: names, addresses, phone numbers etc. It also contains details of libraries in the UK which have sizeable collections of books on Buddhism, publishers and retailers of Buddhist literature and supplies of other Buddhist requisites. It is also fully indexed.

The Society's own publishing activities date back more than 50 years. From time to time it publishes books on Buddhism and related subjects. It has built up a small but select list containing several Buddhist classics.

The Society's most recent publication is 'The Great Way: The Bodhisattva Process in Indian Mahayana Buddhism', by Eric Cheetham, published by the Buddhist Society, London, 2006.

This book is derived from a series of talks delivered by Eric Cheetham beginning in 1990, and it follows on from his previous published work 'An Outline of Indian Mahayana', first published as four booklets by the Buddhist Society and later as a single volume by Tuttle and Co.

GANESHA PRESS
Affiliated to: Dechen Community, UK National Organisations
Telephone Contact: 020 7706 2425
Email: paul.haddon@dechen.org
Website(s): www.dechen.org/shop

The publishing arm of the Dechen Community, Ganesha Press publishes books, booklets and audio tapes on Buddhist thought and practice. For details contact your nearest Dechen centre.

HERITAGE TRUST PUBLICATIONS
Charity No.: SCO 22351
Postal Address: Heritage Buddhist Charitable Trust, Summerlaw, Linton Bankhead, KELSO, TD5 8AF, Scotland
Telephone Contact: 01573 440558
Email: YeshiUK@aol.com
members.aol.com/YeshiUK/index.html

Translations of esoteric Buddhist texts; transcriptions of Buddhist oral teachings; research on Terma.

INTERNATIONAL SACRED LITERATURE TRUST
Postal Address: International Sacred Literature Trust, P.O. Box 54027, London SW20 0YU

The International Sacred Literature Trust was established to promote understanding and open discussion between and within faiths and to give voice in today's world to the wisdom that speaks across time and traditions.

What resources do the sacred traditions of the world possess to respond to the great global threats of poverty, war, ecological disaster, and spiritual despair?

Our starting-point is the sacred texts with their vision of a higher truth and their deep insights into the nature of humanity and the universe we inhabit. The publishing program is planned so that each faith community articulates its own teachings with the intention of enhancing its self-understanding as well as the understanding of those of other faiths and those of no faith.

The Trust especially encourages faiths to make available texts which are needed in translation for their own communities and also texts which are little known outside a particular tradition but which have the power to inspire, console, enlighten, and transform. These sources from the past become resources for the present and future when we make inspired use of them to guide us in shaping the contemporary world.

Our religious traditions are diverse but, as with the natural environment, we are discovering the global interdependence of human hearts and minds. The Trust invites all to participate in the modern experience of interfaith encounter and exchange which marks a new phase in the quest to discover our full humanity.

PALI TEXT SOCIETY

Charity No.: 262216
Postal Address: Eivind Kahrs, Hon Secretary, Pali Text Society, c/o Gazelle, White Cross Mills, Hightown, Lancaster LA1 4XS
Telephone Contact: 01524 528530
Email: pts@palitext.com
Website(s): www.palitext.com

The Pali Text Society is a charity which publishes Pali Texts, translations into English, dictionaries and other reference works. The Society also publishes a Journal on an ad hoc basis. Its aim is to increase public awareness of, and access to, Buddhist Literature in Pali and to encourage scholarship in this field. Research studentships are provided to suitable applicants. AGM held in London. President: Mr L.S.Cousins.

PARINAMA PUBLICATIONS

Email: info@parinama-publications.co.uk
Website(s): www.parinama-publications.co.uk

Exploring the Great Way to Liberation. An in-depth examination and explanation in several phases, of Mahayana Buddhism in India and the rest of Asia

ROUTLEDGE CURZON

Telephone Contact: 020 7017 7720
Website(s): www.routledge.com
www.asianstudiesarena.com

RoutledgeCurzon has for many years been publishing a number of books that form a comprehensive study of the Buddhist tradition as part of wider programme covering Asian studies and other Asian religions. In their RoutledgeCurzon Critical Studies in Buddhism Series they explore the complex and extensive Buddhist tradition from a variety of perspectives, using a range of different methodologies. The series includes scholarly volumes both by established scholars in Buddhist Studies and new authors. It is diverse in its focus, including historical studies, textual translations and commentaries, sociological investigations, bibliographic studies and considerations of religious practice as an expression of Buddhism's integral religiosity. It also publishes materials on modern intellectual historical studies, including the role of Buddhist thought and scholarship in a contemporary, critical context and in the light of current social issues. The series is expansive and imaginative in scope, spanning more than two and a half millennia of Buddhist history. It is receptive to all research works that inform and advance our knowledge and understanding of the Buddhist tradition, maintaining the highest standard of scholarship and promoting the application of innovative research methods.

TEMENOS ACADEMY
Charity No.: 1043015
Postal Address: Temenos Academy, PO Box 203, Ashford, Kent N25 5ZT
Telephone Contact: 01233 813663
Email: temenosacademy@myfastmail.com
Website(s): www.temenosacademy.org

The Temenos Academy is an educational charity which aims to offer education in philosophy and the arts in the light of the sacred traditions of East and West. It regularly features talks on Buddhism in its programme.

THARPA PUBLICATIONS
Affiliated to: New Kadampa Tradition, UK National Organisations
Charity No.: 1015054
Postal Address: Tharpa Publications Conishead Priory Ulverston Cumbria, LA12 9QQ England
Telephone Contact: 01229 588599
01229 483919
Email: tharpa@tharpa.com
Website(s): www.tharpa.com

Tharpa Publications is a publisher of Buddhist books, audiobooks and visual Dharma reproductions, whose main purpose is to preserve and make available the essential teachings of Mahayana Buddhism. The books emphasise the practical application of Buddhist principles to our modern way of life. The author of our books is the highly respected meditation teacher, Geshe Kelsang Gyatso, who has established many centres for the study and practice of Buddhism throughout the world. We also publish authoritative translations of essential sadhanas (prayer booklets) and an extensive range of cards, posters and prints.

Company Registration No 2758093.

Profits received by Tharpa Publications are donated to the NKT - International Temples Project, part of the New Kadampa Tradition (Registered Charity No 1015054), a Buddhist charity, building for world peace.

WINDHORSE PUBLICATIONS
Affiliated to: Friends Of The Western Buddhist Order, UK National Organisations
Charity No.: 272329
Postal Address: Windhorse Publications, 11 Park Road, Moseley, Birmingham B13 8AB
Telephone Contact: 0845 4589514
Or 0121 449 9696(editorial)
Or 0121 449 9191 (Sales and Distribution)
Fax: 0121 449 9191
Email: info@windhorsepublications.com
Website(s): www.windhorsepublications.com

Windhorse Publications is a Buddhist publishing house and book distributor. It specialises in presentations of Buddhism and meditation that are relevant to the western world.

Our publications include: accessible introductions to Buddhism and meditation based upon practical ideas for positive change, modern guides to living a Buddhist life for more experienced practitioners, commentaries, classic texts and inspiration for meditators.

We are the UK and European distributors for Dharma Publishing and Editions Rabten and carry a wide range of books on Buddhism from other publishers.

Please contact us for a free catalogue.

TRAVEL

PALANQUIN TRAVELLER
Postal Address: Palanquin Travels, 92-93 Great Russell Street, London WC1B 3PS
Telephone Contact: 020 7436 9343
www.palanquintravels.com

Palanquin Traveller began with a group of Fellows of the Royal Geographical Society, professional Travellers, Anthropologists, Scientific Explorers, Mountain Leaders and others with Specialist Knowledge of South and Inner Asia. We are dedicated to providing our travellers with a range of opportunities to explore and enjoy unique cultures, wildlife and wilderness.

TRANS HIMALAYA
Postal Address: Trans Himalaya, 16 Skye Crescent, Crieff, Perth & Kinross PH7 3FB
01764 650604
01373 455518
info@trans-himalaya.com
www.trans-himalaya.com

Trans Himalaya, under the direction of Dr Gyurme Dorje, a Tibetologist and Tibet travel writer, organise travel throughout the Tibetan plateau, as well as in Mongolia, China and the Himalayas (Bhutan, Sikkim, Nepal, and Ladakh).

Whether you are a first-time visitor to Central Tibet looking for a simple itinerary, or an experienced Tibet traveller planning an overland journey, trek or expedition in Ngari, Kham or Amdo, Trans Himalaya are the specialists, with a strong client base in the Americas, Europe, SE Asia, Australia and South Africa.

WEBSITES

DIGITAL LIBRARIES

Access to Insight - www.accesstoinsight.org

Sacred Texts - www.sacred-texts.com

Tibetan Buddhist Resource Center - www.tbrc.org

Tibetan & Himalayan Digital Library - www.thdl.org

FORUMS

E-Sangha - www.lioncity.net/buddhism

Beliefnet - www.beliefnet.com

USEFUL LINKS

Buddhanet - www.buddhanet.net

Dharmanet - www.dharmanet.org

Pali Text Society - www.palitext.com

The Zen Site - www.thezensite.com

Zen Guide - www.zenguide.com

Quiet Mountain - www.quietmountain.org

RangyungYesheWiki - rywiki.tsadra.org

Nithartha - www.nitartha.org

A View on Buddhism - www.buddhism.kalachakranet.org

Journal of Buddhist Ethics - www.buddhistethics.org

Dharma The Cat - www.dharmathecat.com

INDEX OF TOWNS AND DISTRICTS

ABERDEEN ....ABERDEEN CITY ....SCOTLAND 139
ABERFELDY ....PERTH AND KINROSS....SCOTLAND 146
ABERYSTWYTH ....CEREDIGION ....WALES 133
ADRIGOLE, BEARA ..CO CORK ....IRELAND..........153
ALLIHIES ....CO CORK ....IRELAND..........153
ASHDON ....ESSEX ....ENGLAND 52
ASHFORD ....KENT ....ENGLAND 65
ASHPRINGTON ....DEVON ....ENGLAND 43
ATHLONE ....CO WESTMEATH ....IRELAND..........157
AYR ....SOUTH AYRSHIRE ......SCOTLAND 146
BAKEWELL ....DERBYSHIRE ....ENGLAND 42
BALLYMENA ....ANTRIM ....IRELAND..........151
BALQHUIDDER ....STIRLING ....SCOTLAND 147
BANBURY ....OXFORDSHIRE ....ENGLAND 104
BATH ....AVON ....ENGLAND 27
BATH/BRISTOL ....AVON ....ENGLAND 27
BAWNBOY ....CO CAVAN ....IRELAND..........152
BEDFORD................BEDFORDSHIRE ....ENGLAND 31
BELFAST ....CO ANTRIM ....IRELAND..........151
BELSAY ..................NORTHUMBERLAND ....ENGLAND 102
BEVERLEY ....HUMBERSIDE ....ENGLAND 63
BIRMINGHAM..........WEST MIDLANDS ....ENGLAND 118
BLACKBURN ....LANCASHIRE ....ENGLAND 67
BOLTON ....Gtr MANCHESTER........ENGLAND 55
BOURNEMOUTH ......DORSET ....ENGLAND 46
BRADFORD ON AVON
............................WILTSHIRE ....ENGLAND 126
BRECON ....POWYS ....WALES 136
BRIGHTON ....EAST SUSSEX ....ENGLAND 48
BRISTOL ....AVON ....ENGLAND 28
BURY ST EDMUNDS..SUFFOLK ....ENGLAND 112
CALDERDALE............WEST YORKSHIRE ......ENGLAND 124
CALNE ....WILTSHIRE ....ENGLAND 127
CAMBRIDGE ............CAMBRIDGESHIRE ......ENGLAND 34
CANTERBURY ....KENT ....ENGLAND 65
CARDIFF..................CARDIFF ....WALES 131
CARLISLE ....CUMBRIA ....ENGLAND 41
CEMAES BAY ....ANGLESEY ....WALES 131
CHEPSTOW ............MONMOUTHSHIRE ......ENGLAND 97
CHESTER ....CHESHIRE ....ENGLAND 36
CHICHESTER ....WEST SUSSEX ....ENGLAND 123
CHIPPENHAM ....WILTSHIRE ....ENGLAND 127
CHITHURST ....WEST SUSSEX ....ENGLAND 124
CIRENCESTER ........GLOUCESTERSHIRE ....ENGLAND 54
COATBRIDGE ....NORTH LANARKSHIRE..SCOTLAND 145
COLCHESTER ....ESSEX........................ENGLAND 52
COLERAINE..............ULSTER ....IRELAND..........157
COLNE....................LANCASHIRE ....ENGLAND 67
CORK ....CO CORK ....IRELAND..........153
CORK CITY ....CO CORK ....IRELAND..........154
CORWEN ................DENBIGHSHIRE ....WALES 133
COVENTRY ....WEST MIDLANDS........ENGLAND 122

CRICCIETH ....GWYNEDD ....WALES 134
CROWBOROUGH ......EAST SUSSEX ....ENGLAND 50
CROYDON ....LONDON: SURREY ......ENGLAND 93
DARTMOOR ....DEVON ....ENGLAND 43
DARWEN..................LANCASHIRE ....ENGLAND 67
DERBY ....DERBYSHIRE ....ENGLAND 42
DONCASTER ....SOUTH YORKSHIRE ....ENGLAND 110
DUBLIN ....CO DUBLIN ....IRELAND..........154
DUBLIN ....DUBLIN ....IRELAND..........154
DUNDEE..................CITY OF DUNDEE ....SCOTLAND 139
DURHAM ....CO DURHAM ....ENGLAND 38
EDGWARE ....LONDON: MIDDLESEX ..ENGLAND 91
EDINBURGH ....EDINBURGH................SCOTLAND 140
ESKDALEMUIR ....DUMFRIES AND GALLOWAY..
....SCOTLAND 140
EXETER ....DEVON ....ENGLAND 43
FORRES ....MORAY ....SCOTLAND 144
GALLOWAY..............DUMFRIES AND GALLOWAY....
....SCOTLAND 140
GALWAY..................CO GALWAY ....IRELAND..........156
GILLINGHAM ....KENT ....ENGLAND 66
GLASGOW ....GLASGOW ....SCOTLAND 143
GLASTONBURY........SOMERSET ....ENGLAND 108
GLOSSOP ....DERBYSHIRE ....ENGLAND 42
GUILDFORD ....SURREY ....ENGLAND 113
HALESOWEN............WEST MIDLANDS........ENGLAND 122
HAM ....LONDON: SURREY ......ENGLAND 93
HARLOW ....ESSEX........................ENGLAND 52
HARROGATE ....NORTH YORKSHIRE ....ENGLAND 100
HARROW..................LONDON: MIDDLESEX ..ENGLAND 91
HASTINGS ....EAST SUSSEX ....ENGLAND 51
HAY-ON-WYE..........POWYS ....WALES 137
HELSTON ....CORNWALL ....ENGLAND 39
HEMEL HEMPSTEAD
............................HERTFORDSHIRE ....ENGLAND 62
HEREFORD ..............HEREFORDSHIRE ....ENGLAND 61
HESTON ....LONDON: MIDDLESEX ..ENGLAND 91
HEXHAM ................NORTHUMBERLAND ....ENGLAND 102
HIGH HURSTWOOD EAST SUSSEX ....ENGLAND 51
HINCKLEY ..............LEICESTERSHIRE ....ENGLAND 70
HONITON ....DEVON ....ENGLAND 45
HOUNSLOW ....LONDON: MIDDLESEX ..ENGLAND 92
HOVE......................EAST SUSSEX ....ENGLAND 51
HUDDERSFIELD ......WEST YORKSHIRE ....ENGLAND 124
HULL ....HUMBERSIDE ....ENGLAND 63
ILFORD ....LONDON: ESSEX ....ENGLAND 90
ILLOGAN ....CORNWALL ....ENGLAND 39
INVERNESS ....HIGHLAND ....SCOTLAND 144
IPSWICH ....SUFFOLK ....ENGLAND 113
KENDAL ....CUMBRIA ....ENGLAND 41
KESWICK ....CUMBRIA ....ENGLAND 41
KETTERING..............NORTHAMPTONSHIRE..ENGLAND..........101

KILLARNEY	CO KERRY	IRELAND	157
KINGSTON UPON THAMES			
	LONDON: SURREY	ENGLAND	93
KNIGHTON	POWYS	WALES	137
LANCASTER	LANCASHIRE	ENGLAND	68
LEAMINGTON SPA	WARWICKSHIRE	ENGLAND	117
LEEDS	WEST YORKSHIRE	ENGLAND	125
LEICESTER	LEICESTERSHIRE	ENGLAND	70
LEIGH ON SEA	ESSEX	ENGLAND	53
LEIGHTON BUZZARD			
	BEDFORDSHIRE	ENGLAND	32
LERWICK	SHETLAND ISLANDS	SCOTLAND	146
LETCHWORTH	HERTFORDSHIRE	ENGLAND	62
LEWES	EAST SUSSEX	ENGLAND	51
LIMERICK	CO LIMERICK	IRELAND	157
LIVERPOOL	MERSEYSIDE	ENGLAND	95
LLANFYLLIN	POWYS	WALES	137
LLANGOLLEN	DENBIGHSHIRE	WALES	133
LLANGUNLLO	POWYS	WALES	137
LONDON E 13	LONDON	ENGLAND	72
LONDON E 2	LONDON	ENGLAND	72
LONDON E 6	LONDON	ENGLAND	73
LONDON EC4	LONDON	ENGLAND	73
LONDON N 1	LONDON	ENGLAND	74
LONDON N 11	LONDON	ENGLAND	74
LONDON N 12	LONDON	ENGLAND	75
LONDON N 15	LONDON	ENGLAND	75
LONDON N 3	LONDON	ENGLAND	75
LONDON N 4	LONDON	ENGLAND	75
LONDON N 5	LONDON	ENGLAND	76
LONDON N 7	LONDON	ENGLAND	76
LONDON N 9	LONDON	ENGLAND	76
LONDON NW 11	LONDON	ENGLAND	77
LONDON NW 3	LONDON	ENGLAND	77
LONDON NW 8	LONDON	ENGLAND	78
LONDON NW 9	LONDON	ENGLAND	78
LONDON NW10	LONDON	ENGLAND	79
LONDON SE 1	LONDON	ENGLAND	79
LONDON SE 11	LONDON	ENGLAND	80
LONDON SE 13	LONDON	ENGLAND	81
LONDON SE 17	LONDON	ENGLAND	81
LONDON SE 18	LONDON	ENGLAND	81
LONDON SE 19	LONDON	ENGLAND	82
LONDON SE 21	LONDON	ENGLAND	82
LONDON SE 24	LONDON	ENGLAND	82
LONDON SW 1	LONDON	ENGLAND	83
LONDON SW 11	LONDON	ENGLAND	83
LONDON SW 19	LONDON	ENGLAND	83
LONDON SW 3	LONDON	ENGLAND	84
LONDON SW 4	LONDON	ENGLAND	85
LONDON W 1	LONDON	ENGLAND	85
LONDON W 11	LONDON	ENGLAND	85
LONDON W 2	LONDON	ENGLAND	86
LONDON W 3	LONDON	ENGLAND	87
LONDON W 4	LONDON	ENGLAND	88
LONDON W 8	LONDON	ENGLAND	88
LONDON W 9	LONDON	ENGLAND	89
LONDON WC 1	LONDON	ENGLAND	89
LOSTWITHIEL	CORNWALL	ENGLAND	40
LUDLOW	SHROPSHIRE	ENGLAND	107
LYME BAY	DORSET	ENGLAND	47
MACCLESFIELD	CHESHIRE	ENGLAND	37
MACHYNLLETH	POWYS	WALES	138
MAIDSTONE	KENT	ENGLAND	66
MANCHESTER	Gtr MANCHESTER	ENGLAND	55
MARLBOROUGH	WILTSHIRE	ENGLAND	128
MARTINSTOWN	DORSET	ENGLAND	47
MATLOCK	DERBYSHIRE	ENGLAND	42
MIDDLESBOROUGH	CLEVELAND	ENGLAND	38
MILTON KEYNES	BUCKINGHAMSHIRE	ENGLAND	33
MORECAMBE BAY	LANCASHIRE	ENGLAND	68
MUNDESLEY	NORFOLK	ENGLAND	97
NARBERTH	PEMBROKESHIRE	WALES	135
NARBOROUGH	LEICESTERSHIRE	ENGLAND	71
NEVERN	PEMBROKESHIRE	WALES	136
NEWBURY	BERKSHIRE	ENGLAND	32
NEWCASTLE EMLYN			
CARMARTHENSHIRE		WALES	132
NEWCASTLE UPON TYNE			
	TYNE AND WEAR	ENGLAND	115
NEWENT	GLOUCESTERSHIRE	ENGLAND	54
NEWPORT	ISLE OF WIGHT	ENGLAND	64
NEWPORT	NEWPORT	WALES	135
NEWPORT	PEMBROKESHIRE	WALES	136
NEWTON ABBOT	DEVON	ENGLAND	45
NORTH CLIFTON, NEWARK			
	NOTTINGHAMSHIRE	ENGLAND	103
NORTH SOMERCOTES			
	LINCOLNSHIRE	ENGLAND	71
NORTHAMPTON	NORTHAMPTONSHIRE	ENGLAND	102
NORTHWICH	CHESHIRE	ENGLAND	37
NORWICH	NORFOLK	ENGLAND	97
NOTTINGHAM	NOTTINGHAMSHIRE	ENGLAND	104
OFF ARRAN	NORTH LANARKSHIRE	SCOTLAND	145
OLDHAM	Gtr MANCHESTER	ENGLAND	68
OLDHAM	LANCASHIRE	ENGLAND	58
OXFORD	OXFORDSHIRE	ENGLAND	104
PENRHOS	MONMOUTHSHIRE	WALES	135
PENZANCE	CORNWALL	ENGLAND	40
PERTH	PERTH	SCOTLAND	145
PERTH	PERTH AND KINROSS	SCOTLAND	146
PETERBOROUGH	CAMBRIDGESHIRE	ENGLAND	36
PORTHMADOG	GWYNEDD	WALES	134
PORTSMOUTH	HAMPSHIRE	ENGLAND	59

Index of Towns and Districts

POTTERS BAR .........HERTFORDSHIRE...........ENGLAND 63
PRESTON ....LANCASHIRE ....ENGLAND 69
READING ....BERKSHIRE ....ENGLAND 32
REDRUTH ....CORNWALL ....ENGLAND 40
RICHMOND ....LONDON: SURREY .....ENGLAND 93
ROMSEY ....HAMPSHIRE ....ENGLAND 60
ROSSENDALE ....LANCASHIRE ....ENGLAND 70
SALE ....Gtr MANCHESTER......ENGLAND 58
SALFORD...................Gtr MANCHESTER......ENGLAND 58
SALISBURY ....WILTSHIRE ....ENGLAND 128
SELSDON ....LONDON: SURREY ....ENGLAND 94
SHEFFIELD ....SOUTH YORKSHIRE ....ENGLAND 110
SHERBOURNE..........WARWICKSHIRE...........ENGLAND 117
SHIPHAM ....SOMERSET ....ENGLAND 109
SHREWSBURY ....SHROPSHIRE..............ENGLAND 108
SIX MILE BRIDGE.....CO CLARE ....IRELAND.............152
SKIPTON ....NORTH YORKSHIRE ....ENGLAND 100
SLOUGH ....BERKSHIRE ....ENGLAND 33
SOUTH BRENT ....DEVON ....ENGLAND 45
SOUTH PETHERTON SOMERSET ....ENGLAND 109
SOUTHALL ....LONDON: MIDDLESEX ..ENGLAND 92
SOUTHAMPTON.......HAMPSHIRE ....ENGLAND 60
SOUTHPORT.............MERSEYSIDE...............ENGLAND 96
SOUTHWOLD............SUFFOLK ....ENGLAND 113
ST PETER PORT ....GUERNSEY ....CHANNEL ISLANDS ..
....149
STEYNING................WEST SUSSEX ....ENGLAND 124
STIRLING.................STIRLING ....SCOTLAND 146
STOCKPORT ....Gtr MANCHESTER.......ENGLAND 59
STOKE-ON-TRENT ....STAFFORDSHIRE ....ENGLAND 112
STROUD ...................GLOUCESTERSHIRE ....ENGLAND 54
SUNDERLAND...........TYNE AND WEAR ....ENGLAND 116
SURBITON.................SURREY ....ENGLAND 114
SURLINGHAM...........NORFOLK ....ENGLAND 99
SUTTON ....LONDON: SURREY ....ENGLAND 94
SUTTON COLDFIELD WEST MIDLANDS..........ENGLAND 122
SWINDON.................WILTSHIRE ....ENGLAND 128
TAPLOW ....BERKSHIRE ....ENGLAND 33
TAUNTON ....SOMERSET ....ENGLAND 109
TELFORD ....SHROPSHIRE ....ENGLAND 108
TOTNES ....DEVON ....ENGLAND 46
TRURO ....CORNWALL ....ENGLAND 40
TWICKENHAM ....LONDON: MIDDLESEX ..ENGLAND 92
UXBRIDGE................LONDON: MIDDLESEX ..ENGLAND 92
VENTNOR ....ISLE OF WIGHT ....ENGLAND 64
WARRINGTON...........CHESHIRE...................ENGLAND 37
WARWICK .................WARWICKSHIRE...........ENGLAND 117
WELLS-NEXT-THE-SEA ....NORFOLK ....
....ENGLAND 99
WESTBURY-ON-TRYM.........................AVON ....
....ENGLAND..........31
WESTER ROSS ....HIGHLAND ....SCOTLAND 144

WEYMOUTH ....DORSET ....ENGLAND 47
WHITCHURCH...........SHROPSHIRE...............ENGLAND 108
WHITECROSS ....CORNWALL ....ENGLAND 40
WHITSTABLE............KENT..........................ENGLAND 67
WILMSLOW..............CHESHIRE ....ENGLAND 37
WIRRAL....................MERSEYSIDE...............ENGLAND 97
WITHERNSEA ....EAST RIDING OF YORKSHIRE ....
....ENGLAND 47
WOKING ....SURREY ....ENGLAND 114
WOLVERHAMPTON WEST MIDLANDS..........ENGLAND 123
WORCESTER ............WORCESTERSHIRE....ENGLAND 129
YORK.......................NORTH YORKSHIRE .....ENGLAND 100

INDEX OF GROUPS BY TITLE

A SHARED OFFERING ....WITHERNSEA 47
ABERDEEN BUDDHIST GROUP (FWBO) ....ABERDEEN 139
ABERDEEN SERENE REFLECTION MEDITATION GROUP .....ABERDEEN 139
ABERFELDY SERENE REFLECTION MEDITATION GROUP .....ABERFELDY 146
ABERYSTWYTH BUDDHIST GROUP ....ABERYSTWYTH....................133
ACRE MOUNTAIN ....OTHER BUDDHIST REQUISITES 195
AGON SHU UK...UK NATIONAL ORGANISATIONS........9
AMARAVATI BUDDHIST MONASTERY ....HEMEL HEMPSTEAD 62
AMARAVATI BUDDHIST MONASTERY ....UK NATIONAL ORGANISATIONS........9
AMARAVATI BUDDHIST RETREAT CENTRE....................HEMEL HEMPSTEAD 62
AMIDA SANCTUARY ....NEWCASTLE UPON TYNE.................115
AMIDA SHEFFIELD CONGREGATION...........................SHEFFIELD 110
AMIDA TRUST ....UK NATIONAL ORGANISATIONS........9
AMRITA DZONG ....LONDON: E 2 72
ANGLESEY THERAVADIN BUDDHIST GROUP ....CEMAES BAY 131
ANGULIMALA: BUDDHIST PRISON CHAPLAINCY ORGANISATION .....RELATED ORGANISATIONS 165
ARMED FORCES CHAPLAINCY ....RELATED ORGANISATIONS 165
ARO BOOKS INC..PUBLISHERS 200
ARRIVING HOME ....SHEFFIELD 110
ARTHUR PROBSTHAIN ....BOOKSHOPS 187
ARUNA RATANAGIRI, HARNHAM BUDDHIST MONASTERY ....BELSAY 102
ASHFORD MEDITATION GROUP ....ASHFORD 65
ASSOCIATION FOR INSIGHT MEDITATION ....ILFORD 90
AWAKENED HEART SANGHA ....CRICCIETH 134
AYR BUDDHIST GROUP (FWBO)...............................AYR 146
BAKEWELL SAMATHA GROUP ....BAKEWELL 42
BANBURY BUDDHIST GROUP...................................BANBURY 104
BARN RURAL RETREAT CENTRE ....TOTNES 46
BATH DIAMOND WAY BUDDHIST CENTRE ....BATH 27
BATH THERAVADA GROUP ....BATH 27
BATH THERAVADA MEDITATION CLASS ....BATH 27
BATH/BRISTOL SAMATHA GROUP ....BATH/BRISTOL 27
BECKMANN VISUAL PUBLISHING ....AUDIO VISUAL 181
BEDFORD AREA BUDDHIST INFORMATION ....BEDFORD.........................31
BERKSHIRE THERAVADAN GROUP ....READING 32
BIRMINGHAM BUDDHIST CENTRE (FWBO) ....BIRMINGHAM 118
BIRMINGHAM BUDDHIST VIHARA.............................BIRMINGHAM 118
BIRMINGHAM DIAMOND WAY BUDDHIST CENTRE ....BIRMINGHAM 119
BIRMINGHAM SAMATHA GROUP ....BIRMINGHAM 119
BIRMINGHAM SERENE REFLECTION MEDITATION GROUP .....BIRMINGHAM 119
BLACK MOUNTAIN ZEN CENTRE...............................BALLYMENA 151
BLACK MOUNTAIN ZEN CENTRE...............................BELFAST 151
BLACK MOUNTAIN ZEN CENTRE...............................COLERAINE........................157
BLACK MOUNTAIN ZEN CENTRE...............................NEWCASTLE UPON TYNE.................115
BLACKBURN & DARWEN SAMATHA GROUP....................DARWEN 67
BLACKBURN BUDDHIST CENTRE (FWBO) ....BLACKBURN 67
BLACKWELLS ....BOOKSHOPS 189
BLUE BANYAN ....OTHER BUDDHIST REQUISITES 195
BODHI GARDEN DHARMA CENTRE ....BRIGHTON 48

BODHICHARYA BUDDHIST GROUP	CHICHESTER	123
BODHICHARYA UK	COATBRIDGE	145
BODHICHARYA UK	UK NATIONAL ORGANISATIONS	10
BODHINYANA GROUP	HEMEL HEMPSTEAD	62
BOLTON MEDITATION GROUP	BOLTON	55
BOURNEMOUTH ZEN DOJO	BOURNEMOUTH	46
BRIGHTON BUDDHIST CENTRE (FWBO)	BRIGHTON	48
BRIGHTON CH'AN GROUP	BRIGHTON	48
BRIGHTON DIAMOND WAY BUDDHIST CENTRE	BRIGHTON	48
BRIGHTON SERENE REFLECTION MEDITATION GROUP	BRIGHTON	49
BRIGHTON SHAMBHALA STUDY GROUP	BRIGHTON	49
BRIGHTON THERAVADAN GROUP	BRIGHTON	49
BRIGHTON TIBET LINK	RELATED ORGANISATIONS	165
BRIGHTON ZEN DOJO	BRIGHTON	49
BRISTOL BUDDHIST CENTRE (FWBO)	BRISTOL	28
BRISTOL CH'AN GROUP	BRISTOL	28
BRISTOL DIAMOND WAY BUDDHIST CENTRE	BRISTOL	28
BRISTOL SHAMBHALA MEDITATION GROUP	BRISTOL	28
BRISTOL SOTO ZEN DOJO	BRISTOL	29
BRITISH BUDDHIST ASSOCIATION	LONDON: W 9	89
BRITISH LIBRARY	LIBRARIES	191
BUDDHA VIHARA	LONDON: E 13	72
BUDDHA VIHARA	SOUTHALL	92
BUDDHADHARMA: THE PRACTITIONER'S QUARTERLY	PUBLICATIONS	199
BUDDHAFIELD (FWBO)	RELATED ORGANISATIONS	165
BUDDHAPADIPA TEMPLE	LONDON: SW 19	84
BUDDHA'S LIGHT INTERNATIONAL ASSOCIATION LONDON (B.L.I.A. LONDON)	LONDON: W 1	86
BUDDHAVIHARA TEMPLE	BIRMINGHAM	119
BUDDHISM NOW	PUBLISHERS	200
BUDDHIST CO-OPERATIVE	RELATED ORGANISATIONS	166
BUDDHIST EDUCATION FOUNDATION (UK)	RELATED ORGANISATIONS	166
BUDDHIST GROUP OF KENDAL (THERAVADA)	KENDAL	41
BUDDHIST HOSPICE TRUST	RELATED ORGANISATIONS	166
BUDDHIST HOUSE	NARBOROUGH	71
BUDDHIST INSIGHT MEDITATION CENTRE OF WEST WALES	NEWCASTLE EMLYN	132
BUDDHIST INSURANCE SCHEMES	OTHER BUDDHIST REQUISITES	195
BUDDHIST INTERHELP AND COMMUNITY OF INTERBEING VIETNAMESE CONTACT	LONDON: SE 13	81
BUDDHIST MEDITATION GROUP	REDRUTH	40
BUDDHIST PUBLISHING GROUP	OTHER BUDDHIST REQUISITES	195
BUDDHIST PUBLISHING GROUP	PUBLISHERS	200
BUDDHIST REALISTS' VIHARA	LONDON: N 11	74
BUDDHIST RESEARCH	PUBLISHERS	201
BUDDHIST SOCIETY	LONDON: SW 1	83
BUDDHIST SOCIETY	UK NATIONAL ORGANISATIONS	10
BUDDHIST SOCIETY	LIBRARIES	191
BUDDHIST SOCIETY	AUDIO VISUAL	181
BUDDHIST SOCIETY	BOOKSHOPS	187
BUDDHIST SOCIETY OF MANCHESTER	SALE	58

BUDDHIST SOCIETY ....PUBLISHERS 201
BURMA CAMPAIGN UK ....RELATED ORGANISATIONS 167
BURY ST EDMUNDS FWBO GROUP ....BURY ST EDMUNDS 112
CALDERDALE ZEN GROUP ....CALDERDALE.................................124
CAMBRIDGE AMARAVATI GROUP ....CAMBRIDGE....................................34
CAMBRIDGE BUDDHIST CENTRE ....CAMBRIDGE....................................34
CAMBRIDGE BUDDHIST INSTITUTE ....RELATED ORGANISATIONS 167
CAMBRIDGE BUDDHIST SOCIETY ....CAMBRIDGE....................................35
CAMBRIDGE CH'AN GROUP ....CAMBRIDGE....................................35
CAMBRIDGE SAMATHA MEDITATION GROUP ....CAMBRIDGE....................................35
CAMBRIDGE SERENE REFLECTION MEDITATION GROUP...CAMBRIDGE...........................36
CANTERBURY BUDDHIST MEDITATION GROUP .....CANTERBURY 65
CANTERBURY DIAMOND WAY BUDDHIST CENTRE...CANTERBURY 65
CANTERBURY TIBET LINK.......................................CANTERBURY 65
CARDIFF BUDDHIST CENTRE ....CARDIFF..132
CARDIFF CH'AN GROUP ....CARDIFF..131
CENTRE FOR MEDITATION AND PSYCHOTHERAPY ...RELATED ORGANISATIONS 167
CHALFORD HILL SHAMBHALA STUDY GROUP ....STROUD..54
CHAM TSE LING BUDDHIST GROUP ....PRESTON 69
CHARITY BANK ....RELATED ORGANISATIONS 167
CHESTER SAMATHA MEDITATION GROUP ....CHESTER 36
CHESTER ZEN GROUP ....CHESTER 37
CHICHESTER SERENE REFLECTION MEDITATION GROUP ...CHICHESTER 123
CHRISTMAS HUMPHREYS MEMORIAL LIBRARY .....AUDIO VISUAL 181
CHRISTMAS HUMPHREYS MEMORIAL LIBRARY .....LIBRARIES 191
CIRENCESTER SERENE REFLECTION MEDITATION GROUP ...CIRENCESTER 54
CIRENCESTER ZEN GROUP ....CIRENCESTER 54
CITTAVIVEKA, CHITHURST BUDDHIST MONASTERY...CHITHURST 124
CLEAR VISION TRUST ....AUDIO VISUAL 182
COLCHESTER BUDDHIST CENTRE (FWBO) ....COLCHESTER 52
COMMUNITY OF INTERBEING ....AUDIO VISUAL 182
COMMUNITY OF INTERBEING ....BOOKS BY POST 184
COMMUNITY OF INTERBEING - ABERDEENSHIRE, BANCHORY SANGHA ...........ABERDEENSHIRE 139
COMMUNITY OF INTERBEING - BIRMINGHAM SANGHA ......BIRMINGHAM 120
COMMUNITY OF INTERBEING - BLUE LOTUS SANGHA ......SHEFFIELD 110
COMMUNITY OF INTERBEING - BORDERS AND LOTHIAN SANGHA......SCOTTISH BORDERS 146
COMMUNITY OF INTERBEING - BOURNEMOUTH SANGHA ......BOURNEMOUTH 46
COMMUNITY OF INTERBEING - BRIGHTON SANGHA ......HOVE 51
COMMUNITY OF INTERBEING - CAMBRIDGE SANGHA ......CAMBRIDGE................................36
COMMUNITY OF INTERBEING - DEEP LISTENING SANGHA ......RELATED ORGANISATIONS ...167
COMMUNITY OF INTERBEING - DULWICH SANGHA ......LONDON: SE 21 82
COMMUNITY OF INTERBEING - DYFI VALLEY SANGHA ......GWYNEDD 133
COMMUNITY OF INTERBEING - EAST MIDLANDS SANGHA......NOTTINGHAM 103
COMMUNITY OF INTERBEING - EDINBURGH SANGHA ......EDINBURGH 140
COMMUNITY OF INTERBEING - GLASGOW SANGHA ......GLASGOW 143
COMMUNITY OF INTERBEING - GUILDFORD SANGHA ......GUILDFORD 113
COMMUNITY OF INTERBEING - HAM / RICHMOND SANGHA ......HAM 93
COMMUNITY OF INTERBEING - HEART OF LONDON SANGHA......LONDON: SW 3 85
COMMUNITY OF INTERBEING - ISLE OF WIGHT SANGHA......ISLE OF WIGHT 64

COMMUNITY OF INTERBEING - LANCASHIRE SANGHA ....MORECAMBE BAY 68
COMMUNITY OF INTERBEING - LEAMINGTON SANGHA ....LEAMINGTON SPA 117
COMMUNITY OF INTERBEING - LEEDS SANGHA ....LEEDS...125
COMMUNITY OF INTERBEING - LEWES SANGHA ....LEWES 51
COMMUNITY OF INTERBEING - LINCOLNSHIRE SANGHA..........................NORTH SOMERCOTES 71
COMMUNITY OF INTERBEING - LYME BAY SANGHA, DORSET ....LYME BAY 47
COMMUNITY OF INTERBEING - MARTINSTOWN SANGHA, DORSET................MARTINSTOWN 47
COMMUNITY OF INTERBEING - MINDFULNESS SANGHA ....DERBY 42
COMMUNITY OF INTERBEING - NORFOLK SANGHA ....NORWICH 97
COMMUNITY OF INTERBEING - NORTH LONDON SANGHA ....LONDON: N 7 76
COMMUNITY OF INTERBEING - NORTHERN LIGHTS SANGHA, FINDHORN ....FORRES 144
COMMUNITY OF INTERBEING - NORTHWEST SANGHA, MANCHESTER ....MANCHESTER 55
COMMUNITY OF INTERBEING - NORTHWICH SANGHA............................NORTHWICH 37
COMMUNITY OF INTERBEING - OXFORD SANGHA ....OXFORD 104
COMMUNITY OF INTERBEING - POPPY SEED SANGHA, FIFE ....FIFE 142
COMMUNITY OF INTERBEING - SOUTH WALES SANGHA ....CARDIFF 131
COMMUNITY OF INTERBEING - SOUTHAMPTON SANGHA.........................SOUTHAMPTON 60
COMMUNITY OF INTERBEING - SUFFOLK SANGHA ....SUFFOLK 112
COMMUNITY OF INTERBEING - THE PATH HOME SANGHA, NORTHAMPTON ......NORTHAMPTON 102
COMMUNITY OF INTERBEING - WEST COUNTRY SANGHA ....EXETER 43
COMMUNITY OF INTERBEING - WHITE CLOUDS SANGHA - W. BERKS, WILTS AND AVON ....
....MARLBOROUGH 128
COMMUNITY OF INTERBEING - WIMBLEDON SANGHA ....LONDON: SW 19 84
COMMUNITY OF INTERBEING - YORKSHIRE SANGHA ....YORK 100
COMMUNITY OF INTERBEING, U.K. ....UK NATIONAL ORGANISATIONS.......12
COPPER PIPE ZEN GROUP OF DUBLIN ....DUBLIN 154
CORK ZEN DOJO..CORK 154
CORNWALL SERENE REFLECTION MEDITATION GROUP ....CORNWALL 39
CROWBOROUGH DIAMOND WAY BUDDHIST CENTRE ....CROWBOROUGH 50
CROYDON BUDDHIST CENTRE ....CROYDON 93
CROYDON BUDDHIST CENTRE BOOKSHOP ....AUDIO VISUAL 182
CROYDON BUDDHIST CENTRE BOOKSHOP ....BOOKSHOPS 186
CULT INFORMATION CENTRE ....RELATED ORGANISATIONS 167
DECHEN COMMUNITY ....UK NATIONAL ORGANISATIONS.......12
DECHEN IN BATH ....BATH 27
DECHEN IN CORNWALL...TRURO 40
DECHEN IN LEEDS ....LEEDS.......................................125
DECHEN IN PEMBROKESHIRE ....NARBERTH 135
DECHEN IN SKIPTON ....SKIPTON 100
DECHEN IN YORK ....YORK 100
DHAMMA THREADS ....AUDIO VISUAL 182
DHAMMAPALA THERAVADA GROUP ....LEEDS.......................................125
DHANAKOSA RETREAT CENTRE (FWBO) ....BALQHUIDDER..........................146
DHARMA CLOUD TRUST ....NEWPORT 135
DHARMA SCHOOL ....RELATED ORGANISATIONS 168
DHARMACHAKRA TAPES ....AUDIO VISUAL 182
DHARMAPALA COLLEGE FWBO STUDY CENTRE ....RELATED ORGANISATIONS 168
DIAMOND WAY BUDDHISM UK..UK NATIONAL ORGANISATIONS.......13
DIGITAL LIBRARIES ....WEBSITES 204

DOGEN SANGHA BUDDHIST GROUP ....BRISTOL 29
DONCASTER DIAMOND WAY BUDDHIST CENTRE ....DONCASTER 110
DRAGON BELL TEMPLE ....EXETER 43
DRUK THEKCHEN CHOEKOR LING ....OXFORD..105
DRUKPA TRUST ....RELATED ORGANISATIONS 168
DUBLIN BUDDHIST CENTRE (FWBO) ....DUBLIN 155
DUBLIN SHAMBHALA STUDY GROUP ....DUBLIN 155
DUBLIN ZEN DOJO ....DUBLIN 155
DUNDEE SERENE REFLECTION MEDITATION GROUP....................DUNDEE 139
DURHAM SAMATHA MEDITATION GROUP ....DURHAM..38
DZOGCHEN BEARA ....ALLIHIES 153
DZOGCHEN BRISTOL ....BRISTOL 29
DZOGCHEN CAMBRIDGE ....CAMBRIDGE..36
DZOGCHEN CARDIFF..CARDIFF 132
DZOGCHEN COMMUNITY UK ....UK NATIONAL ORGANISATIONS........13
DZOGCHEN CUMBRIA..CUMBRIA 41
DZOGCHEN LONDON..LONDON 72
DZOGCHEN MANCHESTER ....MANCHESTER......................................55
DZOGCHEN MIDLANDS ....WEST MIDLANDS 118
EAST DORSET BUDDHIST GROUP ....BOURNEMOUTH 46
EAST LONDON BUDDHIST CULTURAL CENTRE ....LONDON: E 6 73
EDGWARE MEDITATION GROUP ....EDGWARE 91
EDINBURGH BUDDHIST CENTRE ....EDINBURGH 141
EDINBURGH DIAMOND WAY BUDDHIST CENTRE ....EDINBURGH 141
EDINBURGH SAMYE DZONG ....EDINBURGH 141
EDINBURGH SHAMBHALA MEDITATION GROUP ....EDINBURGH 141
EDINBURGH THERAVADA BUDDHIST GROUP ....EDINBURGH 141
ENGLISH BUDDHIST MONASTERY TRUST ....RELATED ORGANISATIONS 169
ENGLISH SANGHA TRUST ....RELATED ORGANISATIONS 169
EUROPEAN BUDDHIST UNION ....RELATED ORGANISATIONS 169
EXETER DIAMOND WAY BUDDHIST CENTRE ....EXETER 44
FEDERATION OF AMBEDKARITE BUDDHIST ORGANISATIONS UK ......LONDON: E 2 73
FEDERATION OF AMBEDKARITE BUDDHIST ORGANISATIONS UK ......UK NATIONAL ORGANISATIONS........14
FINE BOOKS ORIENTAL LTD ....BOOKSHOPS 187
FO GUANG SHAN (MANCHESTER) ....MANCHESTER......................................56
FOREST HERMITAGE (WAT PAH SANTIDHAMMA) ....SHERBOURNE......................................117
FORUMS ....WEBSITES 204
FOUNDATION FOR THE PRESERVATION OF THE MAHAYANA TRADITION............UK NATIONAL ORGANISATIONS........14
FRIENDS OF THE WESTERN BUDDHIST ORDER ....UK NATIONAL ORGANISATIONS........15
FWBO CENTRAL..BIRMINGHAM......................................120
GAIA HOUSE ....NEWTON ABBOT 45
GALLOWAY SERENE REFLECTION MEDITATION GROUP................GALLOWAY 140
GALWAY ZEN DOJO ....GALWAY 156
GANESHA PRESS ....AUDIO VISUAL 183
GANESHA PRESS ....PUBLISHERS 201
GARUDA TRADING - TIBETAN DHARMA SUPPLIES......................AUDIO VISUAL 183
GARUDA TRADING - TIBETAN DHARMA SUPPLIES......................BOOKS BY POST 184
GARUDA TRADING - TIBETAN DHARMA SUPPLIES......................OTHER BUDDHIST REQUISITES 198
GLASGOW BUDDHIST CENTRE (FWBO) ....GLASGOW 143

GLASGOW THERAVADA BUDDHIST GROUP	GLASGOW	143
GLASGOW ZEN DOJO	GLASGOW	143
GLASTONBURY CH'AN GROUP	GLASTONBURY	108
GOLDEN BUDDHA CENTRE	SOUTH BRENT	45
GOLDEN BUDDHA CENTRE	UK NATIONAL ORGANISATIONS	15
GREENSLEEVES	BOOKS BY POST	185
GREENSTREETE SAMATHA GROUP	LLANGUNLLO	137
GUERNSEY BUDDHIST GROUP	GUERNSEY	149
GUERNSEY BUDDHIST ZEN CENTRE	GUERNSEY	149
GUILDFORD CH'AN GROUP	GUILDFORD	113
HAMPSHIRE BUDDHIST SOCIETY	SOUTHAMPTON	60
HAMPSTEAD BUDDHIST GROUP	LONDON: NW 3	77
HARLOW BUDDHIST SOCIETY	HARLOW	52
HARLOW DIAMOND WAY BUDDHIST CENTRE	HARLOW	53
HARROW ZAZENKAI	HARROW	91
HARTRIDGE BUDDHIST MONASTERY (The Devon Vihara)	HONITON	45
HASTINGS AND ROTHER BUDDHIST MEDITATION GROUP	HASTINGS	51
HASTINGS BUDDHIST MEDITATION AND STUDY GROUP	HASTINGS	51
HERITAGE TRUST PUBLICATIONS	PUBLISHERS	201
HEXHAM BUDDHIST GROUP	HEXHAM	102
HEXHAM SERENE REFLECTION MEDITATION GROUP	HEXHAM	102
HIGH PEAK THERAVADA BUDDHIST GROUP	GLOSSOP	42
HOLE FARM GROUP	NEWTON ABBOT	45
HOLLAND PARK GROUP	LONDON: W 11	86
HOLY ISLAND	OFF ARRAN	145
HOUSE OF INNER TRANQUILLITY	BRADFORD ON AVON	126
HUDDERSFIELD SAMATHA GROUP	HUDDERSFIELD	124
HUDDERSFIELD SERENE REFLECTION MEDITATION GROUP	HUDDERSFIELD	124
HULL BUDDHIST FORUM	BEVERLEY	63
HULL SERENE REFLECTION MEDITATION GROUP	HULL	63
ILLOGAN BUDDHIST GROUP (FWBO)	ILLOGAN	39
INFORM: (Information Network Focus on Religious Movements)	RELATED ORGANISATIONS	170
INSIGHT MEDITATION GROUP	DUBLIN	155
INSIGHT TALKS	AUDIO VISUAL	183
INSTITUTE OF ORIENTAL PHILOSOPHY UK	LIBRARIES	190
INTER FAITH NETWORK FOR THE UNITED KINGDOM	RELATED ORGANISATIONS	170
INTERNATIONAL BUDDHIST RELIEF ORGANISATION	RELATED ORGANISATIONS	170
INTERNATIONAL DUNHUANG PROJECT	RELATED ORGANISATIONS	170
INTERNATIONAL MEDITATION CENTRE	CALNE	127
INTERNATIONAL NETWORK OF ENGAGED BUDDHISTS	RELATED ORGANISATIONS	171
INTERNATIONAL SACRED LITERATURE TRUST	PUBLISHERS	201
INTERNATIONAL ZEN ASSOCIATION UK	UK NATIONAL ORGANISATIONS	16
INTERNET BOOKSELLERS	BOOKS BY POST	185
IPSWICH BUDDHIST CENTRE (FWBO)	IPSWICH	113
IRISH VIPASSANA ASSOCIATION	DUBLIN	156
ISLE OF WIGHT BUDDHIST GROUP	NEWPORT	64
ISLE OF WIGHT BUDDHIST GROUP (FWBO)	VENTNOR	64
JAMPA LING BELFAST	BELFAST	152
JAMPA LING TIBETAN BUDDHIST CENTRE	BAWNBOY	152

JAMYANG BRIGHTON	BRIGHTON	50
JAMYANG BUDDHIST CENTRE	LONDON: SE 11	80
JAMYANG BUDDHIST CENTRE LEEDS	LEEDS	126
JAMYANG COLCHESTER	COLCHESTER	52
JAMYANG SALISBURY	SALISBURY	128
JETAVANA BUDDHIST TEMPLE	BIRMINGHAM	120
JOHN RANDALL BOOKS OF ASIA	BOOKSHOPS	189
KAGYU DECHEN DZONG	HARROGATE	100
KAGYU DZONG	COLNE	67
KAGYU LING	MANCHESTER	56
KAGYU OSEL CHOLING	SOUTHPORT	96
KAGYU SAMYE DZONG	DUBLIN	156
KAGYU SAMYE DZONG CHICHESTER	CHICHESTER	123
KAGYU SAMYE DZONG CORK	CORK CITY	154
KAGYU SAMYE DZONG CORNWALL	LOSTWITHIEL	40
KAGYU SAMYE DZONG LONDON	LONDON: SE 1	79
KAGYU SAMYE DZONG NORTHAMPTONSHIRE	KETTERING	101
KAGYU SAMYE LING MONASTERY AND TIBETAN CENTRE - ROKPA TRUST	UK NATIONAL ORGANISATIONS	16
KAGYU SAMYE LING TIBETAN CENTRE - ROKPA TRUST	ESKDALEMUIR	140
KAGYU SHEDRUP LING	LIVERPOOL	95
KAILASH CENTRE	RELATED ORGANISATIONS	171
KANZEON ZEN PRACTICE TRUST	LONDON: NW 3	78
KARMA SHOP	OTHER BUDDHIST REQUISITES	198
KARME CHOLING	WIRRAL	97
KARUNA TRUST AND AID FOR INDIA	RELATED ORGANISATIONS	171
KESWICK SERENE RELECTION MEDITATION GROUP	KESWICK	41
KETUMATI BUDDHIST VIHARA	OLDHAM	58
KHANDRO LING	MACCLESFIELD	37
KINGSWOOD BOOKS	BOOKS BY POST	185
KUNSEL LING	HAY-ON-WYE	137
LAM RIM (WILTS & S.GLOUC)	CHIPPENHAM	127
LAM RIM BRISTOL BUDDHIST CENTRE	BRISTOL	29
LAM RIM BUDDHIST CENTRE	PENRHOS	135
LANCASTER FWBO GROUP	LANCASTER	68
LANCASTER SERENE REFLECTION MEDITATION GROUP	LANCASTER	68
LEEDS BUDDHIST CENTRE (FWBO)	LEEDS	126
LEEDS BUDDHIST COUNCIL	RELATED ORGANISATIONS	172
LEEDS BUDDHIST GROUP	LEEDS	126
LEEDS ZEN DOJO	LEEDS	126
LEI ZANG SI TEMPLE LONDON	LONDON: SE 18	81
LEICESTER BUDDHIST SOCIETY	LEICESTER	70
LEICESTER BUDDHIST VIHARA (East Midlands Buddhist Association)	LEICESTER	70
LEICESTER SERENE REFLECTION MEDITATION GROUP	LEICESTER	71
LEICESTER SHAMBHALA STUDY GROUP	LEICESTER	71
LEIGH BUDDHIST GROUP	LEIGH ON SEA	53
LEIGHTON BUZZARD MEDITATION GROUP	LEIGHTON BUZZARD	32
LETCHWORTH BUDDHIST CENTRE	LETCHWORTH	62
LETCHWORTH FWBO GROUP	LETCHWORTH	63
LINH SON TEMPLE AND MEDITATION CENTRE	LONDON: SE 19	82

LINH SONH PHAT DUONG TEMPLE...LONDON: N 15.................................75
LIVERPOOL AMARAVATI GROUP...LIVERPOOL...................................95
LIVERPOOL DIAMOND WAY BUDDHIST CENTRE ....LIVERPOOL...................................95
LIVERPOOL MEDITATION CENTRE (FWBO).......................................LIVERPOOL...................................96
LIVERPOOL SERENE REFLECTION MEDITATION GROUP ....LIVERPOOL...................................96
LIVERPOOL ZEN GROUP...LIVERPOOL...................................96
LIVING DHARMA TAPES ....AUDIO VISUAL.............................183
LIZARD CH'AN GROUP...HELSTON.....................................39
LLANFYLLIN SAMATHA GROUP...LLANFYLLIN.................................137
LLANGOLLEN BUDDHIST GROUP (FWBO)...LLANGOLLEN................................133
LONDON BUDDHIST ARTS CENTRE (FWBO) ....LONDON: E 2................................73
LONDON BUDDHIST CENTRE (FWBO) ....LONDON: E 2................................73
LONDON BUDDHIST VIHARA..LONDON: W 4...............................88
LONDON BUDDHIST VIHARA BOOKSTALL...BOOKSHOPS 188
LONDON BUDDHIST VIHARA LIBRARY...LIBRARIES...................................192
LONDON BURMESE BUDDHIST VIHARA (BRITAIN BURMA BUDDHIST TRUST) ...LONDON: NW 9.....................79
LONDON DIAMOND WAY BUDDHIST CENTRE.....................................LONDON: WC 1.............................89
LONDON FO GUANG TEMPLE...LONDON: W 1...............................86
LONDON INTER FAITH CENTRE ....RELATED ORGANISATIONS 172
LONDON RETREATS...LONDON: NW 11............................77
LONDON SERENE REFLECTION MEDITATION GROUP ....LONDON: N 1................................74
LONDON SHAMBHALA MEDITATION CENTRE.....................................LONDON: SW 4.............................85
LONDON ZAZEN GROUP..LONDON: W 2...............................87
LONDON-SOUTH DIAMOND WAY BUDDHIST CENTRE ....LONDON: SE 24.............................83
LONGCHEN FOUNDATION...BRISTOL.......................................30
LONGCHEN FOUNDATION...LEIGH ON SEA 53
LONGCHEN FOUNDATION...OXFORD.......................................105
LONGCHEN FOUNDATION...PORTHMADOG 134
LONGCHEN FOUNDATION...LONDON: SE 13.............................81
LONGCHEN FOUNDATION...UK NATIONAL ORGANISATIONS.......16
LOTHLORIEN..RELATED ORGANISATIONS 172
LUDLOW SAMATHA BUDDHIST GROUP ....LUDLOW......................................107
LUMBINI NEPALESE BUDDHA DHARMA SOCIETY UK..........................SLOUGH......................................33
LUMBINI NEPALESE BUDDHA DHARMA SOCIETY UK..........................UK NATIONAL ORGANISATIONS.......18
MACHYNLLETH MEDITATION GROUP ....MACHYNLLETH..............................138
MAIDSTONE MEDITATION GROUP ....MAIDSTONE.................................66
MAIDSTONE MEDITATION GROUP (LONGCHEN FOUNDATION) ....MAIDSTONE.................................66
MAITRI PROJECT..LEICESTER...................................71
MAITRIKARA..BRIGHTON...................................50
MANCHESTER BUDDHIST CENTRE (FWBO)......................................MANCHESTER...............................56
MANCHESTER CENTRE FOR BUDDHIST MEDITATION.........................MANCHESTER...............................56
MANCHESTER CH'AN GROUP ....MANCHESTER...............................57
MANCHESTER DIAMOND WAY BUDDHIST CENTRE ....MANCHESTER...............................57
MANCHESTER SHAMBHALA STUDY GROUP.....................................MANCHESTER...............................57
MANCHESTER ZEN DOJO...MANCHESTER...............................58
MANOR PLACE SAMYE DZONG...LONDON: SE 17.............................82
MARPA HOUSE - Chos Khor Ling...ASHDON......................................52
MATLOCK SERENE REFLECTION MEDITATION GROUP ....MATLOCK.....................................42
MEDICINE BUDDHA GOMPA..MANCHESTER...............................58

MEDWAY CH'AN GROUP ....GILLINGHAM 66
MERIDIAN TRUST ....AUDIO VISUAL 183
MID-KENT AND MEDWAY BUDDHIST GROUP ....MAIDSTONE.....................................66
MIDLANDS BUDDHIST ASSOCIATION [VIETNAMESE] ....BIRMINGHAM 120
MIDLANDS BUDDHIST COMMUNITY ASSOCIATION....................RELATED ORGANISATIONS 173
MIDLANDS INTERNATIONAL BUDDHIST ASSOCIATION IN THE UK ...BIRMINGHAM 121
MILTON KEYNES FWBO ....MILTON KEYNES................................33
MILTON KEYNES SERENE REFLECTION MEDITATION GROUP ....MILTON KEYNES................................33
MODERN BUDDHA WAY ....GUILDFORD.....................................114
MOTILAL (UK) BOOKS OF INDIA ....BOOKS BY POST 185
MYANMAR ASSOCIATION (UK) ....RELATED ORGANISATIONS 173
NETWORK OF BUDDHIST ORGANISATIONS (UK) ....RELATED ORGANISATIONS 173
NETWORK OF ENGAGED BUDDHISTS (UK)...............................UK NATIONAL ORGANISATIONS.......18
NEW KADAMPA TRADITION ....UK NATIONAL ORGANISATIONS.......19
NEWBURY CH'AN GROUP ....NEWBURY 32
NEWCASTLE BUDDHIST CENTRE (FWBO) ....NEWCASTLE UPON TYNE.................115
NEWCASTLE DIAMOND WAY BUDDHIST CENTRE......................NEWCASTLE UPON TYNE.................116
NEWCASTLE SERENE REFLECTION MEDITATION GROUP ....NEWCASTLE UPON TYNE.................116
NEWENT THERAVADA GROUP ....NEWENT..54
NEWPORT SAMATHA GROUP ....NEWPORT.......................................136
NEZANG BUDDHIST MEDITATION GROUP ....CAMBRIDGE.....................................36
NICHIREN BUDDHIST TEMPLE OF LONDON ....LONDON: N 3 75
NIPPONZAN MYOHOJI PEACE PAGODA ....MILTON KEYNES................................34
NIPPONZAN MYOHOJI PEACE PAGODA ....LONDON: SW 11 83
NORTH LONDON BUDDHIST CENTRE (FWBO) ....LONDON: N 7 76
NORTH LONDON ZEN DOJO ....LONDON: N 5 76
NORTH STAFFS ZAZEN GROUP ....STOKE-ON-TRENT 112
NORWICH AMARAVATI MEDITATION GROUP ....NORWICH...98
NORWICH BUDDHIST CENTRE (FWBO).....................................NORWICH...98
NORWICH SERENE REFLECTION MEDITATION GROUP ....NORWICH...98
NORWICH ZEN DOJO ....NORWICH...98
NOTTINGHAM BUDDHIST CENTRE (FWBO) ....NOTTINGHAM 104
NOTTINGHAM CH'AN GROUP ....NOTTINGHAM 104
NOTTINGHAM SERENE REFLECTION MEDITATION GROUP ....NOTTINGHAM 104
OFFICE OF TIBET..RELATED ORGANISATIONS 173
OGYAN CHOKHOR LING ....CANTERBURY 65
OGYAN CHOKHOR LING ....LONDON: N 12..................................75
OGYAN CHOKHOR LING ....UK NATIONAL ORGANISATIONS.......19
OLDHAM SAMATHA MEDITATION GROUP ....OLDHAM...68
ORDER OF BUDDHISTS CONTEMPLATIVES ....UK NATIONAL ORGANISATIONS 20
OXFORD BUDDHIST GROUP (FWBO).......................................OXFORD...105
OXFORD BUDDHIST VIHARA...OXFORD...105
OXFORD CENTRE FOR BUDDHIST STUDIES ....OXFORD...106
OXFORD SAMATHA GROUP ....OXFORD...106
OXFORD ZEN DOJO ....OXFORD...106
PADMA LING ....CAMBRIDGE.....................................36
PADMA LING ....KENT 64
PADMA LING ....MANCHESTER 58
PADMA LING ....LONDON: NW10 79

PADMA LING UK...UK NATIONAL ORGANISATIONS 20
PADMALOKA MEN'S RETREAT CENTRE (FWBO) ....SURLINGHAM 99
PALANQUIN TRAVELLER ....TRAVEL 204
PALI TEXT SOCIETY ....PUBLISHERS 202
PALYUL CENTRE UK ....LONDON: N 1 74
PALYUL CENTRE UK ....UK NATIONAL ORGANISATIONS 21
PARINAMA PUBLICATIONS...PUBLISHERS 202
PASSADDHI MEDITATION CENTRE ....ADRIGOLE, BEARA 153
PENZANCE MEDITATION GROUP......................................PENZANCE 40
PERTH BUDDHIST GROUP (FWBO) ....PERTH 145
PERTH THERAVADA GROUP ....PERTH 146
PETERBOROUGH BUDDHIST GROUP (FWBO) .................PETERBOROUGH 36
PHIROZ MEHTA TRUST...RELATED ORGANISATIONS 174
PORTOBELLO BUDDHIST PRIORY ....EDINBURGH 142
PORTSMOUTH BUDDHIST GROUP....................................PORTSMOUTH 59
PORTSMOUTH CH'AN GROUP...PORTSMOUTH 59
PORTSMOUTH SERENE REFLECTION MEDITATION GROUP ...PORTSMOUTH 59
POTTERS BAR DIAMOND WAY BUDDHIST CENTRE ....POTTERS BAR 63
PRECIOUS WOOD CH'AN GROUP ....CARDIGAN 132
PRESTON DIAMOND WAY BUDDHIST CENTRE ....PRESTON 69
PRESTON SERENE REFLECTION MEDITATION GROUP......PRESTON 69
PURE LAND BUDDHIST FELLOWSHIP ....EDINBURGH 142
PURE LAND BUDDHIST FELLOWSHIP ....UK NATIONAL ORGANISATIONS 21
PURELAND BUDDHISM ....BOOKS BY POST 186
PURELAND RELAXATION AND MEDITATION CENTRE.........NORTH CLIFTON, NEWARK ...103
QUAKER COMMITTEE FOR CHRISTIAN AND INTERFAITH RELATIONS (CIR).........RELATED ORGANISATIONS 174
READING BUDDHIST PRIORY ....READING...32
READING DIAMOND WAY BUDDHIST CENTRE ....READING...32
REDBRIDGE BUDDHIST CULTURAL CENTRE......................ILFORD...90
REIYUKAI CENTRE ....NORWICH..98
RICHARD HUNN ASSOCIATION FOR CH'AN STUDY ....SUTTON...94
RICHMOND SAMATHA MEDITATION GROUP ....RICHMOND..93
RIGPA ATHLONE ....ATHLONE...157
RIGPA BIRMINGHAM ....BIRMINGHAM 121
RIGPA CORK..CORK CITY 154
RIGPA DUBLIN ....DUBLIN 156
RIGPA EDINBURGH ....EDINBURGH 142
RIGPA FELLOWSHIP ....LONDON: N 1 74
RIGPA FELLOWSHIP ....UK NATIONAL ORGANISATIONS 22
RIGPA GALWAY ....GALWAY 157
RIGPA IRELAND ....IRELAND 151
RIGPA KERRY ....KILLARNEY...157
RIGPA LIMERICK..LIMERICK 157
RIGPA NORWICH ....NORWICH..99
RIGPA SOUTH DOWNS ....LEWES 52
RIGPA WICKLOW ....CO WICKLOW 157
RISSHO KOSEI-KAI..WHITSTABLE 67
RISSHO KOSEI-KAI OF THE UK ....UK NATIONAL ORGANISATIONS 22
RIVENDELL RETREAT CENTRE ....HIGH HURSTWOOD 51

ROCHDALE ZEN RETREAT .... BOLTON 55
ROKPA ABERDEEN .... ABERDEEN 139
ROKPA CARDIFF .... CARDIFF 132
ROKPA DUNDEE .... DUNDEE 140
ROKPA GLASGOW .... GLASGOW 144
ROKPA HIGHLANDS .... INVERNESS 144
ROKPA TRUST .... RELATED ORGANISATIONS 174
ROMSEY BUDDHIST GROUP .... ROMSEY 60
ROSSENDALE SAMATHA GROUP .... ROSSENDALE 70
ROUTLEDGE CURZON .... PUBLISHERS 202
SAKYA DECHEN LING - CITY OF LONDON .... LONDON: EC4 73
SAKYA DECHEN LING - NOTTING HILL .... LONDON: W 8 89
SAKYA DECHEN LING - ST. JOHN'S WOOD .... LONDON: NW 8 78
SAKYA GOSHAK CHOLING .... BIRMINGHAM 121
SAKYA THINLEY NAMGYAL LING .... EXETER 44
SAKYA THINLEY RINCHEN LING .... BRISTOL 30
SAKYADHITA INTERNATIONAL - UK CHAPTER .... RELATED ORGANISATIONS 175
SAMADHI MEDITATION CENTRE .... LONDON: N 9 77
SAMATHA CENTRE .... KNIGHTON 137
SAMATHA GROUPS IN IRELAND .... IRELAND 151
SAMATHA TRUST .... UK NATIONAL ORGANISATIONS 22
SAMYE LING TIBETAN CENTRE BOOKSHOP .... OTHER BUDDHIST REQUISITES 198
SANG-NGAK-CHO-DZONG .... BRISTOL 30
SANG-NGAK-CHO-DZONG .... CARDIFF 131
SANG-NGAK-CHO-DZONG .... CARLISLE 41
SANG-NGAK-CHO-DZONG .... CHEPSTOW 97
SANG-NGAK-CHO-DZONG .... CORNWALL 39
SANG-NGAK-CHO-DZONG .... KENT 64
SANG-NGAK-CHO-DZONG .... UK NATIONAL ORGANISATIONS 24
SANG-NGAK-CHO-DZONG .... WEST SUSSEX 123
SANG-NGAK-CHO-DZONG .... YORK 101
SANTISUKHA VIHARA .... HESTON 91
SARANIYA DHAMMA MEDITATION CENTRE .... SALFORD 58
SARASWATI BUDDHIST GROUP .... SOUTH PETHERTON 109
SATIPANYA BUDDHIST TRUST .... RELATED ORGANISATIONS 175
SCHOOL OF ORIENTAL AND AFRICAN STUDIES (SOAS) MEDITATION SOCIETY, THE .... LONDON: WC 1 90
SCHOOL OF ORIENTAL AND AFRICAN STUDIES LIBRARY .... LIBRARIES 192
SGI-UK .... TAPLOW 33
SGI-UK .... UK NATIONAL ORGANISATIONS 25
SHAMBHALA SUN MAGAZINE .... PUBLICATIONS 200
SHANTI GRIHA .... WESTER ROSS 144
SHARPHAM CENTRE FOR CONTEMPORARY BUDDHIST ENQUIRY .... ASHPRINGTON 43
SHEFFEILD SAMATHA BUDDHIST GROUP .... SHEFFIELD 111
SHEFFIELD BUDDHIST CENTRE (FWBO) .... SHEFFIELD 111
SHEFFIELD DIAMOND WAY BUDDHIST CENTRE .... SHEFFIELD 111
SHEFFIELD SERENE REFLECTION MEDITATION GROUP .... SHEFFIELD 111
SHEFFIELD ZEN GROUP - WHITE PLUM .... SHEFFIELD 112
SHEN PHEN THUBTEN CHOELING .... HEREFORD 61

SHETLAND BUDDHIST GROUP (FWBO) .... LERWICK 146
SHINNYO-EN UK .... SURBITON 114
SHREWSBURY BUDDHISM AND MEDITATION GROUP (FWBO) .... SHREWSBURY 108
SHRIMALA TRUST .... RELATED ORGANISATIONS ... 176
SLSCO-FLAME .... HOUNSLOW 92
SMILING MOUNTAIN MEDITATION GROUP .... HALESOWEN 122
SOCIETY FOR THE WIDER UNDERSTANDING OF THE BUDDHIST TRADITION ...... OXFORD 106
SOUTH DEVON CH'AN GROUP .... DARTMOOR 43
SOUTH DORSET BUDDHIST GROUP .... WEYMOUTH 47
SOUTH LONDON BUDDHIST GROUP (FWBO) .... LONDON: SE 24 83
SOUTH LONDON ZEN DOJO .... LONDON: SE 1 80
SOUTHAMPTON BUDDHIST GROUP (FWBO) .... SOUTHAMPTON 60
SOUTHAMPTON SHIN SANGHA .... SOUTHAMPTON 61
SRI SADDHATISSA INTERNATIONAL BUDDHIST CENTRE .... LONDON: NW 9 79
STEYNING MEDITATION GROUP .... STEYNING 124
STILLPOINT .... RELATED ORGANISATIONS ... 176
STIRLING BUDDHIST GROUP (FWBO) .... STIRLING 147
STOCKPORT SAMATHA MEDITATION GROUP .... STOCKPORT 59
STROUD BUDDHIST GROUP .... STROUD 54
STROUD CH'AN GROUP .... STROUD 55
SUKHAVATI BUDDHIST TEMPLE .... LONDON: N 7 77
SUNDERLAND SAMATHA GROUP .... SUNDERLAND 116
SUNYATA RETREAT CENTRE .... SIX MILE BRIDGE 152
SURREY THERAVADA BUDDHIST GROUP .... WOKING 114
SUTTON COLDFIELD BUDDHISM AND MEDITATION GROUP (FWBO) ...... SUTTON COLDFIELD 122
SWINDON CH'AN GROUP .... SWINDON 128
TARA COLLEGE OF TIBETAN MEDICINE .... RELATED ORGANISATIONS ... 176
TARA ROKPA EDINBURGH & THE INSTITUTE FOR TIBETAN MEDICINE ...... EDINBURGH 142
TARA ROKPA NORFOLK .... MUNDESLEY 97
TARALOKA RETREAT CENTRE FOR WOMEN .... WHITCHURCH 108
TASHI KHYIL TRUST .... RELATED ORGANISATIONS ... 176
TASHI LHUNPO MONASTERY UK TRUST .... RELATED ORGANISATIONS ... 176
TAUNTON MEDITATION GROUP .... TAUNTON 109
TEA CIRCLE .... OTHER BUDDHIST REQUISITES ... 198
TEESIDE SERENE REFLECTION MEDITATION GROUP .... MIDDLESBOROUGH 38
TEESSIDE THERAVADIN BUDDHIST GROUP .... MIDDLESBOROUGH 38
TELFORD BUDDHIST PRIORY .... TELFORD 108
TEMENOS ACADEMY .... PUBLISHERS 203
THAMES BUDDHIST VIHARA .... SELSDON 94
THARPA PUBLICATIONS .... PUBLISHERS 203
THEOSOPHICAL SOCIETY .... BOOKSHOPS 188
THERAVADA BUDDHISM (SW WALES) .... NEVERN 136
THERAVADA BUDDHIST CENTRE .... BRISTOL 31
THERAVADA BUDDHIST GROUP .... CARLISLE 41
THRANGU HOUSE BUDDHIST CENTRE .... OXFORD 107
THREE WHEELS .... LONDON: W 3 87
THROSSEL HOLE BUDDHIST ABBEY .... HEXHAM 103
THROSSEL HOLE BUDDHIST BOOKSHOP .... AUDIO VISUAL 184
THROSSEL HOLE BUDDHIST BOOKSHOP .... BOOKSHOPS 189

THROSSEL HOLE BUDDHIST BOOKSHOP ....OTHER BUDDHIST REQUISITES 198
TIBET FOUNDATION ....RELATED ORGANISATIONS 177
TIBET HOUSE TRUST...RELATED ORGANISATIONS 177
TIBET SHOP ....AUDIO VISUAL 184
TIBET SHOP ....BOOKSHOPS 188
TIBET SHOP ....OTHER BUDDHIST REQUISITES 198
TIBET SOCIETY AND TIBET RELIEF FUND UK...........................RELATED ORGANISATIONS 178
TIRATANALOKA WOMEN'S ORDINATION RETREAT CENTRE ....BRECON 136
TISARANA VIHARA...TWICKENHAM 92
TRANS HIMALAYA ....TRAVEL 204
TREVOR LEGGETT ADHYATMA YOGA TRUST.............................SOUTHWOLD 113
TRICYCLE: THE BUDDHIST REVIEW ....PUBLICATIONS 200
UK ASSOCIATION FOR BUDDHIST STUDIES..............................RELATED ORGANISATIONS 178
UK FA YUE BUDDHIST MONASTERY...BIRMINGHAM 122
UNIVERSITY OF BRISTOL SAMATHA GROUP ....BRISTOL...31
USEFUL LINKS ....WEBSITES 204
UXBRIDGE SAMATHA MEDITATION GROUP ....UXBRIDGE..92
VAJRALOKA BUDDHIST MEDITATION CENTRE FOR MEN (FWBO) ....CORWEN 133
VAJRASANA RETREAT CENTRE (FWBO) ....BURY ST EDMUNDS 112
VIPASSANA FELLOWSHIP ....UK NATIONAL ORGANISATIONS 25
VIPASSANA MEDITATION GROUP ....CORK CITY 154
VIPASSANA TRUST ....HEREFORD 61
W HEFFER & SONS ....BOOKSHOPS 186
WARRINGTON SAMATHA GROUP ....WARRINGTON 37
WARWICK BUDDHISM AND MEDITATION GROUP ....WARWICK 117
WARWICK UNIVERSITY BUDDHIST SOCIETY ....COVENTRY 122
WAT SANGHATHAN ....BIRMINGHAM 122
WATERSTONES (Formerly Dillons)...BOOKSHOPS 189
WATKINS BOOKS...BOOKSHOPS 189
WELLS-NEXT-THE-SEA ZEN GROUP (IZAUK) ....WELLS-NEXT-THE-SEA 99
WEST CORNWALL ZEN CENTRE ....HELSTON 39
WEST LONDON BUDDHIST CENTRE (FWBO) ....LONDON: W 2 87
WEST MIDLANDS BUDDHIST COUNCIL ....RELATED ORGANISATIONS 179
WESTBURY ON TRYM MEDITATION GROUP ....WESTBURY-ON-TRYM 31
WESTERN CH'AN FELLOWSHIP...UK NATIONAL ORGANISATIONS 25
WHITECROSS BUDDHIST MEDITATION CENTRE.......................WHITECROSS 40
WILMSLOW (SAMATHA) BUDDHIST MEDITATION GROUP ....WILMSLOW 37
WIMBLEDON SAMATHA MEDITATION GROUP ....LONDON: SW 19 84
WINDHORSE IMPORTS ....OTHER BUDDHIST REQUISITES 199
WINDHORSE PUBLICATIONS ....BOOKS BY POST 186
WINDHORSE PUBLICATIONS ....PUBLISHERS 203
WINTERHEAD RETREAT HOUSE ....SHIPHAM 109
WISDOM BOOKS ....BOOKS BY POST 186
WISDOM BOOKS ....BOOKSHOPS 189
WOLVERHAMPTON BUDDHA VIHARA..WOLVERHAMPTON 123
WORCESTER BUDDHISM AND MEDITATION GROUP (FWBO) ....WORCESTER 129
WORLD CONGRESS OF FAITHS (The Interfaith Fellowship) ....RELATED ORGANISATIONS 179
WORLD FELLOWSHIP OF BUDDHISTS ....RELATED ORGANISATIONS 179
YORK CH'AN BUDDHIST GROUP ....YORK 101

Index of Groups by Title

YORK DIAMOND WAY BUDDHIST CENTRE...YORK 101
YOUN-HWA-SA (LOTUS HOUSE) ....KINGSTON UPON THAMES 93
ZAM...BOOKS BY POST 186
ZAZEN (Sacred Icons) ....OTHER BUDDHIST REQUISITES 199
ZEN LONDON..LONDON: N 4.......................................75
ZEN LONDON..LONDON: W 4 88
ZEN PRACTICE CENTRE TRUST ....HINCKLEY...70
ZEN PRACTICE CENTRE TRUST ....HULL..64
ZEN PRACTICE CENTRE TRUST ....MAIDSTONE...67
ZEN PRACTICE CENTRE TRUST ....PRESTON 69
ZEN PRACTICE CENTRE TRUST (Affiliated to the Kanzeon Sangha) ....UK NATIONAL ORGANISATIONS 26

INDEX OF GROUPS BY TRADITION

Please note that groups which do not declare allegiance to a specific tradition have been omitted from this index.

Agon Shu
AGON SHU UK..UK NATIONAL ORGANISATIONS........9

Chinese: Ch'an
BRIGHTON CH'AN GROUP ....BRIGHTON 48
BRISTOL CH'AN GROUP ....BRISTOL...............................28
BUDDHA'S LIGHT INTERNATIONAL ASSOCIATION LONDON (B.L.I.A. LONDON) ....LONDON: W 1 86
CAMBRIDGE CH'AN GROUP ....CAMBRIDGE.........................35
CARDIFF CH'AN GROUP ....CARDIFF 131
FO GUANG SHAN (MANCHESTER) ....MANCHESTER 56
GLASTONBURY CH'AN GROUP ....GLASTONBURY 108
GUILDFORD CH'AN GROUP ....GUILDFORD 113
LIZARD CH'AN GROUP ....HELSTON............................39
LONDON FO GUANG TEMPLE ....LONDON: W 1 86
MANCHESTER CH'AN GROUP ....MANCHESTER 57
MEDWAY CH'AN GROUP ....GILLINGHAM 66
NEWBURY CH'AN GROUP ....NEWBURY 32
NOTTINGHAM CH'AN GROUP ....NOTTINGHAM 104
PORTSMOUTH CH'AN GROUP ....PORTSMOUTH.....................59
PRECIOUS WOOD CH'AN GROUP ....CARDIGAN 132
RICHARD HUNN ASSOCIATION FOR CH'AN STUDY ....SUTTON..............................94
SOUTH DEVON CH'AN GROUP ....DARTMOOR 43
STROUD CH'AN GROUP ....STROUD..............................55
SWINDON CH'AN GROUP ....SWINDON...........................128
WESTERN CH'AN FELLOWSHIP...UK NATIONAL ORGANISATIONS 25
YORK CH'AN BUDDHIST GROUP ....YORK 101

Chinese: True Buddha School
LEI ZANG SI TEMPLE LONDON...LONDON: SE 18 82

FWBO
ABERDEEN BUDDHIST GROUP (FWBO) ....ABERDEEN 139
AYR BUDDHIST GROUP (FWBO)..AYR....................................146
BIRMINGHAM BUDDHIST CENTRE (FWBO) ....BIRMINGHAM 118
BLACKBURN BUDDHIST CENTRE (FWBO) ....BLACKBURN 67
BRIGHTON BUDDHIST CENTRE (FWBO) ....BRIGHTON 48
BRISTOL BUDDHIST CENTRE (FWBO) ....BRISTOL 28
BUDDHAFIELD (FWBO)..RELATED ORGANISATIONS 165
BURY ST EDMUNDS FWBO GROUP ....BURY ST EDMUNDS 112
CAMBRIDGE BUDDHIST CENTRE ....CAMBRIDGE.......................34
CARDIFF BUDDHIST CENTRE ....CARDIFF 132
COLCHESTER BUDDHIST CENTRE (FWBO) ....COLCHESTER 52
CROYDON BUDDHIST CENTRE ....CROYDON 93
DHANAKOSA RETREAT CENTRE (FWBO) ....BALQUHIDDER.....................146
DHARMAPALA COLLEGE FWBO STUDY CENTRE ....RELATED ORGANISATIONS 168
DUBLIN BUDDHIST CENTRE (FWBO) ....DUBLIN 155
EDINBURGH BUDDHIST CENTRE ....EDINBURGH 141
FRIENDS OF THE WESTERN BUDDHIST ORDER ....UK NATIONAL ORGANISATIONS........15

FWBO CENTRAL	BIRMINGHAM	120
GLASGOW BUDDHIST CENTRE (FWBO)	GLASGOW	143
ILLOGAN BUDDHIST GROUP (FWBO)	ILLOGAN	39
IPSWICH BUDDHIST CENTRE (FWBO)	IPSWICH	113
ISLE OF WIGHT BUDDHIST GROUP (FWBO)	VENTNOR	64
LANCASTER FWBO GROUP	LANCASTER	68
LEEDS BUDDHIST CENTRE (FWBO)	LEEDS	126
LETCHWORTH FWBO GROUP	LETCHWORTH	63
LIVERPOOL MEDITATION CENTRE (FWBO)	LIVERPOOL	96
LLANGOLLEN BUDDHIST GROUP (FWBO)	LLANGOLLEN	133
LONDON BUDDHIST ARTS CENTRE (FWBO)	LONDON: E 2	73
LONDON BUDDHIST CENTRE (FWBO)	LONDON: E 2	73
MANCHESTER BUDDHIST CENTRE (FWBO)	MANCHESTER	56
MILTON KEYNES FWBO	MILTON KEYNES	33
NEWCASTLE BUDDHIST CENTRE (FWBO)	NEWCASTLE UPON TYNE	115
NORTH LONDON BUDDHIST CENTRE (FWBO)	LONDON: N 7	76
NORWICH BUDDHIST CENTRE (FWBO)	NORWICH	98
NOTTINGHAM BUDDHIST CENTRE (FWBO)	NOTTINGHAM	104
OXFORD BUDDHIST GROUP (FWBO)	OXFORD	105
PADMALOKA MEN'S RETREAT CENTRE (FWBO)	SURLINGHAM	99
PERTH BUDDHIST GROUP (FWBO)	PERTH	145
PETERBOROUGH BUDDHIST GROUP (FWBO)	PETERBOROUGH	36
RIVENDELL RETREAT CENTRE	HIGH HURSTWOOD	51
SHEFFIELD BUDDHIST CENTRE (FWBO)	SHEFFIELD	111
SHETLAND BUDDHIST GROUP (FWBO)	LERWICK	146
SHREWSBURY BUDDHISM AND MEDITATION GROUP (FWBO)	SHREWSBURY	108
SOUTH LONDON BUDDHIST GROUP (FWBO)	LONDON: SE 24	83
SOUTHAMPTON BUDDHIST GROUP (FWBO)	SOUTHAMPTON	60
STIRLING BUDDHIST GROUP (FWBO)	STIRLING	147
SUTTON COLDFIELD BUDDHISM AND MEDITATION GROUP (FWBO)	SUTTON COLDFIELD	122
TARALOKA RETREAT CENTRE FOR WOMEN	WHITCHURCH	108
TIRATANALOKA WOMEN'S ORDINATION RETREAT CENTRE	BRECON	136
VAJRALOKA BUDDHIST MEDITATION CENTRE FOR MEN (FWBO)	CORWEN	133
VAJRASANA RETREAT CENTRE (FWBO)	BURY ST EDMUNDS	112
WARWICK BUDDHISM AND MEDITATION GROUP	WARWICK	117
WEST LONDON BUDDHIST CENTRE (FWBO)	LONDON: W 2	87
WORCESTER BUDDHISM AND MEDITATION GROUP (FWBO)	WORCESTER	129

Korean

YOUN-HWA-SA (LOTUS HOUSE)	KINGSTON UPON THAMES	93

Kwan Um School

COPPER PIPE ZEN GROUP OF DUBLIN	DUBLIN	154

Nepalese

LUMBINI NEPALESE BUDDHA DHARMA SOCIETY UK	UK NATIONAL ORGANISATIONS	18

Nichiren

GUERNSEY BUDDHIST GROUP	GUERNSEY	149
SGI-UK	UK NATIONAL ORGANISATIONS	25

Nichiren: Myohoji shu

NIPPONZAN MYOHOJI PEACE PAGODA	LONDON: SW 11	83

Nichiren: Nichiren Shu
NICHIREN BUDDHIST TEMPLE OF LONDON.................LONDON: N 3................75
NIPPONZAN MYOHOJI PEACE PAGODA ....MILTON KEYNES................34
Nichiren: Reiyukai
REIYUKAI CENTRE.................NORWICH................98
Pure Land
PURE LAND BUDDHIST FELLOWSHIP ....UK NATIONAL ORGANISATIONS 21
PURELAND BUDDHISM ....BOOKS BY POST................186
Pure Land: Amida Buddhism
MAITRI PROJECT.................LEICESTER................71
Pure Land: Amida-Shu
AMIDA SANCTUARY.................NEWCASTLE UPON TYNE................115
AMIDA SHEFFIELD CONGREGATION.................SHEFFIELD................110
AMIDA TRUST.................UK NATIONAL ORGANISATIONS........9
BUDDHIST HOUSE ....NARBOROUGH................71
SUKHAVATI BUDDHIST TEMPLE ....LONDON: N 7................76
Pure Land: Jodo Shin Shu
SOUTHAMPTON SHIN SANGHA ....SOUTHAMPTON................61
THREE WHEELS.................LONDON: W 3................87
Shingon
SHINNYO-EN UK.................SURBITON................114
Theravada
AMARAVATI BUDDHIST MONASTERY.................HEMEL HEMPSTEAD................62
AMARAVATI BUDDHIST MONASTERY.................UK NATIONAL ORGANISATIONS........9
AMARAVATI BUDDHIST RETREAT CENTRE.................HEMEL HEMPSTEAD................62
ANGLESEY THERAVADIN BUDDHIST GROUP ....CEMAES BAY................131
ARUNA RATANAGIRI, HARNHAM BUDDHIST MONASTERY ....BELSAY................102
ASHFORD MEDITATION GROUP.................ASHFORD................65
BAKEWELL SAMATHA GROUP.................BAKEWELL................42
BATH THERAVADA GROUP ....BATH................27
BATH THERAVADA MEDITATION CLASS ....BATH................27
BATH/BRISTOL SAMATHA GROUP ....BATH/BRISTOL................27
BERKSHIRE THERAVADAN GROUP ....READING................32
BIRMINGHAM BUDDHIST VIHARA ....BIRMINGHAM................118
BIRMINGHAM SAMATHA GROUP ....BIRMINGHAM................119
BLACKBURN & DARWEN SAMATHA GROUP.................DARWEN................67
BODHINYANA GROUP.................HEMEL HEMPSTEAD................62
BOLTON MEDITATION GROUP.................BOLTON................55
BRIGHTON THERAVADAN GROUP.................BRIGHTON................47
BUDDHA VIHARA.................LONDON: E 13................72
BUDDHAPADIPA TEMPLE ....LONDON: SW 19................84
BUDDHAVIHARA TEMPLE ....BIRMINGHAM................119
BUDDHIST GROUP OF KENDAL (THERAVADA).................KENDAL................41
BUDDHIST MEDITATION GROUP.................REDRUTH................40
BUDDHIST SOCIETY OF MANCHESTER ....SALE................58
CAMBRIDGE AMARAVATI GROUP.................CAMBRIDGE................34
CAMBRIDGE SAMATHA MEDITATION GROUP ....CAMBRIDGE................35
CANTERBURY BUDDHIST MEDITATION GROUP ....CANTERBURY................65

Index of Groups by Tradition

CHESTER SAMATHA MEDITATION GROUP ....CHESTER 36
CITTAVIVEKA, CHITHURST BUDDHIST MONASTERY..........CHITHURST 124
DHAMMA THREADS ....AUDIO VISUAL 182
DHAMMAPALA THERAVADA GROUP ....LEEDS 125
DURHAM SAMATHA MEDITATION GROUP ....DURHAM 38
EAST LONDON BUDDHIST CULTURAL CENTRE ....LONDON: E 6 73
EDINBURGH THERAVADA BUDDHIST GROUP ....EDINBURGH 141
FOREST HERMITAGE (WAT PAH SANTIDHAMMA) ....SHERBOURNE 117
GLASGOW THERAVADA BUDDHIST GROUP ....GLASGOW 143
GREENSTREETE SAMATHA GROUP ....LLANGUNLLO 137
HAMPSTEAD BUDDHIST GROUP ....LONDON: NW 3 78
HARLOW BUDDHIST SOCIETY ....HARLOW 52
HARTRIDGE BUDDHIST MONASTERY (The Devon Vihara) ....HONITON 45
HEXHAM BUDDHIST GROUP ....HEXHAM 102
HIGH PEAK THERAVADA BUDDHIST GROUP ....GLOSSOP 42
HOLE FARM GROUP ....NEWTON ABBOT 45
HOLLAND PARK GROUP ....LONDON: W 11 87
HUDDERSFIELD SAMATHA GROUP ..................HUDDERSFIELD 124
KETUMATI BUDDHIST VIHARA ....OLDHAM 58
LEICESTER BUDDHIST VIHARA (East Midlands Buddhist Association) ....LEICESTER 70
LEIGH BUDDHIST GROUP ....LEIGH ON SEA 53
LETCHWORTH BUDDHIST CENTRE ....LETCHWORTH 62
LIVERPOOL AMARAVATI GROUP ....LIVERPOOL 95
LLANFYLLIN SAMATHA GROUP ....LLANFYLLIN 137
LONDON BUDDHIST VIHARA ....LONDON: W 4 88
LONDON BUDDHIST VIHARA BOOKSTALL ....BOOKSHOPS 188
LONDON BURMESE BUDDHIST VIHARA (BRITAIN BURMA BUDDHIST TRUST) ....LONDON: NW 9 79
LUDLOW SAMATHA BUDDHIST GROUP ....LUDLOW 107
MAIDSTONE MEDITATION GROUP ....MAIDSTONE 66
MANCHESTER CENTRE FOR BUDDHIST MEDITATION ....MANCHESTER 56
MID-KENT AND MEDWAY BUDDHIST GROUP ....MAIDSTONE 66
MIDLANDS INTERNATIONAL BUDDHIST ASSOCIATION IN THE UK ....BIRMINGHAM 121
NEWENT THERAVADA GROUP ....NEWENT 54
NEWPORT SAMATHA GROUP ....NEWPORT 136
NORWICH AMARAVATI MEDITATION GROUP ....NORWICH 98
OLDHAM SAMATHA MEDITATION GROUP ....OLDHAM 68
OXFORD BUDDHIST VIHARA ....OXFORD 105
OXFORD SAMATHA GROUP ....OXFORD 106
PENZANCE MEDITATION GROUP ....PENZANCE 40
PERTH THERAVADA GROUP ....PERTH 146
PORTSMOUTH BUDDHIST GROUP ....PORTSMOUTH 59
REDBRIDGE BUDDHIST CULTURAL CENTRE ....ILFORD 90
RICHMOND SAMATHA MEDITATION GROUP ....RICHMOND 93
ROSSENDALE SAMATHA GROUP ....ROSSENDALE 70
SAMADHI MEDITATION CENTRE ....LONDON: N 9 77
SAMATHA CENTRE ....KNIGHTON 137
SAMATHA GROUPS IN IRELAND ....IRELAND 151
SAMATHA TRUST ....UK NATIONAL ORGANISATIONS 22
SANTISUKHA VIHARA ....HESTON 91

SATIPANYA BUDDHIST TRUST .... RELATED ORGANISATIONS 175
SOAS MEDITATION SOCIETY, THE .... LONDON: WC 1 90
SHEFFIELD SAMATHA BUDDHIST GROUP .... SHEFFIELD 111
SLSCO-FLAME .... HOUNSLOW 92
SOUTH DORSET BUDDHIST GROUP .... WEYMOUTH 47
SRI SADDHATISSA INTERNATIONAL BUDDHIST CENTRE ...... LONDON: NW 9 79
STEYNING MEDITATION GROUP .... STEYNING 124
STOCKPORT SAMATHA MEDITATION GROUP ...... STOCKPORT 59
STROUD BUDDHIST GROUP .... STROUD 54
SUNDERLAND SAMATHA GROUP .... SUNDERLAND 116
SUNYATA RETREAT CENTRE .... SIX MILE BRIDGE 152
SURREY THERAVADA BUDDHIST GROUP .... WOKING 114
TAUNTON MEDITATION GROUP .... TAUNTON 109
TEESSIDE THERAVADIN BUDDHIST GROUP .... MIDDLESBOROUGH 38
THAMES BUDDHIST VIHARA .... SELSDON 94
THERAVADA BUDDHISM (SW WALES) .... NEVERN 136
THERAVADA BUDDHIST CENTRE .... BRISTOL 31
THERAVADA BUDDHIST GROUP .... CARLISLE 41
TISARANA VIHARA .... TWICKENHAM 92
UNIVERSITY OF BRISTOL SAMATHA GROUP ...... BRISTOL 31
UXBRIDGE SAMATHA MEDITATION GROUP .... UXBRIDGE 92
VIPASSANA MEDITATION GROUP .... CORK CITY 154
WARRINGTON SAMATHA GROUP .... WARRINGTON 37
WAT SANGHATHAN .... BIRMINGHAM 122
WILMSLOW (SAMATHA) BUDDHIST MEDITATION GROUP ...... WILMSLOW 37
WIMBLEDON SAMATHA MEDITATION GROUP ...... LONDON: SW 19 84

Theravada: Ambedkarite
BUDDHA VIHARA .... SOUTHALL 92
FEDERATION OF AMBEDKARITE BUDDHIST ORGANISATIONS UK ...... UK NATIONAL ORGANISATIONS.......14
FEDERATION OF AMBEDKARITE BUDDHIST ORGANISATIONS UK ...... LONDON: E2 73
JETAVANA BUDDHIST TEMPLE .... BIRMINGHAM 120
WOLVERHAMPTON BUDDHA VIHARA .... WOLVERHAMPTON 123

Theravada: Vipassana
ASSOCIATION FOR INSIGHT MEDITATION .... ILFORD 90
BUDDHIST INSIGHT MEDITATION CENTRE OF WEST WALES ...... NEWCASTLE EMLYN 132
GAIA HOUSE .... NEWTON ABBOT 45
HOUSE OF INNER TRANQUILLITY .... BRADFORD ON AVON 126
INSIGHT MEDITATION GROUP .... DUBLIN 155
INTERNATIONAL MEDITATION CENTRE .... CALNE 127
IRISH VIPASSANA ASSOCIATION .... DUBLIN 156
PASSADDHI MEDITATION CENTRE .... ADRIGOLE, BEARA 153
SARANIYA DHAMMA MEDITATION CENTRE .... SALFORD 58
VIPASSANA FELLOWSHIP .... UK NATIONAL ORGANISATIONS 25
VIPASSANA MEDITATION GROUP .... CORK CITY 154
VIPASSANA TRUST .... HEREFORD 61

Tibetan
BODHICHARYA BUDDHIST GROUP .... CHICHESTER 123
BODHICHARYA UK .... UK NATIONAL ORGANISATIONS.......10
BODHICHARYA UK .... COATBRIDGE 145

CANTERBURY TIBET LINK...CANTERBURY 65
KAILASH CENTRE ....RELATED ORGANISATIONS 171

Tibetan: Dzogchen
DZOGCHEN BRISTOL...BRISTOL 29
DZOGCHEN CAMBRIDGE..CAMBRIDGE..................................36
DZOGCHEN CARDIFF...CARDIFF...132
DZOGCHEN COMMUNITY UK ....UK NATIONAL ORGANISATIONS.......13
DZOGCHEN CUMBRIA..CUMBRIA 41
DZOGCHEN LONDON..LONDON 72
DZOGCHEN MANCHESTER ....MANCHESTER 55
DZOGCHEN MIDLANDS ....WEST MIDLANDS 118
KUNSEL LING ....HAY-ON-WYE 137

Tibetan: Gelugpa
JAMPA LING BELFAST ....BELFAST 152
JAMPA LING TIBETAN BUDDHIST CENTRE ....BAWNBOY 152
JAMYANG BRIGHTON..BRIGHTON 50
JAMYANG BUDDHIST CENTRE ....LONDON: SE 11.............................80
JAMYANG BUDDHIST CENTRE LEEDS ....LEEDS...126
JAMYANG COLCHESTER ....COLCHESTER 52
JAMYANG SALISBURY ....SALISBURY 128
LAM RIM (WILTS & S.GLOUC)..CHIPPENHAM 127
LAM RIM BRISTOL BUDDHIST CENTRE............................BRISTOL 29
LAM RIM BUDDHIST CENTRE ....PENRHOS......................................135
SARASWATI BUDDHIST GROUP ....SOUTH PETHERTON......................109
SHEN PHEN THUBTEN CHOELING....................................HEREFORD 61
TASHI KHYIL TRUST ....RELATED ORGANISATIONS 176
TASHI LHUNPO MONASTERY UK TRUST ....RELATED ORGANISATIONS 176

Tibetan: Gelugpa / Kagyu
CHAM TSE LING BUDDHIST GROUP..................................PRESTON 69

Tibetan: Kagyu
DRUK THEKCHEN CHOEKOR LING......................................OXFORD..105

Tibetan: Kagyu/Drikung
DRUKPA TRUST ....RELATED ORGANISATIONS 168

Tibetan: Kagyu-Nyingma
AWAKENED HEART SANGHA ....CRICCIETH 134
BRIGHTON SHAMBHALA STUDY GROUP ....BRIGHTON 49
BRISTOL SHAMBHALA MEDITATION GROUP....................BRISTOL 28
CHALFORD HILL SHAMBHALA STUDY GROUP ....STROUD..54

Tibetan: Kagyu-Nyingma
DUBLIN SHAMBHALA STUDY GROUP ....DUBLIN 155
EDINBURGH SHAMBHALA MEDITATION GROUP ....EDINBURGH 141
LEICESTER SHAMBHALA STUDY GROUP ....LEICESTER....................................71
LONDON SHAMBHALA MEDITATION CENTRE....................LONDON: SW 4..............................85
LONGCHEN FOUNDATION ....UK NATIONAL ORGANISATIONS.......16
LONGCHEN FOUNDATION ....PORTHMADOG 134
LONGCHEN FOUNDATION ....BRISTOL 30
LONGCHEN FOUNDATION ....LONDON: SE 13 81
LONGCHEN FOUNDATION ....OXFORD..105

LONGCHEN FOUNDATION .... LEIGH ON SEA 53
MAIDSTONE MEDITATION GROUP (LONGCHEN FOUNDATION) ..... MAIDSTONE 66
MANCHESTER SHAMBHALA STUDY GROUP .... MANCHESTER 57
SHRIMALA TRUST .... RELATED ORGANISATIONS 176

Tibetan: Kagyu-Sakya
DECHEN COMMUNITY .... UK NATIONAL ORGANISATIONS.......12
DECHEN IN BATH .... BATH 27
DECHEN IN CORNWALL .... TRURO 40
DECHEN IN LEEDS .... LEEDS 125
DECHEN IN PEMBROKESHIRE .... NARBERTH 135
DECHEN IN SKIPTON .... SKIPTON 100
DECHEN IN YORK .... YORK 100
KAGYU DECHEN DZONG .... HARROGATE 100
KAGYU DZONG .... COLNE 67
KAGYU LING .... MANCHESTER 56
KAGYU OSEL CHOLING .... SOUTHPORT 96
KAGYU SHEDRUP LING .... LIVERPOOL 95
KARME CHOLING .... WIRRAL 97
SAKYA DECHEN LING - CITY OF LONDON .... LONDON: EC4 73
SAKYA DECHEN LING - NOTTING HILL .... LONDON: W 8 89
SAKYA DECHEN LING - ST. JOHN'S WOOD .... LONDON: NW 8 78
SAKYA GOSHAK CHOLING .... BIRMINGHAM 121
SAKYA THINLEY NAMGYAL LING .... EXETER 44
SAKYA THINLEY RINCHEN LING .... BRISTOL 30

Tibetan: Karma-Kagyu
AMRITA DZONG .... LONDON: E 2 72
BATH DIAMOND WAY BUDDHIST CENTRE .... BATH 27
BIRMINGHAM DIAMOND WAY BUDDHIST CENTRE .... BIRMINGHAM 119
BRIGHTON DIAMOND WAY BUDDHIST CENTRE .... BRIGHTON 48
BRISTOL DIAMOND WAY BUDDHIST CENTRE .... BRISTOL 28
CANTERBURY DIAMOND WAY BUDDHIST CENTRE................. CANTERBURY 65
CROWBOROUGH DIAMOND WAY BUDDHIST CENTRE .... CROWBOROUGH 50
DIAMOND WAY BUDDHISM UK .... UK NATIONAL ORGANISATIONS.......13
DONCASTER DIAMOND WAY BUDDHIST CENTRE .... DONCASTER 110
EDINBURGH DIAMOND WAY BUDDHIST CENTRE .... EDINBURGH 141
EDINBURGH SAMYE DZONG .... EDINBURGH 141
EXETER DIAMOND WAY BUDDHIST CENTRE .... EXETER 44
HARLOW DIAMOND WAY BUDDHIST CENTRE .... HARLOW 53
HOLY ISLAND .... OFF ARRAN 145
KAGYU SAMYE DZONG .... DUBLIN 156
KAGYU SAMYE DZONG CORK .... CORK CITY 154
KAGYU SAMYE DZONG CORNWALL..................................... LOSTWITHIEL 40
KAGYU SAMYE DZONG LONDON .... LONDON: SE 1 79
KAGYU SAMYE DZONG NORTHAMPTONSHIRE .... KETTERING 101
KAGYU SAMYE LING MONASTERY AND TIBETAN CENTRE - ROKPA TRUST ....UK NATIONAL ORGANISATIONS.......16
KAGYU SAMYE LING TIBETAN CENTRE - ROKPA TRUST .... ESKDALEMUIR 140
LIVERPOOL DIAMOND WAY BUDDHIST CENTRE .... LIVERPOOL 95
LONDON DIAMOND WAY BUDDHIST CENTRE........................ LONDON: WC 1 89
LONDON-SOUTH DIAMOND WAY BUDDHIST CENTRE .... LONDON: SE 24..............................83

MANCHESTER DIAMOND WAY BUDDHIST CENTRE ....MANCHESTER 57
MANOR PLACE SAMYE DZONG...LONDON: SE 17 82
MARPA HOUSE - Chos Khor Ling ....ASHDON 52
NEWCASTLE DIAMOND WAY BUDDHIST CENTRE........................NEWCASTLE UPON TYNE 116
NEZANG BUDDHIST MEDITATION GROUP ....CAMBRIDGE.....................36
POTTERS BAR DIAMOND WAY BUDDHIST CENTRE ....POTTERS BAR 63
PRESTON DIAMOND WAY BUDDHIST CENTRE ....PRESTON 69
READING DIAMOND WAY BUDDHIST CENTRE ....READING............................32
ROKPA ABERDEEN...ABERDEEN 139
ROKPA CARDIFF ....CARDIFF 132
ROKPA DUNDEE ....DUNDEE 140
ROKPA GLASGOW ....GLASGOW 144
ROKPA HIGHLANDS...INVERNESS 144
ROKPA TRUST ....RELATED ORGANISATIONS 174
SHEFFIELD DIAMOND WAY BUDDHIST CENTRE...........................SHEFFIELD 111
TARA ROKPA EDINBURGH & THE INSTITUTE FOR TIBETAN MEDICINE ....EDINBURGH 142
TARA ROKPA NORFOLK ....MUNDESLEY 97
THRANGU HOUSE BUDDHIST CENTRE ....OXFORD 107
YORK DIAMOND WAY BUDDHIST CENTRE....................................YORK 101

Tibetan: New Kadampa Tradition

NEW KADAMPA TRADITION ....UK NATIONAL ORGANISATIONS.......19

Tibetan: Nyingma

DZOGCHEN BEARA ....ALLIHIES 153
MAITRIKARA...BRIGHTON 50
OGYAN CHOKHOR LING ....UK NATIONAL ORGANISATIONS.......19
OGYAN CHOKHOR LING ....CANTERBURY 65
OGYAN CHOKHOR LING ....LONDON: N 12 75
PADMA LING UK ....UK NATIONAL ORGANISATIONS 20
PALYUL CENTRE UK ....UK NATIONAL ORGANISATIONS 21
RIGPA ATHLONE ....ATHLONE..........................157
RIGPA BIRMINGHAM ....BIRMINGHAM 121
RIGPA CORK...CORK CITY 154
RIGPA DUBLIN ....DUBLIN 156
RIGPA EDINBURGH ....EDINBURGH 142
RIGPA FELLOWSHIP ....UK NATIONAL ORGANISATIONS 22
RIGPA GALWAY ....GALWAY 157
RIGPA IRELAND ....IRELAND 151
RIGPA KERRY ....KILLARNEY.......................157
RIGPA LIMERICK...LIMERICK 157
RIGPA NORWICH ....NORWICH 99
RIGPA SOUTH DOWNS ....LEWES 52
RIGPA WICKLOW ....CO WICKLOW 157
SANG-NGAK-CHO-DZONG ....UK NATIONAL ORGANISATIONS 24
SANG-NGAK-CHO-DZONG ....BRISTOL 30
SANG-NGAK-CHO-DZONG ....CARDIFF 131
SANG-NGAK-CHO-DZONG ....CARLISLE...........................41
SANG-NGAK-CHO-DZONG ....CHEPSTOW......................97
SANG-NGAK-CHO-DZONG ....CORNWALL 39
SANG-NGAK-CHO-DZONG ....WEST SUSSEX 123

SANG-NGAK-CHO-DZONG ....KENT 64
SANG-NGAK-CHO-DZONG ....YORK 101
Tibetan: Nyingma / Rime
KHANDRO LING ....MACCLESFIELD 37
Vietnamese
LINH SON TEMPLE AND MEDITATION CENTRE.................................LONDON: SE 19 82
MIDLANDS BUDDHIST ASSOCIATION [VIETNAMESE] ....BIRMINGHAM 120
Vietnamese: Mahayana
LINH SONH PHAT DUONG TEMPLE..LONDON: N 15.................75
Vietnamese: Thich Nhat Hanh
BUDDHIST INTERHELP AND COMMUNITY OF INTERBEING ....LONDON: SE 13 81
COMMUNITY OF INTERBEING ....AUDIO VISUAL 182
COMMUNITY OF INTERBEING ....BOOKS BY POST 184
COMMUNITY OF INTERBEING - BIRMINGHAM SANGHA ....BIRMINGHAM 120
COMMUNITY OF INTERBEING - BORDERS AND LOTHIAN SANGHA.............SCOTTISH BORDERS 146
COMMUNITY OF INTERBEING - BOURNEMOUTH SANGHA ....BOURNEMOUTH 46
COMMUNITY OF INTERBEING - BRIGHTON SANGHA ....HOVE.............................51
COMMUNITY OF INTERBEING - CAMBRIDGE SANGHA ....CAMBRIDGE...................36
COMMUNITY OF INTERBEING - DULWICH SANGHA ....LONDON: SE 21 82
COMMUNITY OF INTERBEING - EDINBURGH SANGHA ....EDINBURGH 140
COMMUNITY OF INTERBEING - GLASGOW SANGHA ....GLASGOW 143
COMMUNITY OF INTERBEING - GUILDFORD SANGHA ....GUILDFORD...................113
COMMUNITY OF INTERBEING - HAM / RICHMOND SANGHA ....HAM............................93
COMMUNITY OF INTERBEING - HEART OF LONDON SANGHA ....LONDON: SW 3 85
COMMUNITY OF INTERBEING - LEAMINGTON SANGHA ....LEAMINGTON SPA 117
COMMUNITY OF INTERBEING - LEWES SANGHA ....LEWES..........................51
COMMUNITY OF INTERBEING - LINCOLNSHIRE SANGHA.......................NORTH SOMERCOTES 71
COMMUNITY OF INTERBEING - NORFOLK SANGHA ....NORWICH 97
COMMUNITY OF INTERBEING - NORTHERN LIGHTS SANGHA, FINDHORN ....FORRES 144
COMMUNITY OF INTERBEING - NORTHWEST SANGHA, MANCHESTER ....MANCHESTER 55
COMMUNITY OF INTERBEING - OXFORD SANGHA ....OXFORD 104
COMMUNITY OF INTERBEING - POPPY SEED SANGHA, FIFE ....FIFE............................142
COMMUNITY OF INTERBEING - SOUTH WALES SANGHA.......................CARDIFF 131
COMMUNITY OF INTERBEING - SOUTHAMPTON SANGHA......................SOUTHAMPTON 60
COMMUNITY OF INTERBEING - SUFFOLK SANGHA ....SUFFOLK 112
COMMUNITY OF INTERBEING - WEST COUNTRY SANGHA ....EXETER 43
COMMUNITY OF INTERBEING - WHITE CLOUDS SANGHA - W. BERKS, WILTS AND AVON
....MARLBOROUGH 128
COMMUNITY OF INTERBEING, U.K. ....UK NATIONAL ORGANISATIONS.......12
Zen
CIRENCESTER ZEN GROUP ....CIRENCESTER 54
GUERNSEY BUDDHIST ZEN CENTRE ....GUERNSEY 149
SMILING MOUNTAIN MEDITATION GROUP ....HALESOWEN 122
TREVOR LEGGETT ADHYATMA YOGA TRUST ....SOUTHWOLD 113
WINTERHEAD RETREAT HOUSE ....SHIPHAM 109
Zen: Kwan Um School
ZEN LONDON...LONDON: N 4..................75
ZEN LONDON...LONDON: W 4 88

Zen: Soto

ABERDEEN SERENE REFLECTION MEDITATION GROUP ....ABERDEEN 139
ABERFELDY SERENE REFLECTION MEDITATION GROUP ....ABERFELDY 146
BIRMINGHAM SERENE REFLECTION MEDITATION GROUP ....BIRMINGHAM 119
BLACK MOUNTAIN ZEN CENTRE...BELFAST 151
BLACK MOUNTAIN ZEN CENTRE...NEWCASTLE UPON TYNE.............115
BLACK MOUNTAIN ZEN CENTRE...BALLYMENA................................151
BLACK MOUNTAIN ZEN CENTRE...COLERAINE.................................157
BOURNEMOUTH ZEN DOJO ....BOURNEMOUTH 46
BRIGHTON SERENE REFLECTION MEDITATION GROUP............................BRIGHTON 49
BRIGHTON ZEN DOJO...BRIGHTON 49
BRISTOL SOTO ZEN DOJO...BRISTOL 29
CAMBRIDGE SERENE REFLECTION MEDITATION GROUP.........................CAMBRIDGE.................................36
CHESTER ZEN GROUP...CHESTER 37
CHICHESTER SERENE REFLECTION MEDITATION GROUP ....CHICHESTER 123
CIRENCESTER SERENE REFLECTION MEDITATION GROUP ....CIRENCESTER 54
CORK ZEN DOJO...CORK 154
CORNWALL SERENE REFLECTION MEDITATION GROUP ....CORNWALL 39
DHARMA CLOUD TRUST...NEWPORT 135
DOGEN SANGHA BUDDHIST GROUP ....BRISTOL 29
DRAGON BELL TEMPLE ....EXETER 43
DUBLIN ZEN DOJO...DUBLIN 155
DUNDEE SERENE REFLECTION MEDITATION GROUP...............................DUNDEE 139
GALLOWAY SERENE REFLECTION MEDITATION GROUP ....GALLOWAY 140
GALWAY ZEN DOJO ....GALWAY 156
GLASGOW ZEN DOJO...GLASGOW 143
HARROW ZAZENKAI ....HARROW 91
HASTINGS AND ROTHER BUDDHIST MEDITATION GROUP ....HASTINGS.....................................51
HEXHAM SERENE REFLECTION MEDITATION GROUP ....HEXHAM 102
HUDDERSFIELD SERENE REFLECTION MEDITATION GROUP ...................HUDDERSFIELD..........................124
HULL SERENE REFLECTION MEDITATION GROUP ....HULL...63
INTERNATIONAL ZEN ASSOCIATION UK..UK NATIONAL ORGANISATIONS.......16
KESWICK SERENE RELECTION MEDITATION GROUP.................................KESWICK.......................................41
LANCASTER SERENE REFLECTION MEDITATION GROUP ....LANCASTER...................................68
LEEDS ZEN DOJO ....LEEDS...126
LEICESTER SERENE REFLECTION MEDITATION GROUP ....LEICESTER.....................................71
LIVERPOOL SERENE REFLECTION MEDITATION GROUP ....LIVERPOOL 96
LONDON SERENE REFLECTION MEDITATION GROUP ....LONDON: N 1 74
LONDON ZAZEN GROUP ....LONDON: W 2 87
MANCHESTER ZEN DOJO ....MANCHESTER...............................58
MATLOCK SERENE REFLECTION MEDITATION GROUP ....MATLOCK 42
MILTON KEYNES SERENE REFLECTION MEDITATION GROUP ....MILTON KEYNES 33
NEWCASTLE SERENE REFLECTION MEDITATION GROUP ....NEWCASTLE UPON TYNE 116
NORTH LONDON ZEN DOJO ....LONDON: N 5 76
NORWICH SERENE REFLECTION MEDITATION GROUP ....NORWICH 98
NORWICH ZEN DOJO ....NORWICH 98
NOTTINGHAM SERENE REFLECTION MEDITATION GROUP ....NOTTINGHAM 104
ORDER OF BUDDHISTS CONTEMPLATIVES ....UK NATIONAL ORGANISATIONS 20
OXFORD ZEN DOJO ....OXFORD 106

PORTOBELLO BUDDHIST PRIORY ....EDINBURGH 142
PORTSMOUTH SERENE REFLECTION MEDITATION GROUP ....PORTSMOUTH 59
PRESTON SERENE REFLECTION MEDITATION GROUP..PRESTON 69
READING BUDDHIST PRIORY ....READING.......................................32
ROCHDALE ZEN RETREAT ....BOLTON 55
SHEFFIELD SERENE REFLECTION MEDITATION GROUP ....SHEFFIELD 111
SOUTH LONDON ZEN DOJO ....LONDON: SE 1 80
TEESIDE SERENE REFLECTION MEDITATION GROUP.........................MIDDLESBOROUGH 38
TELFORD BUDDHIST PRIORY ....TELFORD 108
THROSSEL HOLE BUDDHIST ABBEY ....HEXHAM 103
WELLS-NEXT-THE-SEA ZEN GROUP (IZAUK) ....WELLS-NEXT-THE-SEA 99

Zen: Soto/Rinzai

ARRIVING HOME ....SHEFFIELD...............................110
CALDERDALE ZEN GROUP..CALDERDALE 124
KANZEON ZEN PRACTICE TRUST ....LONDON: NW 3............................78
LIVERPOOL ZEN GROUP ....LIVERPOOL 96
SHEFFIELD ZEN GROUP - WHITE PLUM...SHEFFIELD.................................112
ZEN PRACTICE CENTRE TRUST ....HULL...64
ZEN PRACTICE CENTRE TRUST ....MAIDSTONE................................67
ZEN PRACTICE CENTRE TRUST ....PRESTON 69
ZEN PRACTICE CENTRE TRUST ....HINCKLEY 70
ZEN PRACTICE CENTRE TRUST (Affiliated to the Kanzeon Sangha) ....UK NATIONAL ORGANISATIONS 26

Zen: Thich Nhat Hanh

COMMUNITY OF INTERBEING - ABERDEENSHIRE, BANCHORY SANGHA ...........ABERDEENSHIRE 139
COMMUNITY OF INTERBEING - BLUE LOTUS SANGHA ....SHEFFIELD.................................110
COMMUNITY OF INTERBEING - DEEP LISTENING SANGHA ....RELATED ORGANISATIONS 167
COMMUNITY OF INTERBEING - DYFI VALLEY SANGHA ....GWYNEDD 133
COMMUNITY OF INTERBEING - EAST MIDLANDS SANGHA................NOTTINGHAM 103
COMMUNITY OF INTERBEING - ISLE OF WIGHT SANGHA.................ISLE OF WIGHT 64
COMMUNITY OF INTERBEING - LANCASHIRE SANGHA ....MORECAMBE BAY 68
COMMUNITY OF INTERBEING - LEEDS SANGHA ....LEEDS.......................................125
COMMUNITY OF INTERBEING - LYME BAY SANGHA, DORSET ....LYME BAY 47
COMMUNITY OF INTERBEING - MARTINSTOWN SANGHA, DORSET..................MARTINSTOWN 47
COMMUNITY OF INTERBEING - MINDFULNESS SANGHA....................DERBY 42
COMMUNITY OF INTERBEING - NORTH LONDON SANGHA ....LONDON: N 7..............................76
COMMUNITY OF INTERBEING - NORTHWICH SANGHA......................NORTHWICH 37
COMMUNITY OF INTERBEING - THE PATH HOME SANGHA, NORTHAMPTON ......NORTHAMPTON 102
COMMUNITY OF INTERBEING - WIMBLEDON SANGHA ....LONDON: SW 19..........................84
COMMUNITY OF INTERBEING - YORKSHIRE SANGHA.........................YORK 100

Zen / Ch'an

WEST CORNWALL ZEN CENTRE ....HELSTON......................................39